The

S

Online

There are more than one hundred and fifty
Rough Guide travel, phrasebook and music titles,
covering destinations from Amsterdam to Zimbabwe,
languages from Czech to Vietnamese,
and musics from World to Opera and Jazz

www.roughguides.com

Credits

Text editor: Paul Simpson
Contributors: Victoria Williams, Helen Rodiss, Ian Cranna, Ann Oliver,
Caroline Green, Emma Young, Susan Aldridge, Caroline Elliott,
Ali MacArthur, Richard Pendleton, James Werry-Easterbrook,
Thanks to: Sue Weekes, Simon Kanter, Mark Ellingham, Mark Payton
Photographs: CSA Plastock/Photonica

Publishing Information

This first edition published October 2000 was prepared by
Haymarket Customer Publishing for Rough Guides Ltd,
62–70 Shorts Gdns, London WC2H 9AH

Distributed by the Penguin Group

Penguin Books Ltd, 27 Wrights Lane, London W8 5TZ

Typeset in Adobe Clarendon and Helvetica to an **original design by**
Cathy Constable, Sarah Jane Voyce, Sarah Carter,
Jon Butterworth, Alison Lane, Martin Tullett.
Printed in Spain by Graphy Cems.

A catalogue record for this book is available from the British Library.
ISBN 1-85828-768-5

The publishers and authors have done their best to ensure
the accuracy and currency of all the information in
The Rough Guide to Shopping Online however,
they can accept no responsibility for any loss, injury or
inconvenience sustained as a result of information
or advice contained in the guide.

CONTENTS

Contents

A public safety announcement

Remember that web sites can go down as well as up. Although this book was produced to the tightest production schedule possible (pages flying over to Spain to be printed little more than a month before the book arrived at a bookshop near you), some of the sites, addresses and prices which are quoted here will have changed by the time you peruse this. As the book went to press, the web addresses here actually worked and the recommendations made were accurate.

Since then some websites may have closed down, others will have radically revamped their sites. We're sorry but there is nothing much we can do about it except to say that even so, with information on online shops in 63 types of product from arts to wine and spirits, with well over 1700 web addresses quoted and with specific guidance on where you can buy anything from works of art made of old fruit crates to Jim Rosenthal's autograph and the smallest car in the world you should find this guide really very useful indeed. Anyway, let us know how you get on by email the editor at paul.simpson@haynet.com.

Part one

The secret of successful (and safe)
shopping over the World Wide Web

THE BASICS

Save money, save time and
save your blushes...

ONLINE
SHOPPING

Don't believe what you read in the papers.
The Internet isn't about to revolutionise
the way we have sex but it is already
revolutionising the way we shop, whether
we're buying a new car or the week's food

Is the Internet shopping revolution all hype?
Not at all. The best evidence suggests that by the middle
of this year, more than three million Britons were
using the Net to buy stuff. And by "stuff" we mean anything from cheaper electricity (***www.buy.co.uk/Personal/
Index.asp***) to a 27-acre island off Panama (***www.vladi-
privateislands.de/sales_islands/sites/06_gallo.html***) or a
new car (through *Which Online*'s ***www.carbusters.com***).
And in many cases, i.e. with the notable exception of that
aforementioned Panamanian paradise, you can save
money if you buy over the Internet.

So how does online shipping work? Economically, it's
supposed to be a very simple model. Traditional retailers
invest millions in expensive high-street real estate and
countless shop assistants in the belief, sadly not always

vindicated, that you will pop in and buy something. **Freed from such financial shackles,** e-tailers, as they like to refer to themselves, only have to worry about taking your order on their web site, ensuring they've got the item you want stored somewhere and organising its delivery.

Some of the money they save on not having a bricks and mortar presence at your local shopping centre can be passed on to you, the buyer. This is why so many online stores offer savings of **at least 20 per cent** over high-street prices. The added bonus, as Tesco has discovered with its online grocery service, is that people buying online spend more: at Tesco's trial service in Kent online shoppers spent four times as much as those who shopped in store. (The

> **More than three million Brits are using the Internet to go shopping**

other model, which cuts out retailers entirely, is that you buy direct from the manufacturer. Again, big savings are promised but manufacturers have to work out a way of selling their wares over the Net without upsetting their traditional retail stockists.)

There is, of course, a catch. For a start, many online

ONLINE VS OFFLINE

E-TAIL

No queue for car parks

No embarrassing public incidents with screaming offspring

No having to rush from work to catch 'late night opening'

No chance of being surprised by friends or colleagues when making embarrassing purchases (eg that video about the biggest dog in the world)

No opportunity for your spouse to look pained when trying on new clothes

RETAIL

No repercussions for your phone bill

No junk email to add to the junk mail

No known incidence of customers being rejected from a high-street store because they don't have the right software

No real chance a computer crash will stop you making your purchase

No chance that your postman will become overly familiar with your shopping habits ("Hmm, it's another Ann Summers parcel, sir!")

businesses soon realised that there was rather more to the mundane business of delivering product than met the eye.

Online shops also discovered that, although they saved on logistics and staffing, they had to invest between 60 and 83 per cent of their earnings to market themselves, a level which would prove ruinous in the long term. There is also evidence that online shoppers are even less loyal than high-street shoppers although, again, no one can say if this will be true in five years time.

So is the online shopping revolution stuffed? No, because even the most pessimistic forecasters say that five per cent of our shopping will be done over the Internet by the end of this decade. Besides, **only 10 million Brits** are actually online at the moment. The government has set a target of giving everyone Internet access over the next five years. Even if they miss this target as spectacularly as they failed to meet visitor targets for the Dome, **it will still mean 30 million Brits will be online by 2005.** But browsing isn't the same as shopping, is it? And isn't shopping over the Net a risky business?

Sadly for those who prefer to see the Internet through the eyes of *Sunday Sport* ("Click here to buy a **World War II bomber** found on the moon!") it is very hard to buy ballistic missiles, human kidneys or illegal drugs over the Net. It is, alas, all too easy to buy the greatest hits of Brotherhood of Man. And that ultimately is what online shopping is all about: giving you the **freedom of choice,** which is one of the things capitalism was supposed to guarantee but, in an increasingly monopolistic age, found it too often uneconomic to do so.

A FEW TIPS FOR YOU...

1 Use two search engines for the bulk of your surfing.

2 Configure your search engine so that it either looks only at UK sites or at UK sites first. This is usually simple to do from the engine's home page.

3 Plug in as little software as you can.

4 If you're searching for "Tommy Hilfiger", some sites search better with a "+" sign between the names. Others won't.

5 It's worth keying the item you want into your search engine's shopping area. As well as key auctions. And be sure to compare UK and US prices - you may save money even after paying shipping costs.

Welcome to a world
where you can...

SHOP STILL
YOU DROP

Online shopping needn't be technically arduous, financially hazardous or even unduly time-consuming, as long as you abide by a few simple principles. This chapter is designed to explain the ins and outs, dos and don'ts, ifs and buts, etc, for beginners

How to buy over the Internet

Let's assume, for the sake of argument, that you want to buy a copy of Leonard Nimoy's seminal album *Highly Illogical*, a must-have for every connoisseur of truly bad singing. Composed, in unequal parts, of songs sung in character as the first science officer of the *USS Enterprise* and his own versions of such standards as *If I Had A Hammer*, these recordings explain why his post-*Enterprise* career as a cabaret artiste was so shortlived.

There are two ways to proceed. You can key **Leonard Nimoy** into the shopping part of a general search engine like Yahoo and see what comes up, or you can go straight to a specific site like Amazon which you suspect may stock the goods you're after. The advantage of going to a specific site is that you might feel that much safer dealing with a company known to you, or recommended by a friend, by one of the multitude of Internet magazines, or indeed by a convenient little guide like this.

Log on to your online shop

For the purposes of illustration, log on to your favourite browser and key *http://www.amazon.co.uk* into the address bar. In the time it takes to say "Live long and prosper" your screen should fill up with a page which says **"Welcome to Amazon.co.uk"**. Like most such pages, Amazon's bombards you with a bewildering array of apparent bargains designed to tempt the online shopper who wants to buy something but isn't sure what.

Be single-minded and go to the box beneath the search button (top right) and key in **Leonard Nimoy**. As you know you want a CD, not one of his vulcanised volumes of memoirs, you can change the **"all products"** strap to **"music"** to save time and click on **"Go"**.

You are then presented with a choice of three items, only one of which is the real thing and two of which are inferior versions with the 'bonus' of even more embarrassing

Amazon's home page is typical of the genre: clear, packed with advice and compelling reasons for you to spend money

A quick search provides three choices of CD, but the one that matches our spec is Highly Illogical, and if you click on "Read more..." you get the full, awesome track listing

performances by William Shatner. The price, £12.99, does not include postage and packing (that comes later). The delivery time, 1-2 weeks, is not bad for such an obscure artefact of popular culture. More mainstream stuff should arrive within 1-3 days.

Often a product will be accompanied by a customer's review but these may well be written by true devotees, people with an axe to grind or people for whom penning reviews on such sites is their nearest brush with fame.

So now you've found what you want...

Sometimes, you can inspect the product in closer detail (by seeing a track listing or a larger photo of the cover). If you're buying a book, you will usually get a paragraph-long synopsis. To buy Nimoy's finest hour, click on the **"add to shopping basket"** button which says you have one item in your basket, costing £12.99 and gives you a chance to order more than one copy.

Click on **"proceed to checkout"** and you will then be asked whether you're a new customer or not. If you are,

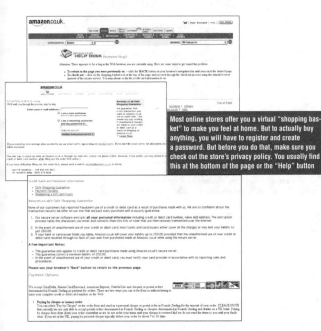

Most online stores offer you a virtual "shopping basket" to make you feel at home. But to actually buy anything, you will have to register and create a password. But before you do that, make sure you check out the store's privacy policy. You usually find this at the bottom of the page or the "Help" button

clicking on the right button takes you to a form which asks for the usual details (name, address, email, etc).

It's at this point that new online shoppers may have a few qualms about just handing over this information, wondering just what else this personal data might be used for. Most reputable online stores have a button at the foot of the page marked something like **"Privacy policy"**. If you click on this you should find a statement which will explain what information they need, why, what they use it for, how they protect this data, and whether this information will be given to anyone else. (For more detailed info on these issues see chapter 3.) But if a site does not have such a policy then you should only buy an item if it really is not available anywhere else.

What happens if things go wrong?

While you're checking out the online store, it's probably worth examining their policies on returns, refunds and delivery. Some, like Amazon, have a **"no quibble"** guarantee which says that if you are unhappy for any reason and can be bothered to wrap up the goods you've bought and send it back they'll refund the purchase price. These policies may be buried beneath a **"help"** button on the home page but too often a casual browse will fail to reveal any obvious policy on these mundane but vital issues, in which case email or phone them for the low-down. Also, global as the Internet now is, its centre of gravity is still America and you may find the company which sells the ugly plastic false teeth you've been looking for only ships to North America.

After filling in all the correct fields you will be invited to enter a password and re-enter it. Best practice is to use a unique word which has personal significance so your memory won't need jogging, throw in a couple of numbers if you can be bothered and use this all the time.

Having read the privacy policy (and chapter 5 of this guide) you should feel confident enough to enter your credit or debit card details and click **"continue"**. Most online stores let you key in your details on what is known as a **"secure server"**. With the almost daily reports of hackers pillaging the Pentagon's database, you may be wondering if "secure server" is an oxymoron. Suffice to say these services wrap an extra layer of code around your confidential details to protect them (for more on this see chapter 3).

You can pay by cheque, but Amazon says this delays orders by 7-10 days, or you can just enter the last five digits of your

Check the returns policy which is often buried under the "Help" button

card number and the expiry date on the site and phone up to give the rest of your number. Some companies have experimented with a separate pin number so financial details do not have to be given out over the Net.

Let's assume you go for the full online shopping experience and hit that **"continue"** button. You are then invited to confirm your address and delivery method. Many online shoppers like to have stuff delivered to work rather than find a card telling them they have a package at a local sorting office which can't be found without the purchase of a local A to Z for £5.99 but it depends on how much trust you place in your company's postroom.

You're only a few clicks away now

If you order more than one item, you will be offered the choice to have them all delivered at once (cheaper but can you wait that long?) or have them delivered individually (more expensive but faster and you help postie's campaign to get a six-pack stomach).

Another click and you get to confirm your debit or credit card number and then you are presented with the electronic "invoice" which tells you

You should be able to check price, delivery time, and method before doing anything irrevocable, like buying

Purchase Details

Order # : cathy constable

cathy constable
rough guide
somerset house
teddington surrey W6 7JP
United Kingdom
edit

Subtotal of Items:	£12.99
Offering:	£0.00
Postage & Packing:	£1.74
Promotional Gift Certificate:	-£0.00
Total Before VAT:	£12.54
VAT:	£2.19
Total:	£14.73
Gift Certificate:	-£0.00
Total for this Address:	£14.73

Dispatch method:
Dispatch Preference: Dispatch this order when complete
edit

Order Items

Highly Magical
Leonard Nimoy
Availability: Usually ships in 1-2 weeks

Qty: 1   Wrap: None
Message: No Message
add

Your order is not complete until you click here.   ► Place Your Order

One click to go, and by now you should have seen an electronic invoice which sets out all the costs of delivery, VAT, etc

how much you have to pay for postage and packing. (Some sites deliver for free but you usually find "free delivery" is reflected in the purchase price.) You are now a click away from doing something which will lead to pounds and pence being withdrawn from your account. Time to take stock and decide if you are that keen on Nimoy. If you are and click on **"place your order"** a "mean that most sincerely" thank you page will pop up.

You may want to print out a copy of what you have ordered. Some online stores (and Amazon does this) email confirmation of your order and tell you when they've got around to sticking the item(s) in the post. Within two weeks, you should hear that soon to be familiar scraping noise as the postie tries to squeeze the cardboard-wrapped CD through your spatially challenged letterbox.

If not, most reputable online sellers have some kind of button (usually marked **"Your account"**) which you can click on to check what's happening to your order. On some sites your account buttons are less helpful, proving, on inspection, only to tell you your order is in progress.

Buying on the Internet really is (almost) that easy and, despite the scare stories, only a miniscule percentage of online shoppers find that, having disclosed their financial information to a respectable online store, their bank accounts are mysteriously depleted of large sums which are eventually traced to international drug syndicates.

Sometimes it's not as easy as it looks...

So why is Internet shopping only "almost" that simple? Partly because many online stores have very different user interfaces. The late, unlamented (except by people who worked there or invested in it) **Boo.com** had the kind of user interface which gave visitors a headache and feelings of deep technological inferiority. Even mainstream sites like Habitat demand you download a certain software package to make the most of their virtual shelves. First-time shoppers can get lost in the process. While buying a CD from Amazon or CD Now is pretty straightforward, buying your week's groceries can take up to an hour the first time and that's if your computer doesn't crash. Even on well-tried sites like Amazon, if you click back to look at the preceding page, you sometimes get a page popping up with the intriguing headline **"Browser bug?"**. Usually, it's easy to get back on track but nervous buyers might get lost.

SO WHAT ARE PEOPLE BUYING ONLINE?

Forrester Research, one of those US consultants who make a mint from Internet surveys, say that in 1999 seven million Europeans spent £490 per head online. They expect those figures to grow so that by 2003 131m people in Europe will spend an average of £1,774 online, i.e. almost a fiver a day.

The amazing thing so far is that most studies show it doesn't matter whether an online shopper is in Birmingham, Alabama or Birmingham, West Midlands, they tend to use the Web to buy similar types of goods: books (some 8% of UK online spending), software (6%), CDs and videos (5%) and then, finally, computer peripherals (4%).

... especially the delivery part

Then there's the delivery, which is where online shopping too often goes wrong. Last Christmas the press were full of sob stories about online shoppers who didn't get what they'd ordered when they'd been promised they would. Indeed, the US government fined seven US e-tailers for late delivery and several irate customers even took out a class action suit against ToysRUs for spoiling their 25 December. When Mick Jagger famously said you can't always get what you want, he almost certainly wasn't thinking of online shopping but the sentiment is certainly applicable.

Even apparently reputable e-tailers have been known to send the wrong CD in a box with a fat **"postage to pay"** sticker planted erroneously on it. And yet surveys continue to show that seven out of every ten online shoppers are satisfied with the service they get, the most conclusive result since Whiskas first consulted cat owners.

The right product, the right price

For simplicity's sake, the purchase of Leonard Nimoy's CD was followed through just one site. In reality, once you'd found Amazon had the product and the price (£12.99) you might be tempted to see if you could find it cheaper elsewhere. So let's type in **_www.Yahoo.com_** and click on the word **"shopping"** just below the slit where you normally type whatever you're trying to find.

Up comes a natty little page snappily captioned **"Welcome, Guest"** and, in the search box just below, you type in those mesmerising words **leonard+nimoy** and lo and behold, you discover there are 199 products associated with the pointy-eared personage, available from 15 stores.

One of them is another collection of Nimoy's greatest hits which may only cost $15-16 (under £11). Upon further inspection you see that you can buy it from a company called cd world and they even deliver to the UK. However, you are stymied in your attempt to see how much postage and packing will cost so you give up.

This experience has not been totally in vain because new though you are, you have realised that although online shopping is usually an intensely exhilarating experience, it can also be as frustrating as those January sales where you spend hours flicking through racks of CDs marked down to £5.99 only to discover that they have cut the price of every Talking Heads album apart from the one you haven't got.

And finally, a few words of advice...

Be organised. If you just surf hopefully in the belief that you'll find the right present for Dad's birthday, you could drown in cyberspace. Generally, the more specific you are about what you want to buy, the faster, and more pleasureable, shopping online will be.

Set a budget. Virtual shopping still uses real money but somehow it doesn't feel as financially painful when you just click a button on your computer screen. Sticking to a budget is particularly vital if you are buying through an online auction (see chapter 4).

Consider using your credit card. If you do use a credit card, your consumer rights will be protected as Visa points out in its round up of handy hints (**www.visa.com/nt/ecomm/consumer/main.html#tips**), although obviously it could be more expensive if you don't pay off the £250 you lavished on that rarest of F Scott Fitzgerald's books, *Turkey Remains And How To Inter Them With Numerous Scarce Recipes from The Note-Books of F Scott Fitzgerald.*

Don't rush. Online shopping still takes time, especially if you're looking for something rare, so check delivery times and don't leave it to the last possible minute.

Trust your instincts. If you don't feel comfortable buying something because you suspect you're buying from a cyber Del Boy, back off. The American-based Internet Fraud Watch (**www.fraud.org/internet/intset.htm**) says that high-pressure sales tactics are often a sign that there's something fishy going on.

You may find these sites of help.

http://uk.kelkoo.com/ helps you compare prices before you buy.

www.bizrate.com rates companies in the online shopping business.

www.consumerworld.org/ is big, brash and American and has everything from product reviews to the news that 76% of email response systems at 1000 e-commerce operators failed to, err, respond to emails.

www.which.net/ now have their own e-tailer accreditation scheme.

www.zdnet.com/pcmag/features/e-comm_sites/sb2.htm "Shop safely in unknown corners" is this site's boast and it almost lives up to that promise.

**How to shop online
and not feel paranoid**

SAFE AS HOUSES

"I'd like to go shopping online but..." The 'but' in that sentence invariably refers to a fear that shopping over the Internet is likely to expose yourself to all sorts of frauds, scams and cybercrimes, many of which you may not even be aware of. With online bank accounts appearing to be about as private as the post-PE lesson shower in your schooldays, and daily headlines about an epidemic of cyberfraud, shopping over the Internet seems fraught with unacceptable risk. In truth, there's no conclusive evidence that online shoppers are more likely to be the victim of fraud than those who do their shopping offline

If it's so safe why do I read so many scare stories?

The Federal Trade Commission, the US government body which keeps an eye on this, says "There's a general public concern about transmitting credit card numbers over the Internet which is not well-founded. All in all, **it's much riskier to give your credit card to a waiter** or waitress than it is to send it over the Internet." Many reports of online credit fraud actually relate to breaches of security in offline databases and not to misuse on the Internet itself. That said, there is obviously a risk but you can reduce your chances of becoming a victim.

When am I most at risk?

For a full rundown of potential dangers see the "take precautions" section below, but generally **avoid products sold on junk email**, which seem to be offered at ludicrous prices, by companies you've never heard of whose only offline location is a post box in a remote island republic whose major export is fraud.

When I'm online, can people steal information from my hard disk?

Theoretically yes, but this is one **urban legend** which has never been proved. If you really want to investigate how much data you are giving away while surfing, try visiting ***http://privacy.net/analyze.***

What are cookies and are they dangerous?

No, but neither are they as cute as the name suggests. Cookies are basically small text files which some sites store on your hard disk. For instance, you might have booked a holiday and this file will store the pages you visited when buying so the travel company can customise its pages for you next time you visit their site. These text files can only contain information you provide and can only be read by the site which created them. Nor, as small text files, are they likely to be the carriers of the next I Love You! electronic plague. If you're using Internet Explorer, you can see what cookies are on your hard disk by selecting "Preferences" from the "Edit" menu and scrolling down to "Receiving Files". In Netscape, you can decide how to manage cookies by pulling down"Preferences" and clicking on "Advanced".

What are firewalls?

At its simplest, a firewall is a cyberforce which protects corporate IT networks from external communications systems such as the Internet. Often, the firewall will be a physical computer with a couple of network interface cards: it will check every packet of data going between the internal and external network and reject those it is programmed to consider inappropriate. You need to be aware of this if you're buying from work, because some corporate **firewalls can actually prevent your order** from being processed without you realising.

If a site has 'UK' in its address, can I assume that it's a British company?

No. Which is why you're better off checking their physical location (or "snail mail" address) to be sure.

Any other general advice?

Beware of sites/email offers which use capital letters for NO APPARENT REASON, promise "secrets of success", have ludicrous testimonials from customers defined only as "Mrs S, Canada" and start their pitch with the protest-too-much headline "This is not a scam!". Also, watch out for **"shopping baskets"**. Some sites stick stuff in them when you click for more info and others don't let you pull items at the last minute. If in doubt, crash the terminal.

Security guards

http://www.ftc.gov/bcp/conline/pubs/online/sitesee/index. html is the Janet-and-John guide to surfing for the ultimate

newbie, from those nice folks in the US government
http://www.oft.gov.uk/html/shopping/index.html is the
British version of the above, aimed at online shopping
www.which.net/shopping/guide.html is the commendably
unhysterical approach from *Which?* to the pitfalls of
online shopping
www.scambusters.com does exactly what it says on the
web address but be warned – it may make you paranoid
http:/privacy.net covers similar territory and will leave
you even more paranoid
www.web-police.org is Interpol's electronic arm, which
comes complete with a comedy western sheriff's badge,
a string of Java error messages and, seven out of ten
times, a crash to your terminal.

You can take precautions...

1 **When you visit a site, check how secure it is**. Sites
which are encrypted may have an address which
begins 'https' (the extra "s" indicates the site is using a bit
of technical know-how called Secure Sockets Layer to
encode your data). If you're using Internet Explorer or
Netscape Communicator, a secure site should have
a little golden padlock at the bottom of your screen.
(But remember that this lock may only appear when you
enter the part of the site where you actually buy
something.) In Netscape version 4.6 onwards, there is a
security button on the toolbar next to "Print" which, if
you click on it, will tell you whether the site you're on
uses encryption. If you're still uncertain, check their web
address with a service like ***www.enonymous.com*** which
will tell you, for instance, if the online store you're
visiting will give out your data to other companies without specifically asking your permission.

2 **Don't use a simple password** when registering on a
site. Dates of birth, mother's maiden names, etc, can
easily be guessed. Try something more obscure (often
mixing letters and numbers) which you can still easily
remember. If you're really worried, use really complex

passwords and store them in a software program like Password Keeper (***www.gregorybraun.com/PassKeep. html***) which will cost you the equivalent of $20 in your English pounds. Or surf the Web anonymously with free trial software from ***www.anonymizer.com***.

3 **Don't buy anything you hear about in junk email.** According to those awfully vigilant people at Internet ScamBusters (***www.scambusters.com***), your chances of getting anything at all from such a source are less than 45 per cent and your chances of actually getting what you ordered are a statistically unimpressive one in 20. Also, take care if a seller is using a free email service. While most people using these services are as honest as the 21st of June is long, these services make it easier for a seller to hide their real identity.

4 **Use a credit card.** It limits your liability if you're ripped off. Barclaycard, for example, guarantees you against any fraudulent use of your card providing you haven't done anything seriously daft like junk email your credit card number and expiry date to everyone in your electronic address book.

5 **Don't buy anything from a website which doesn't have a physical location.** If that physical address happens to begin and end with a post box number, consider moving on. Similarly, if a person you're buying from at an auction won't give you their real name, address and phone number, take your business elsewhere. The European Union's distance-selling directive, which was due to be implemented in all countries in the EU by June 2000, states that if you're paying in advance you have to be told the identity of the supplier and their address before concluding the contract to buy.

6 **Buy branded names from known sources**. One estimate suggests that 10-20 per cent of luxury goods sites are selling fakes. Okay, that estimate did come from an Internet security company but the best way to ensure your branded stuff is the genuine article is to shop at known stores rather than the dot com equivalent of

IF THINGS GO WRONG...

Complain to the e-tailer with the usual info. Most will have a help button with a contact address and their returns policy.

If you're still not happy, you can: call your local Trading Standards department; see if they belong to a trade association (and if it runs an arbitration scheme); sue; complain to the Office of Fair Trading, the Advertising Standards Authority, your MP or, if desperate, *Watchdog*. For the full rundown and for issues with an overseas e-tailer, see *www.oft.gov.uk/html/ shopping/index.html*.

You can also use the free consumer watchdog service belonging to the Interactive Media In Retail Group (IMRG) on *www.imrg.org*. Set up to raise awareness of online shopping, it has its own code of practice.

If you don't get delivery in 30 days, and haven't agreed to another date, you should be able to cancel and/or get your money back.

Trotters Independent Traders. There are various accreditation schemes (such as Trust UK and Which Web Trader) which are designed to make sure you're dealing with reputable company.

7 Save copies of every email and document related to your purchase. It might just help you get some redress if you're ripped off.

8 Check every little detail. Bargain headline prices may be offset by ludicrous shipping costs, especially if you want the item delivered yesterday. On the plus side, some e-tailers will have goodwill policies which mean they'll refund your money if you're not happy for any reason.

9 Be careful with your personal info. We're all smart enough not to paste a Post-It with our passwords onto our keyboard, but don't give out any other info about yourself (addresses etc) unless you're on a secure site.

10 Remember: if you do decide to buy from an individual, your rights of redress will probably not be as good as if you had bought the item from a company.

11 Know your software. Both Explorer and Communicator have devices which can help you to shop more safely. For example, in the way most Internet users have their browsers set up, their name and email address are available to every website they happen to visit. If you don't want this to be the case, you can leave these fields blank.

Auctions are for everybody, not just Hugh Scully or Arthur Daley

GOING GOING, GONE

A uctions are no longer the preserve of art collectors or dealers in dodgy motors. The current glut of auction sites allows folk all over the world to recycle their stuff. That is not to say that online auctions are problem-free but the more way-out rumours about desperate people selling their kidneys for transplant or buying nuclear weapons from the former Soviet Union are unfounded

Know the ground rules

E ven if someone were trying to offload their internal organs to the highest bidder, reputable auction sites are pretty strict about what they will accept as a lot. They are subject to the same laws as any high-street retailer about what they can sell, although individuals who sell through the sites are not governed by consumer laws, which can lead to problems for the buyer (see *How Not To Get Conned* p37). But sellers who try to break the rules will find their auction accounts terminated and very possibly replaced by an intimate tête-a-tête with the constabulary.

That's not to say that you won't still find some bizarre and compelling items. If you missed your chance in 1981, you can now pick up a Charles & Diana Commemorative Wedding Coin for a very reasonable price. Others may decide they must have a 1914 edition of *Golf Monthly*. Where caution is required is the urge to possess any number of strange items that will end up collecting dust until you finally get around to auctioning them yourself.

How auctions work

Most online auction sites, whether they offer general or specialist merchandise, work in the same way. On general sites, like eBid or QXL, the offerings are broken down first into rough categories such as computer hardware or household goods, with further sub-categories appearing as you progress through the site. There are usually featured auctions on the home page, as well as on the main page for each category, but these are not necessarily the best bargains on the site; the sellers probably paid for their lots to get extra publicity.

Auction sites are free to buyers. They make their money by charging sellers small fees to list an item, and another if a sale is successful. On specialist auction sites it helps to know exactly what you are looking for, or to be very careful in assessing what's on offer.

A computer package may seem like an extraordinary deal, but look closely and you may find that it comes minus small details, like a monitor. This may not worry you, but if you were looking for a

---

IN THE BAG

Most auction sites have a special charity section to browse in case you're feeling philanthropic.

The charity Breast Cancer Care was lucky enough to bag a legend when they persuaded Margaret Thatcher to relinquish her grip on her beloved black Ferregamo handbag, still doubtless bearing the imprints of out-of-favour cabinet ministers.

It was further enhanced by a letter of authentication signed by the Iron Lady herself. Auctioned via Handbag.com and eBay, it was eventually won by a Scottish collector for a whopping £100,000.

ready to plug in PC, it's not the deal for you.

If you are just surfing auction sites to see if anything appeals to you, you don't need to register on most sites. But once you decide to buy or sell, you will have to register to show that you are a real person and can be contacted if there's a dispute.

EBay is the most famous auction site on the Internet. But if you're selling stuff on it, check out the fees

Private sellers usually have to provide more information about themselves than buyers, including credit card details. After a number of online shouting matches about deals that didn't go through or goods that never turned up, some sites now insist that you provide an email address that is registered either at your home or place of work (a Hotmail address that can be run from a cyber café is much too worryingly anonymous).

The art of selling

Once you have decided which site will benefit from the contents of your attic, you need to list your item as a lot on the site. The first things you will be asked for are fairly obvious – a title for your lot, a brief, accurate but attention-grabbing description and a starting price.

After that it can get a little more complicated. You will have the option to upload a picture of your item, and to put a reserve amount on your lot. So if your rollerblades cost you £150 and a broken wrist, and you don't want to sell them for less than half of what you paid, a good trick is to make the starting price very low to attract attention, but then place a reserve price of £75 on them.

Some sites discourage reserve prices, which they say make a sale less likely. This is true, but their concern is really more for their sale fees than for your profit. Other decisions to make include: the duration of the auction, who pays for shipping (almost always the buyer), and what forms of payment you will accept. It is also vital to let potential buyers know a little bit about yourself in order to allay fears that you might be a criminal.

If someone wins your auction and is now looking forward to breaking bones of their own, you are legally obliged to sell the rollerblades to them. The auction site will forward you details of who has won the bidding and it is up to you to arrange payment and delivery.

The art of buying

Before you do anything, remind yourself that any bid you place is a binding contract and if you win the lot, you cannot change your mind, so don't bid for anything just for a laugh or that stuffed badger could be yours.

Make all the checks you want (see *How Not To Get Conned*) and if everything looks good, the best and most efficient way to proceed is to decide the maximum you are prepared to pay, and then ask the site to bid on your behalf up to that amount. If no one bids above you, and the reserve has been met, the blades are yours, hopefully below your maximum price. If someone outbids your maximum, the site will notify you to see if you want to bid again. This is when auction fever can set in. Don't fall into the "oh, it's only another tenner" trap. Go and make a cup of tea. Then rush back, throw caution to the winds and bid like crazy until they're yours. You know you're going to, at least once.

Once you have fought off the other contenders, the seller will contact you to let you know the final price of the rollerblades, including their shipping cost. Think about this extra expense before you make your final bid.

Don't fall into the 'oh, it's only another tenner' trap. Go and make a cup of tea

HOW NOT TO GET CONNED

According to The National Fraud Information Center (**_www.fraud.com_**), 87 per cent of Internet fraud last year was on auction sites. This is not surprising. Personal auctions are like carboot sales with the added thrill of not knowing if the goods will even turn up. Placing a lot for sale, or bidding on an item, is in theory a binding contract but in practice it is unlikely to be worth the effort and cost to try to enforce it. The big sites have introduced tighter security measures, but you can reduce the risks.

Start small. It's not the end of the world if you lose a fiver on something that turns out to be dodgy.

Try to buy only from rated sellers. You can check out other buyers' experiences with sellers in the feedback section of the site. See if the seller is a regular on the site's message boards and is open about what they're selling.

Buying from the auction site or a registered company using the site as a sales tool is a lot safer than buying from an individual. Most consumer protection laws don't deal with private sales, so disputes could be hard to settle.

If you do buy from an individual, get an address and other identifying information before sending your money.

If buying from a company or the auction site, check details of returns, warranties and service if the product is faulty. Ask that higher priced items are insured while in transit.

Be aware that some sellers get friends ('shills') to bid on items to raise the price artificially. Don't always rush to bid back on an item you want (unless the auction is about to close). This will reveal how keen you are to win the lot.

Pay by the safest way you can. If a seller insists on cash, think twice. If possible, pay by credit card (more and more sites are offering individuals a way to accept credit card payments) because you can dispute the charges if the goods are misrepresented or never arrive.

Tell the auction site if you come across dodgy dealings, as the site can (and will) investigate on your behalf.

Remember the golden rule of auctions If it sounds too good to be true, it probably is.

General Auctions Something for everyone

Auction Town

www.auctiontown.co.uk

Despite the cutesy category titles (Miscellaneous Mews!) there are bargains to
be nabbed here, though when we browsed on a Mac, it kept causing Internet
Explorer to abort. You have to register just to look at lots, but basic listings are
free to sellers (you pay if you want your lot highlighted), and there are
comprehensive instructions for beginners.

Bluecycle

www.bluecycle.com

Backed by the insurance giant CGU, this is where to come for items seized by
the police and never claimed or left after the insurers paid out. Head for the
Salvage section for incredible bargains on some truly bizarre lots.

EBay

www.ebay.co.uk

The first (and still one of the biggest) auction site, with items ranging from rare
Victorian stamps to modern furniture. The homepage may look hectic, but it's
a great site offering lots of info about each lot and lively message boards. It's
free to buyers, but for sellers there is a complex fee structure – check before
deciding what to list. On each sale there's an insertion fee (between $0.25 and
$5), plus a final value fee based on a percentage of the sale price. Other fees
include one to put a reserve price on your item (refundable if it doesn't sell).

EBid

www.ebid.co.uk

A real mixed bag of items on this site, including a trip to France for five people
or a domain name for selling Rolex watches. They charge a handling fee for
any lot that reaches its reserve price, plus a closing charge based on your
final sale price. You can easily check which lots are getting extra attention, or
are about to close, from useful links on the home page.

E-Base 5

www.ebase5.com

Small compared to the giant sites, but worth a look if you're after bargain

Beanie Babies or Pokémon cards. Listing items is free, and the seller only pays if they want their lot in bold (10p) or featured (50p). The site makes money by encouraging users to advertise with them, for which they charge a basic fee plus 5p per person who accesses their page from this site.

EZ-Auctions

www.ez-auctions.net

This site was short of content as we went to press – a shame as it's one of the best for ease of navigation and clarity of instructions. Hopefully traffic will improve. Placement fees range from 75p to £5 and commission fees depend on the final price of the object. Students are entitled to a 25 per cent fee discount, and the site runs occasional specials like no commission for a month.

QXL

www.qxl.com

QXL works in three different ways. An item can be auctioned by QXL itself, by one of its Merchant Partners, or by individuals. There is no insertion fee, but they charge success fees (although a credit for new sellers effectively makes your first £185 from sales commission free). Any queries not answered online are dealt with by an excellent phone support line. The site also features Hugh Scully's Online Valuations where you can get your antiques valued by experts and then auction them online with a certificate declaring their authenticity.

Yahoo Auctions

http://uk.auctions.yahoo.com/uk

Plenty to browse through, and easy to find your way around. It's free to list lots on this site, although they do insist on holding any seller's credit card details for security purposes. Buyers are only allowed to bid on a few items at a time until they have some positive feedback from a seller. The better their rating, the more lots they can bid on.

Bluecycle is the place to go for really hot merchandise: many products on this site come from police raids

Specialist Auctions — Something in particular

Art
www.sothebys.com
Be prepared to add a lot of noughts to your usual auction maximum, but there's a brilliant online chat system to introduce you to the world of high art. See also www.bonhams.com and www. christies.com, or for something a little less highbrow, www.artconte. com – paintings, drawings and sculpture from both young and established artists, many of them based in the US.

Business equipment
www.morgan-auctions.co.uk
Outstanding site for nearly new and refurbished office equipment, especially computers and computer parts. Bidding process is simple and speedy. See also www.business-auctions.com – office clearance goods and refurbished computers, aimed at business-to-business but bargains for home offices too.

Collectibles
www.icollector.co.uk
Quality antiques, art and collectibles from bone china to classic sports cars, from professional dealers and auction houses only (many US-based).

Computers
www.cnet.com
US-based computer hardware and software – worth looking at but some lots may have export problems. See also www.computers4sale.co.uk – UK site for private sellers to offload anything to do with computing.

Sports Memorabilia
www.sports-memorabilia.co.uk
Plenty of unique sporting items up for grabs here – such as boxing gloves signed by Muhammad Ali or a cricket bat signed by Don Bradman.

Stamps
www.sandafayre.com
Stamp collectors' paradise with vast selection of countries on offer. Online bids are put against postal bids, and all lots come with no-quibble guarantee.

**How to make sure
it's worth your while**

BUYING STUFF
FROM ABROAD

It seems so simple. An international site
has the camcorder you want at a price
that turns local retailers pale. Tap in your
credit card details, await delivery and you're
quids in, right? Well, not always. Those
huge savings can be wiped out by irritating
extras like shipping, import duty and VAT,
so for the real low cost lowdown, read on

Things to remember

Some goods, particularly in the electronic and computing
markets, may not be available for shipping overseas.
Many US-based companies restrict which goods can be
exported to protect their international markets. So you
could find a website with exactly the 3COM Palm Pilot
you're after, and at a mind-boggling price, only to be told
at checkout that it can't be shipped overseas.

You should also check if the manufacturer will honour
warranties if the goods have been shipped overseas, or
offers technical support for international users. Many do
not. This isn't such a problem if you want Calvin Klein
underwear, but if it's anything electrical or electronic, do

some research before you click "buy". If you're looking for a video product, be it a camcorder or DVD player, remember that many countries use formats incompatible with UK television sets. We use PAL video, so check that anything you buy can be converted to that format.

Make sure it's worth it

Once you find the right thing to buy, shipping can often be worked out online before you finalise the order, but be prepared to provide credit card details and start the buying process before you find out how much delivery will be. Less savvy sites may have to email you separately. Either way, be sure to check costs thoroughly, as a FedEx delivery can add a shocking amount to the price.

Once shipping costs are clear, and you still think you've got a bargain, you then face the tricky business of

EXAMPLES OF CUSTOMS DUTY RATES (%)

AUDIO-VISUAL		Skis	3.7
Compact discs	3.5	**GARMENTS**	
DVD player	14	Women's and girls'	12.8
DVD discs	3.5	Men's & boys'	12.8
Colour televisions	14	Baby	10.5
Video cameras & camcorders	4.9	**JEWELLERY**	
Video games	2.2	Of precious metals	2.5
Video tape recorders *(domestic)*	14	*(inc. jewellery with pearls*	
Bicycles *(including children's)*	15	*or semi-precious stones)*	
Computers *(Including peripherals)*	FREE	Imitation jewellery	4
Fax machines	FREE	Microwave ovens	5
FOOTWEAR		Mobile phones	1.6
Ski boots & board boots	17	**PHOTOGRAPHIC**	
With uppers of leather	8	Still cameras	4.2
FURNITURE		Digital still cameras	FREE
Metal, wood & plastic	FREE	Skin care products *(inc. make-up)*	FREE
GAMES & SPORT		Spectacles and sunglasses	2.9
Golf clubs and tennis rackets	2.7	Tools	2.7

CUSTOMS AND EXCISE ADVICE CENTRES

IPSWICH:	01473 235951	NOTTINGHAM:	0115 971 2107
LONDON CENTRAL:	020 7865 4400	PLYMOUTH:	01752 777123
LONDON SOUTH:	020 7202 4227	READING:	0118 964 4355
NEWCASTLE-UPON-TYNE:	0191 201 1719	SOUTHAMPTON:	023 8082 7536

import duty and VAT on goods entering the UK. You don't have to pay extra tax on imports of less than £18 in value, but tobacco, alcohol and perfume are liable from the first penny.

All international parcels must have a standard label on them declaring the contents so Customs and Excise can assess the duty and level of VAT to apply. If this label is missing, incomplete or unclear, they will open the parcel to inspect the contents.

Some web sites tried putting misleading information on packages to foil the tax man, but they're cracking down on this, so don't rely on it as a ruse to lower costs. If they do open your parcel and find that its contents are illegal in the UK – in the unlikely event that you're importing, say, nunchuka – the goods will be confiscated, and you may be prosecuted.

As with most tax matters, the amount of duty and VAT payable on personal imports is not one simple calculation applied to all goods. Taxes are charged at differing rates depending on the type of product imported and its place of manufacture. We've compiled a duty table for items you're more likely to find while shopping online, but this is only a fraction of the complete Customs Tariff, which reads like advanced calculus.

If you are unsure what category your purchase falls under (and you probably will be), ring your local Customs and Excise Advice Centre or try

WORK OUT THE TAX

1. Look up the item's duty rate % and VAT %.

2. Multiply the Purchase Price Abroad (PPA) by the duty rate %. This is the amount of duty to be paid (AMOUNT A).

3. Add AMOUNT A to the PPA and multiply the result by the VAT %. This is the amount of VAT to be paid (AMOUNT B).

4. Add AMOUNTS A & B together and that will be how much tax you have to pay on your order.

EXAMPLE:

You've ordered some CDs from abroad. The cost, including postage and packing, was £100. So, you find out that the duty rate is 3.5% and that VAT is 17.5%. Multiplying the cost of the CDs by the duty rate gives you £3.50. Add this to the original £100 and you get £103.50. Multiply that by the VAT rate, which is 17.5%, and that all comes to £18.11. So £121.61 is what you'll pay for your CDs in all, of which £21.61 will be your total Customs and Excise charge.

www.hmce.gov.org for online guidance. Rather unfairly, the charges you pay for shipping are counted as part of the purchase price, so don't forget to factor this in too.

Pay the tax man and bag a bargain

If your order is sent by post, the Post Office will collect duty and VAT on behalf of Customs and Excise, or store the goods if Customs needs to make further inquiries. Usually the Post Office will collect charges on delivery (a label will be slapped on the package at the Customs Postal Depot, showing the charge as well as any Post Office fee), and it adds a small charge for doing this – Royal Mail charges £1.20 and Parcelforce charges £5.25 for standard deliveries and £10.25 for express. Sometimes collection of these charges can be a bit random, but don't count on a dozy postman to save your pennies. If there's any query, they will send you a form to complete and return to them before your parcel can be delivered.

If your order is sent by an international courier, such as Federal Express, DHL or UPS, they will pay any taxes due and invoice you for reimbursement. Federal Express (*www.federalexpress/com/gb*) and DHL (*www.dhl.co.uk*) do not charge for this service, although you may have to pay a £10 Customs admin charge for dealing with a courier.

> With a bit of online detective work you can save £100 on a Canon camera

But don't let all this bureaucracy, tax and abstruse mathematical calculations put you off. There are loads of things worth seeking out on foreign sites, such as camera equipment, fax machines and some furniture, which are low rated (or even free) for duty, leaving only VAT and shipping that you need to worry about.

A bit of online detective work can lead to some stunning bargains. For example, a Canon Powershot S10 digital still camera, quoted at £478 (inc VAT) on a leading British

If you love him tender, this is the obvious place to go for more Elvis memorabilia than you'll find anywhere outside Graceland itself

website, is only $434.99 on US-based The Camera Club (**www.thecameraclub.com**). When you convert that, add VAT and shipping (about $40), you're looking at a total price of about £378 – a saving of around £100.

Savings can also be made on less expensive items such as CDs, books or clothing if you buy several at one time. A best-selling CD might cost $13.28 (about £9.09) on **CdNow.com** compared to £11.99 on **Amazon.co.uk**, but you'd have to buy at least 11 titles before shipping and taxes were overtaken by savings. Similarly, high-quality cotton men's t-shirts from Lands End are £12.50 each on **www.landsend.co.uk**, but only $12.00 (about £8.22) on **www.landsend.com**. But after taxes and shipping, you're only saving around £1 per shirt even if you buy a dozen.

Some foreign websites offer items that are just not available in the UK. This could be anything from Elvis memorabilia (**www.elvis-presley.com**) to authentic Italian deli food (**www.gourmet2000.it**). There's piles of stuff out there that will never reach your high street, but it can come to your front door. Above all, online shopping should be fun. If that Okuma Titus TG50 fishing reel ($199.99 from **www.gofishin.com**) looks like it could bring a bureaucratic headache rather than an awesome saving, think again. But after a bit of surfing and a few price comparisons, you should be able to catch an international bargain to brag about for months to come.

**How the Web
helps you shop**

USING THE
INTERNET

Okay, you've been to your local PC World
and put a snazzy beige box on your
credit card. You've listened to your
modem gurgling and clicked on the
browser and you can see something which
the manual describes as a homepage. And
the rest, as they say, is mystery. Don't click
on the "Help!" button until you've read this

Searching the Web

A search engine is exactly that. A means of searching
the Net for whatever you want. Just type in key
words and click on **"Search"** or **"Go"**. Hundreds of
links of some relevance to your chosen topic should
appear. But type in Madonna and you may find yourself
reading reams of religious sermons instead of quirky
facts about the Queen of Pop.

The granddaddy of all search engines has got to be
www.yahoo.com. Its straightforward design gives you
the choice of browsing through the categories listed, such

as **"travel"**, or just typing in your chosen topic. Yahoo can search sites in a specific country or the whole web.

A wealth of young pretenders have emerged to challenge Yahoo with new technology and new ways of linking you to your request. For example, **www.google.com** delivers results based on sites which have been linked to by the most other sites. So Google should lead you to the most useful, if you accept that the most useful are also the most popular. If you want quantity rather than quality, **www.altavista.com** claim to hold the largest index available, with 350 million web pages.

From the best of the rest, **www.alltheweb.com** is a parallel search tool, exploring a range of other engines to find results, **www.dogpile.com** gets good word of mouth recommendation whereas **www.askjeeves.co.uk** could be called the idiot's guide to the Net as you can type in the exact question you want answered. But Jeeves can focus on the if's and but's rather than the real question.

Making sense of directories

If you lack the patience to browse the thousands of pages that most search engines list, directories provide a narrower field of enquiry. They group together URLs of like mind so if you want to know about skiing, a directory will offer a list of sites all relating to the ski world.

For specific help, you can find online equivalents of Yellow Pages

The best UK specific directories include **www.yahoo.co.uk**, **www.looksmart.co.uk** and **www.ukplus.co.uk**. Click on a particular category and browse through the list of related URLs. Many, such as UK Plus, review each site so you can sift the best and the worst. There are directories defined by age (**www.seniorsearch.com/ssuk/homedirectory.htm** for fiftysomethings) or where you live (**www.250000.com** lists sites by geographical location).

If you want a one-click process, some sites act as online equivalents of Yellow Pages. If you're moving house or moving country, ***www.yell.co.uk*** contains property and travel guides with resort guides, insurance quotes, removal men etc while ***www.scoot.co.uk*** can find products from furniture to your local Chinese take-away.

Shopping Bots

With many couples' Saturday ritual being to hit the high street at 11am, have the men lose interest at around lunchtime and both head home at around 2pm with not a shopping bag in sight, shopping on the high street has ceased to be a pleasure and become something which causes **57 per cent of arguments** between couples in the UK. Shopping from your computer could ease the tension if you know **how (and where)** to look.

Help is at hand. Shopping directories are the online equivalent to shopping malls. Most, like ***www.just35.com***, ***www.shopsafe.co.uk*** and ***www.shop andwin.co.uk*** offer a list of popular shopping categories alongside reviews and ratings. Many are taking directories that one-step further by creating **shopping bots**. Most sites advertise themselves as cutting high-street prices so you should get some kind of bargain but a shopping bot searches cyberspace to find the best deals for you. This sounds too good to be true and in some cases it is, but many good bots will do just what it says on the box.

All you do is tell them what you're looking for, they take a few seconds to scan the globe and return with a list of the best bargains. One of the best bots is ***www.kelkoo.com*** with a database of 25,000 online stores. Categories include music, film, wines, electrical appliances and computing, and you can make your search as simple or as complex as you like. For obvious reasons, they'll only look at companies that deliver to the UK. ***http://uk.shopsmart.com*** and ***www.mytaxi.co.uk*** are other solid sites to follow. Although the price comparisons are limited to CDs, videos, games and books, the vast selection can see you save up to 30 per cent on high-street prices, paying just £2.50 for a Harry Potter book.

If you're after a specific bargain, simply type **"price comparison"** and then whatever you're looking for into your search engine. Most search engines come up with something but try ***http://wine-searcher.com*** for the boozy bargains, ***www.bookbrain.co.uk*** for literature and ***www.computerprices.co.uk*** for the obvious.

Some shopping bots only search the vendors which they have deals with so you won't always get the ultimate deal. An easy way to check this is to do a simple search for quite a common item and see how many different stores are listed. If it's limited to only a couple you may find better deals elsewhere. Some companies such as ***www.pricescan.com*** and ***www.mysimon.com*** make a point of saying they don't accept money from vendors.

If you're still not convinced, both ***www.botspot.com*** and ***www.smartbots.com*** offer guides to the best around. In the future, bots will constantly email you with new bargains. Some of them might even be relevant to you. Either way, you need never face Harrods sale again.

Group buying power

If you've got enough friends, group buying is another way to save. Sites such as ***www.letsbuyit.com*** and ***www.mercata.com*** work on the premise that the more people who buy an item, the cheaper it becomes. It's a bit more complicated than that but not much – just make sure you look out for the Best Price marking. Even if you persuade your whole family to join in, you'll never knock the price so low you get a digital camera for £10. They usually state a **cut-off price point** which may be **40 per cent off** the normal price. Lets Buy offers the chance to bid at the current price or only on the best possible price, so you can decide in advance how much you'll be stung for. You can also tip off a friend about the latest great deals.

www.buyasone.com   Buy as One
www.mobshop.com   Mob Shop

Getting the best reviews

The Internet is teeming with review sites for everything from film and music to computer and household goods. There are even sites reviewing other websites so you can find the best site to start your online search from.

Of the more general review sites, ***www.epinions.com***, ***www.productreviewnet.com*** and ***www.consumer guide.com*** are probably the best. Each covers popular online buys, CDs and computer equipment, as well as more unusual stuff like cigars, sleeping bags and shampoo. You can submit your own reviews or read those from independent punters. Product Review also offers buying guides and shopping tips, and Consumer Guide offers a concise history of each item and a guide to what the technical nonsense in handbooks means. Useful if you still can't set the timer on your video.

Don't be put off by the countless computer reviews that you'll find during your searches. There's a review site

You're never alone when you're online shopping: not with sites like Product Review around to advise

on the Net to cover every product and topic imaginable. Book reviews are posted on the sites of some e-tailers like BOL, Waterstones and WHSmith. Or you could peruse. ***www.booksonline.co.uk*** from the *Daily Telegraph* allows you to search by author, title or genre. *The Times*, the *Independent* and the *Guardian* also run online review sections and links to independent sellers. With ***www.blether.com*** you can discuss the book you've just read and say whether you loved or hated it.

Review sites can give you what no retailer can: an objective opinion

For an alternative to the perhaps over-familiar film reviews of Barry Norman, you can always try ***www.popcorn.co.uk*** which covers reviews of every movie currently showing in the UK and lets you submit your own. ***www.odeon.com*** follows a similar premise with the added bonus of being able to buy online.

If you want computer reviews and can't face looking at every Tom, Dick and Harry's entry, one of the best is ***www.zdnet.com***. Covering PCs, peripherals and digital technology, ZD collects reviews from different sources and offers simple overviews, full reviews and test scores for a good all-round picture of the product before you buy.

Internet review sites are infinite in number, especially if you're looking for something like a car or a computer But even if you're after something more specialised, the Internet can help. If you're just getting into scuba diving but aren't sure what to use, ***www.scubadiving.com*** will help you decide if the Aqua Lung Impulse 2 or the Zeagle Flex is the best snorkel.

Review sites give you what you'll never get from the mumbling sales assistants who can barely recall the name of the products they're selling: an objective, informed opinion. A site like ***www.audioreview.com*** will offer you the opinions of punters and experts. At ***www.buy.co.uk*** they'll help you decide what deal best suits you, rather than what suits them. If you're after a mobile phone you just answer a set of questions, from which they'll determine what kind of phone to get, if any. They will then link you to reputable retailers who stock the product you need.

www.reviewfinder.com   Review Finder

And now for the bad news...

Veteran online shoppers have one big beef about buying over the Web and, surprisingly, it's not about the time it takes to deliver, but where stores deliver to.

Years ago, when the idea of buying stuff from your computer seemed like another sci-fi myth, a bit like the idea that we'd eat all our meals in a single white pill, the theory was that some day goods could be sent anywhere we wanted without us having to join a post office queue.

The reality isn't that good. Yet. Some sites, like wine seller Bordeaux Direct, do let you specify a different address but many, including Toys "R" Us, don't. Partly, it has to be said, because of legitimate security concerns about possible misuse of credit cards. But a solution must be found because sending present A to address B or C is a big part of what online shopping is supposed to be about.

One final beef from those buying goods from abroad is that too many sites make it very hard to discover: a) whether they deliver outside the US and b) if so, what they will charge. Sites should be more upfront about the extra costs and not force users to read the electronic small print. Some sites even add an admin fee without warning when you're halfway through your electronic checkout. Stunts like that give online shopping a bad name it doesn't deserve. They'd never try that at your local Woolies.

Part two

How to buy everything online
from azaleas to zithers

THE DIRECTORY

Antiques

The world's newest mass medium is probably the fastest growing marketplace for the world's oldest treasures. Even your old teddy can get in on it

Abercrombie Antiques
www.abercrombie.fsnet.co.uk
Specialising in antique glassware, jewellery and toys, along with collectible stamps and postcards, this Powys-based site has plenty to offer besides its online catalogue pages. There are details of antiques sales and fairs in the Mid-Wales area, training courses for both professionals and amateurs, and house-clearance services in Mid-Wales and nearby districts – Shropshire, Cheshire and Staffordshire.

Antiques.Co.Uk
www.antiques.co.uk
This speedy and beautifully laid out site promises antiques which have been vetted and guaranteed by a team of experts for sale and delivery all over the world. You can build up your own portfolio wish-list, arrange to view an item (the business is London-based), or even just go ahead and buy it, all online. You can pay by credit card, cheque or a wire-transfer from your bank, and delivery charges are calculated online so there won't be any nasty surprises in store. A very professional and impressive site.

Antiques UK
www.antiques-uk.co.uk
This antiques portal offers links to many regional stores and auction houses, from specialist dealers to salvage warehouses. There's an excellent classified section where you can post a message if you're looking for a particular item and any dealer with a matching piece can get in touch through the site.

Arts And Crafts Furniture
www.artsandcraftsantiques.co.uk
An online catalogue of restored late-19th and early-20th century furniture from the Art and Crafts movement. David Bona's store is based in Manchester, but there are good photos on an otherwise basic site, so you can get an idea of the beauty of some of the pieces. You can email for details or phone for a viewing.

The Bath Antiquities Centre

www.bathantiquities.freeserve.co.uk

If you like your antiques on the ancient side, this Bath-based site for a group of ten independent UK dealers is the place to come for real antiquities, with prehistoric items such as flint arrowheads or Ammonite fossils at surprisingly affordable prices. For a more recent treasure, an amulet of the Egyptian god Shu will cost you £110, but do check that it comes without one of those Howard Carter-style curses. Purchases can be made vie email or the phone, and all items are shipped with a certificate of guaranteed authenticity.

Christer Schulz Antiques

www.schultz-antiques.com

This site is the easy-to-use online current catalogue of a South East England-based dealer who specialises in high-quality English and Northern European antiques, ranging from Georgian secretaires to Victorian chandeliers. Christer Schulz will accept enquiries online, and the web site has contact details for his various retail outlets. There are also links to various other antiques information sites.

Christer Schulz will deal with your online queries, and the site also offers links to various antiques information sites

The Howard Gallery

www.thehowardgallery.article7.co.uk

This well-stocked antiques dealer is a specialist in 17th- and 18th-century furniture, and has a limited range of clocks and porcelain. The site is simply designed with good photos of available pieces, each of which you can make an online enquiry about. The Gallery will call you back within a few days.

Invaluable

www.thesaurus.co.uk

This isn't really an online shop, but a very useful collection of news articles, information on forthcoming auctions and tips for antiques enthusiasts. They have a comprehensive search facility through auction catalogues and dealers' stock lists if you're looking for a particular item, and offer contact details for dealers all over the world. A great online starting point for amateur collectors.

Lassco

www.lassco.co.uk

If a side table or chaise longue is simply not on a grand enough scale for you, what about getting into architectural antiques? Lassco is a salvage company offering a glorious selection of antique fixtures and fittings which have been saved from old buildings undergoing renovations or demolition. Items among their collection on offer when we investigated were Grinling Gibbons-style wood carvings taken from the old Lloyds of London building, and cabinets, some still containing botanical specimens, from the old Museum at Kew Gardens in London.

AMERICAN ANTIQUES

Old things from the New World are growing in popularity, particularly craft items such as rugs and quilts. Antique Quilts (*www.antiquequilts.com*) is one of the best sites for original American quilts; it also stocks other genuine Americana such as Quimper and Bennington pottery. There is plenty to browse online, or you can buy the full catalogue for $10. Other good sites for antiques with a transatlantic flavour include:

Time Travelers
www.tias.com

Leigh Keno American Antiques
www.leighkeno.com

Antique Fest
www.antiquefest.com

Essex River Antiques
www.essexriver antiques.com

Dawn Hill Antiques
www.dawnhillantiques.com

Mir Russki

www.russiansilver.co.uk
Should you find yourself with an overwhelming urge to collect Fabergé, Mir Russki can help you drop some serious cash on exquisite silver and enamelled pieces made during Imperial Russia. Not many people have £895 to spend on a matchbox cover, but if you do, you can contact the company through its web site, although for security's sake, they recommend the final cash transaction takes place over the phone.

Old Bear

www.oldbear.co.uk
Antique teddy bears are big business, so before you despatch your ragged childhood friend to the car-boot sale, take a look at this site to see if he's worth a bob or two. Toy collectors can get their fill of Steiff teddies and stuffed animals here, along with other famous manufacturers' items and teddy-related memorabilia. There's an online form to complete if you are seriously interested in any of the teddies featured for sale, and the site can send you more detailed information and photographs before you actually decide to buy.

Richard Gardner Antiques

www.richardgardnerantiques.co.uk
Cautiously and curiously rather ponderously billed as "possibly the largest single antique dealer web site in the world", this is actually a very smooth site which displays an enormous selection of truly lovely pieces of furniture and decorative items. The Miscellaneous section includes lots and lots of fun items, with clockwork birdcages and crocodile handbags to browse through. The company's showroom is in historic Petworth, Sussex.

Arts

The Internet is now the biggest art market in the world. You can buy almost anything, from a painting of Madonna and Child to vintage Polish posters to furniture made out of old fruit crates

General   For those with an artistic temperament

Art 123

http://ART123.com

Neat, uncluttered art news and opinion site with an online art market. The only slight downside is that, after you finish filling in the online order form, you notice you can only pay by cheque or money order. The market has a decent selection of contemporary art in a mix of styles, and even if you don't want to buy, you can still read up on which antique dealer has been done for fraud or which VIP has been offended by which work of art at which museum.

Art.com

www.art.com

The obvious address for all things arty offers limited editions, photographs, prints and posters, animation and even Mona Lisa mugs. The catalogue is massive. If you key in Edvard Munch, you will be bombarded with no fewer than 73 permutations of *The Scream* but you also get some of his less famous (but equally fine) work like *Vampire*. The site ships globally and if you spend more than $400 you get 50 per cent off your shipping charges.

Art Crimes

www.graffiti.org

It's graffiti, Jim, but not as we know it. None of that "Kilroy woz 'ere" stuff here – just an introduction to a network of artists who indulge in the world's biggest (and most debased) participation art, some of whom will do graffiti to order. All that and a catalogue of magazines with great names like *Molotov Cocktail*. This site is definitely worth a bookmark.

Art Is A Tart

www.art-is-a-tart.com

Limited edition paintings by contemporary artists, bronze resin sculptures and greetings cards (delivered free) are all on sale at a site which never quite lives up to the chutzpah in its title. The ordering system was temperamental and the visitor isn't given enough clear cues to find their way around easily.

Art Planet

www.artplanet.com

There are enough art links here to condemn the aficionado to a lifetime in cyberspace. Want to check what contemporary Lithuanian artists are up to? Follow the links and your curiosity will be satisfied on www.culture.lt/ArtDB/. The only criticism you can make of this site is that there is just too much here and some of the links are not always that relevant.

Christies

www.christies.com

If you happen to have $82.5m burning a hole in your pocket or purse, this is the place to buy a Van Gogh. But not everything on this site run by the famous (and thoroughly wired) auction house costs that much: you can buy a Warhol print for less than $9000. Failing that, a subscription to the company's *Living With Art magazine* will cost you a measly £14. A word of warning: once you've visited this site you will want to keep coming back, if for no other reason than to hang around in a very classy part of cyberspace.

Eyestorm

www.eyestorm.com

Flashy site which offers contemporary art and art photography from A (Marina Abramovic) to W (James Welling) and enables the technologically challenged to enter a "quick, simple" version. If you use credit card-ordering (there's a handling charge of $1) your item will be delivered free, usually within two working days of the order being processed. Although the breadth of artists on display is impressive, the work on show may not always be their finest.

New British Artists

www.newbritishartists.co.uk

Reasonably priced selection of work from British artists you may not have heard of, complete with potted biographies of each prodigy and an email ordering service. There's also a good money-back guarantee if the work of art you get doesn't look quite as tasty as it did on the computer screen.

Red Dot

www.reddot.co.uk

This site's exhibition of the month typically features a select number of artists with prices starting at about £125. The site has an understandable, but still slightly irritating, habit of showing work that has already been sold. Pictures can be returned if you contact the gallery within three days and pay for delivery. If you're a new buyer, you should find the excellent back-up info (advice, terms and conditions etc) helpful. You can't yet buy online but you can reserve a painting by email.

Sothebys
www.sothebys.com

It may be just the colour scheme but this site feels more formal than Christies. But you can register to bid online and, as with Christies, there's no shortage of stuff to bid for. Those of you who find yourselves, almost against your will, glued to Loyd Grossman's *Through The Keyhole* may find the catalogues intriguing, especially the one devoted to the estate of the late Jacqueline Kennedy Onassis. After all, £90 is a small price to pay for such prurience.

 Artists Lords, thin white dukes and tramps

David Bowie
www.bowieart.com

The return of the Thin White Duke throwing darts into eyes of art lovers everywhere. After close inspection of just one of the works displayed here, all but the most hardcore Bowie fan would probably decide there are cheaper ways of getting his autograph. The site is uncluttered by any information such as its returns policy, how they ship the stuff to you... When emailed, the site responded that it delivers within 14 days of a credit card order and will refund or exchange any item if the customer is not happy. These policies weren't posted on the site, the email explained helpfully, because BowieArt is not a big company. So that's all right then.

Jack Lord
sites.inka.de/sites/edruta/jlmaler.htm

In the 1950s Jack Lord, aka The Lord of Hawaii aka Steve McGarrett of *Hawaii Five-O*, tried to make a living as a painter. On this Anglo-German site you can find a collection of his work in the style of various masters such as Van Gogh and Gaugin. The drawings suggest there was genuine talent before he became more famous for being the world's most conspicuous consumer of hair lacquer. You can't buy Lord's work online, but you can buy the work of another US TV cop Buddy Ebsen (who played Barnaby Jones) from www.buddyebsencreations.com/gallery/fine1.html – but please don't.

Daniel Strawser
http://strawserart.com/trampartbio.html

If art was a stock market, now would be a good time to buy as many shares as you could in in 'tramp art'. The term applies to those artists who take everyday debris like fruit crates and pallets and make small pieces of furniture out of them. It's called tramp art because it's how American hobos allegedly amused themselves in the early 1800s and the 1930s. Daniel Strawser's contemporary work is typical of the genre although this display doesn't really do him justice – some of the links don't work and the close-ups aren't that close up. But you can email him an enquiry about any of the work on show.

Andy Warhol
www.warholstore.com
Andy's official online art mart contains the less-than-reassuring statement to potential customers outside the US: "We will attempt to honor all international orders" Pity really, because there's a massive range of stuff on sale here and much of it is on offer at good discount prices.

 Galleries Fine art, butterflies and flowers

20th Century Fine Art Gallery
www.geocities.com/SoHo/Den/6243/index.html
The title is slightly misleading, omitting as it does the key word "Russian", but this is a lovely, almost naive, site which simply showcases some wonderful paintings from (among others) the Leningrad school and simply asks you to email the gallery if you are interested in buying any of the work on display.

Animation Art
www.animationartgallery.com
There aren't many works of art which Joe Public can afford, but just $400 at this online gallery will buy you an original piece of animation art from *The Simpsons*. The site – which showcases cartoons and animation from Dr Seuss through to Disney and Matt Groening – is slightly chaotic, but there is secure online ordering (although you only find that out when you try to buy).

Flowers East
www.flowerseast.co.uk
East End warehouse art gallery which has been showcasing the best of British art for over 30 years. You can buy special-offer prints by email or view original works from such artists as Carole Hodgson, whose sculpture *Standing Form* is quoted at £3500. All in all, a seductive, low-key site where you want to linger. It's also worth following the link to Flowers West, in Santa Monica.

Les Pabillons
www.galerie-dcor.com
There's no easy way to say this: this is a French gallery which sells butterflies made out of banknotes. And for roughly four £10 notes one of these financial butterflies can be yours. This could be the next big thing. Or it could just be the daftest thing to do with banknotes apart from setting fire to them.

Tate Gallery

www.tate.org.uk

The site sells mostly posters, prints, books, cards and slides. Buying seems easy with the electronic order form, but when you go to key in your credit card details, they say, "If sending your order by email, please note the transaction is not taking place on a secure commerce server. Your credit card details will not be encrypted during transmission to the Tate." Nice of them to let us know.

Posters & Prints   You owe it to your wall

Art Republic

www.artrepublic.com

Impeccably designed, superbly presented, incredibly easy to search, commendably unpretentious, it's impossible to overstate what a refreshing change ArtRepublic is from from the average online shopping emporium. Affiliated to BT's Watchdog security scheme, the site's single-sentence privacy statement reads: "We do not sell, trade or rent your personal information to outside parties." All this is backed up by a fine selection of posters and prints which you can search by artist and, for newbie art lovers, an explanation of artistic terms.

Contemporary Posters

www.contemporaryposters.com/

Rather like the Russian fine arts gallery, this site's name is missing a key word, the word in question this time being "Polish". With that caveat, it has to be said that there are some very cool posters here including the classic Solidarity poster from 1980. Sadly, you can only view this site to the accompaniment of a piece of music that sounds as if it's been pirated from the soundtrack of one of those short animated Czech films which used to fill the cracks in the BBC2 schedule. So persistent is this music that you actually have to quit Internet Explorer to turn it off. Does anyone know the Polish for user-friendly?

GORILLAS ON CANVAS

Even in the crazy world of cyberspace, Koko stands out. He is the first (and so far only) gorilla to host his own online chat session (no Sylvester Stallone jokes please). With his friend Michael, he is also one of two gorillas to have his own paintings for sale over the Net.

Surprised by the fact that gorillas like to paint? Well, US psychology professor Roger Fouts says, "It's in their nature. They like to use crayons, pencils and finger paints. Of course, they also like to eat them."

You can see the art they produce before hunger took hold on www.koko.org/koko/gorilla_art/. Prices start at $25. And it's all in a good cause: to save the species.

EasyArt

www.easyart.com

This site can occasionally take a while to download the art available in a specific category (eg seascapes and landscapes) but everything else about this site lives up its name. Registering is simple and minimal, ordering is secure, the pop-up windows do just pop up, delivery is within five working days and free on framed prints. Someday all Web sites will be this easy to use. Hopefully.

You'll find enough of Roy's stuff on Rare Posters to make even the Lichtenstein family say "Enough already!"

GB Posters

www.gbposters.co.uk

If you suffer from a deep-rooted fear of being original, this is the poster store for you: only the obvious selections for the obvious subjects (the Beatles, Digemon, Austin Powers). If you're after movie posters, you'll find a much greater collection at the site of the mysterious Dr Z with the equally mysterious URL www.blarg.net/~dr_z/Movie/Posters_IJK.html/, And yes, it is worth the effort keying all that in, although the site could be better organised.

The NAS Gallery

www.ndirect.co.uk/~nas

Before retro becomes so outro, visit this Old Masters site and order a print of that Constable painting your auntie always had on her wall. If you want something less naff, you'll also find some Gaugins here. There's even a button which says "Commission your own painting" which is surely taking Internet democracy too far. You can order online but you still have to send a cheque.

Rare Posters

www.rareposters.com

A stonking collection of exhibition and museum posters, with more Roy Lichtensteins than even the Lichtenstein family might want on their walls. Rare Posters is a nifty, unpretentious site which could lighten your wallet by $12 or a considerably more substantial $8000 if you were tempted by a signed and numbered Lichtenstein limited edition print.

Visoni Poster Art

www.visoni.com/index1.html

Nice-looking site which has a good, if small, stock of classic posters, mostly from the tourism industry. Special offers (like 10% off if you buy more than five posters) are often run and there's secure online ordering.

Babycare & Maternity

Call on the Internet to feed the baby's brain in the womb, ease the sting of childbirth (very slightly), cure junior's nappy rash and deliver champers to the new mum

 **When there's a bun in the oven...**

Active Birth Centre
www.activebirthcentre.com
North London mothers-to-be flock to this organisation, which was among the first to pioneer the idea that giving birth shouldn't necessarily be all about misery and enemas. This straightforward site has the same stock on sale as in the shop, including baby and mother massage oils. There's advice, too, on why massaging your wriggler is a good thing. Expectant mums can even buy oil to be massaged into the perineum – supposed to prevent it from tearing during labour. Delivery (ho ho) is £2.95: items come within seven days.

Blooming Marvellous
www.bloomingmarvellous.co.uk
For anyone who refuses to wear a tent during pregnancy, this site has a great selection of fashionable clothes, plus some lovely baby clothes. It's a good site for buying presents for pregnant friends or new parents, for example the witty New Mum Kit, which has some pampering goodies and earplugs to help you survive noisy hospital wards. Deliveries within 2-10 days, cost £3.95.

Jojo Maman Bebe
www.jojomamanbebe.co.uk
An easy to use site which offers the same good quality range as in the catalogue. The maternity section includes some useful business clothes and there are some pretty nursing tops to help with discreet breastfeeding. You'll find plenty of attractive kids' clothes too, plus useful gadgets and basic

Zen and the art of maintaining mum's morale in maternity: the holistic midwife's cure for feeling lousy

equipment. The Clearance Sale section has some neat discounts on maternity and children's clothes, although there aren't always pictures. Deliveries cost £2.99 and take five working days.

Pregnancy Shop
www.pregnancy-shop.com
For those who fancy a zen-like pregnancy, well-known holistic midwife and acupuncturist Zita West has her own site, which offers a small range of products to pamper and soothe the expectant mother. The Feeling Lousy kit, for anyone spending too much time with their chin on the toilet bowl, includes acupressure magnets, ginger and various essential oils, while the Belly Balm is designed to stop stretchmarks. This site doesn't guarantee security, so best call in with your order. Delivery costs £2 and it comes by first class post.

Precious Cargo
www.preciouscargo.co.uk
Not the hippest collection of maternity clothes around, as the slightly old-fashioned name might suggest. Still there are some useful outfits for special occasions such as weddings, including brides' gear, so it's obviously modern enough in its thinking. Some of the day stuff is a bit on the mumsy side, but a useful feature is that you can order clothes in different fabrics and even get some samples sent to you beforehand. Most deliveries will take up to ten working days, and cost £2.50 for orders to £75 and £3.50 for over.

 How to cope without getting out of your pram

Babies "R" Us
www.babiesrus.co.uk
The baby Toys R offers nappies and gadgets as well as more heavy-duty items like prams and high chairs. Its own-branded nappies are cheaper than Boots' own, but it's not worth buying single packets because the postage and packing evens things out. Bulk buying with friends could be a winner.

Babycare Direct
www.babycare-direct.co.uk
Winner of the 1999 Shops on the Net Awards, this is a comprehensive site with a wide range of products, from the basics to prams and car seats. There

are also some good discounts on offer. However, it's not without faults; for a start, there's an annoying ordering system where you have to write down the details of what you want to buy, which means going back a page to note it down. And if you want to phone to double check something, the customer service number isn't that easy to get through to. Deliveries are within five working days and cost £3.95, free for orders over £200.

Babycentre

www.babycentre.co.uk/

You'll feel in safe hands at this professional and comprehensive site. It offers a wide range of information along with a good selection of products, clothes and equipment to buy. Really eager types can start shopping for baby gear as soon as they've checked out their ovulation calendar. You can shop by the child's age or lifestyle; for example 'trendy baby' and 'city baby' and there's some unusual stuff here too, like a special cot that folds in a way that lets you sleep alongside your pride and joy. There's a choice of delivery options, starting at £2.50 for 3-4 days, or £6 for next day.

Babyworld

www.babyworld.co.uk

A good solid site that offers lots of useful tips including a discussion forum and an "ask the experts" panel (one free question: what makes them experts?). There's an intriguing range of products on offer here. Among those you may not have heard of is a handy, reasonably priced, Scandinavian sunblock mousse, a much more sensible option than the lardy goop parents usually have to try and slap on flailing infant limbs. Deliveries arrive promptly in two working days and are free on orders over £75.

Boots

www.boots.co.uk

After some teething problems (excuse the pun), this site is running well. As you'd expect from Boots, it's dependable. You can buy all the basics, plus a range of toys, clothes and equipment – and the big advantage is that it offers many more products than you'd find in your average store. Registration is required to shop, but it's simple and once you've done it, you instantly get a personalised shopping page. Deliveries, which take five days, are free for orders over £50 and for under, £2.95 per basket of goods.

Cribs2Go

www.cribs2go.com

An American site that delivers to the UK at decent rates. It works out worthwhile on some items such as sports strollers (those trendy three-wheel buggies). There's one here for a good price that only costs £35 to ship, so it's still much cheaper than buying one here. But don't be tempted by the child safety items, which are a lot more expensive than you'll find at home. A professional service that e-mails instantly with answers to queries.

Diaper Goop

www.innopharm.com

Here's a top product for parents of babies with a tendency to get nappy rash. This American site sells a highly recommended cream for treating sore botties. If you can stand the name (it really is called Diaper Goop), this stuff really seems to work. The company charges $3 to deliver single jars to the UK. It costs about £5 for a 60g pot, and arrives promptly in 2-3 days.

Genius babies

www.geniusbabies.com

Hilarious American site that offers all sorts of products designed to hothouse your own little prodigy. The Embryonics section includes a range of goods that "encourage" a brainy foetus, like the Mozart Womb Songs CD. And what concerned parent could be without a Baby Shakespeare video? Joking aside, this is a great site with lots of witty ideas for presents. There are a range of delivery options to the UK and they'll email you with costs beforehand.

Katies playpen

www.katiesplaypen.co.uk

There's a good selection of goods and some decent discounts can be found on the larger items. But it doesn't make it easy for you to hand over your cash, as you have to e-mail for prices on many products, which makes you wonder what it's keeping quiet. The site also has a split screen, which is fiddly to use. The delivery prices, at least, are clear. It costs £2.50 for smaller items and £7.50 for big stuff.

Mothercare

www.mothercare.com

It was no great surprise when many of the country's branches of Mothercare closed down last year, as the service and range in many of the shops were often found to be woefully lacking. But with this site, it won't compete on the Internet either, unless some major work is carried out on the registration process. It's clunky and cumbersome and currently seems to have trouble with UK addresses. Apart from that, there's a decent range of products, and prices include delivery within five days.

Planet Baby

www.planetbaby.co.uk

A very professional site that is also a break from the overly busy designs of many other mother

---

BABY TALK

Web Baby (www.webbaby co.uk) is an online baby store with a difference.

There's lots of useful info not just on the usual stuff such as feeding, but employees' rights and even mobile phones. There's also an online clinic session, so you can ask questions without having to trudge down to your local surgery.

The Baby Boutique has a big range of products and there's a handy Wish List, a bit like a wedding list. All that and there's free delivery in the UK.

and baby pages. You'll find lots of good ideas for equipment, toys and nursery products with some unusual stuff, such as the Tooth Timer, a toy to encourage tots to brush their teeth. It's helpfully divided into sections with nice headings such as "It's my room" and "The great outdoors". It offers next day delivery for just £2.95 and makes a point of stating that all its toys comply with European safety regulations.

Premier baby direct
www.babygoods.co.uk

You'll find some useful nursery equipment here that you might not have seen anywhere else, such as a special baby bath that attaches handily to an adult bath, and an unusual sunshade to prevent your slumbering baby from being roasted alive in the car seat. The ordering system is a pain in that you have to do it by fax or phone, but it's worthwhile for the stuff on offer. It won't commit to a delivery time, saying that it should take 10-14 days but might take 28. If you get a lurid yellow page about a car seat, scroll on down the page and you'll see a small text hyperlink to the Premier Baby Direct store which, confusingly, has the same URL.

The Total Baby Shop
www.thetotalbabyshop.com

Some brilliant bargains can be found at the Total Baby Shop, both on equipment and baby food, which is worth buying in bulk. Baby Organix baby food costs around 10p a jar less than the supermarkets and its Baby Bjorn slings are much cheaper than in the shops. There's a nice range of reasonably priced clothes, too. A whole newborn kit, with several changes of clothes, costs just £30. An excellent site that's well worth checking out. Deliveries take 2-5 working days and cost £2.99.

 **Clothes** The fashion parade starts here

Baby clothes direct
www.babyclothesdirect.co.uk

A basic site, which specialises in clothes for children up to the age of 18 months. There isn't a huge variety of clothes and styles on offer here, but what they do have is good value. You'll find decent quality packs of two sleep suits, for example, for well under a tenner. Postage and packing is £3.50 and deliveries take three working days. Ordering is secure and there's no registration, but you're moved to another site to order, which can confuse.

Cute as a bug
www.cuteasabug.com

This American site is for anyone who wants to buy high-quality babies' and kids' clothes that aren't going to be seen on the neighbours' offspring. The collection includes some cute stuff for babies, toddlers and older kids and they charge $8 for posting to the UK on items below $30. Check out the boys' pyjamas, which are much nicer than most of the offerings over here. Charges vary above that, so you won't be saving any money, but it's well worth it if you're looking for something a bit different from the norm.

Mischief kids
www.mischiefkids.co.uk
What concerned parent could be without a Donna Karan romper suit for their *bambino*? This site has a warm, personally written approach, which helps take the sting out of the prices. Annoyingly, a lot of the stuff listed is marked as sold out; a whole page worth of clothes in the case of the DKNY new arrivals. Still, if you're happy to pay designer prices, there's a great range of clothes here; delivery will cost from 75p to £10, and be with you the next day.

Sunday Best
www.sundaybest.co.uk
A British baby clothes site that seems to be pitched at Americans, which seems odd until you check out what it's selling. The Christening outfits have names such as The Fauntleroy, The Country Squire and The Bronte, which might give you a clue about what to expect. There's a lot of velvet and lace on offer here and more frills and froth than you could shake a rattle at. UK deliveries cost £5 and take just two days if the item's in stock.

 Gifts Champagne and personalised sick cloths

Baby bloomers
www.babyblooms.com
Everything has been handmade on this US site which specialises in ultra-twee memorabilia such as baby bracelets and personalised first curl boxes. Your baby can even have their very own personalised sick cloths, which may come in useful if you linger too long here. But if this is your (hand-embroidered) bag, shipping rates to the UK are pretty low at $6 an order. You might have to wait for three weeks for delivery because of the handmade nature of each item.

Stork basket
www.storkbasket.co.uk
If you don't want to buy new parents the usual gift of flowers and soft toys, this site offers a series of gift baskets with goodies for babies and their proud new owners. The cheapest packages, which include basics like bibs and teething rings, cost around £35. Mum's Treat basket includes champagne and luxury chocolates. For a princely £100 you get stuff for sprogs and mums in the Premium Selection basket. These gifts make a nice change if you can afford it. Payment is carried out by phone and deliveries cost £4.95.

Beauty
Why the Internet is a truly gorgeous place to be

Mirror, mirror, on the wall, which is the loveliest site of all...? While the newer, trendier brand names seem surprisingly shy of selling online, good grooming is there for those who know it's chic to click...

Cosmetics
Save a bundle on big-name beauty

Avon
www.uk.avon.com
The world's favourite budget cosmetics online. Sadly, you have to add items to your basket before the Avon lady deigns to tell you how much they cost. The Avon concept of offering a wide range of product categories features here: trouble is, there aren't sufficient products under each. Unenticing.

Class Cosmetics
www.classcosmetics.com
Cheap and cheerful, Class Cosmetics' real giveaway, once you've hit the site, is the www.amazoncosmetics.co.uk/class/ URL... Almay and Revlon are the main names here, though there are Ultima II and Elizabeth Arden products if you look. The site's strong on lipsticks and nail polishes, the goods are a third of the high street price and delivery, in 3-4 working days, is a snip at a £1.

Direct Cosmetics
www.directcosmetics.com
At up to 90% off RRPs, Direct Cosmetics is as cheap as you're likely to find. Obviously this doesn't apply to everything but the majority of goods, from hair care to accessories (including the bizarre inclusion of Elvis tapes and odd items from long-dead lines such as Charles of the Ritz: very 80s), can be bought half price. Searching is simple and top brands include high street stores, Boots and Superdrug alongside Calvin Klein and Clarins (their Eau Dynamisante is a bit of a bargain here). However, Direct sneakily fail to provide details of delivery charges; not good. Contact them and insist on being told before you order so much as a toothpick.

Island Trading

www.island-trading.com

Stylewise this resembles a tacky US online beauty magazine, but this Brighton based company do at least discount most of the big franchise brands, including Estée Lauder, Revlon, Almay, Clinique and Bobbi Brown. Savings ranging from £1 to £25 plus free shipping. Read the wording carefully, particularly in the two-for-one offers. And would you really buy 60 Borghese eye compresses for £19, far less their original £54?

General It's the details that make the difference

A QUICK PLUCK?

Definitely one of the more lurid sites we've come across, Eyebrowz is the DIY way to perfect eyebrows – the stencil.

Advertised like painting by numbers, Eyebrowz offers a range of 60 brow shapes to choose from, plus Hollywood celebrity visual aids, including Madonna and Jennifer Aniston, to help you choose the stencil to suit you. The whole package costs £19.95, or powder refills, $5.

Men can pluck, too, with their own kits. Of course it is an American site, but with a mere $3 shipping charge, what's to lose?

----

www.eye-browz.com

Allcures

www.allcures.com

Beautifully designed, totally navigable and unfeasibly fast, this dream pharmacy site is where to come for those bulk orders of toothpaste, cleanser and Matey bubble bath. All the household names are there, with specials such as Roger & Gallet bath products; the house cosmetics line is the ever-reliable Bourjois. Orders take 1-4 working days to arrive, depending on whether you want the Priority service for £5.99 or Standard for £3.49, and Standard orders of over £35 are delivered free.

Body Reform

www.bodyreform.co.uk

With poor navigation and lacking any distinct shopping route, Body Reform's site at least offers a range of specialised anti-ageing products and treatments. It seems to be aimed at the 'tried everything else, might as well give this a go' market. Despite costly items (£19.99 for anti-ageing serum), this is not a branded site and the packaging resembles the freebies you pick up in hotel rooms. However, shopping is simple once you get in, with easy ordering and cheap delivery (79p per item).

Look Fantastic

www.lookfantastic.com

Don't be put off by the busy homepage: this is the place to buy those expensive hair products your hairdresser tries to sell you. Get reductions on Aveda, Kerastase and Tigi by becoming a member. Could be improved with cheaper delivery and let-

...ting you in on the great reductions before you click to buy.

Lush

www.lush.co.uk

If you're using Navigator, this one will be a bit of a faff to get into, but if you're a fan of Lush's exceptionally smelly products with silly names like Pea Green soap and Draught of Immortality moisturiser, you'll love it. Delivery takes a somewhat sluggish 14 working days and costs £2.95, orders over £25 being free.

Manpack

www.manpack.com

One of the few sites tailored for men, the plain black home page is obviously specifically designed to ensure men aren't embarrassed to be seen shopping for girly beauty products. It's personalisable – once you've subscribed they'll re-send your order whenever you feel the need. Manpack offer reputable brands at typical high street prices and delivery is free unless you order their entire stock. No huge savings, but it's mega-convenient.

Molton Brown

www.moltonbrown.com

Lovely products, but the navigation's all over the place. With no sub-categories you are forced to scroll through images of what they have to sell, all in no particular order, Sea Moss Stress Relieving Soak next to Hand Wash. Alternative categories include Chinese Remedies and Travel Companions alongside the usual cosmetics and bathing products. Sadly off-putting.

 The sweet smell of the web

Augustus Oils

www.augustus-oils.ltd.uk/

Perfume, indeed – but in its rawest form. Hampshire-based Augustus sells essential oils, aromatherapy oils, highly concentrated absolutes and floral waters, by the drum. But although it supplies mainly to the trade and industry, Augustus will sell 500g/1lb, (or 100g in the case of absolutes), to customers who make their own scented soaps and candles. Buy with friends and share.

Fragrance Net
www.fragrancenet.com

Virtually every difficult-to-find fragrance lurks on these pages. Creed, Annick Goutal – and Jean Couturier, Coriandre fans – are all represented. Search by product or scroll down the alphabetical list. Soaps and body washes are also available. Although an American site, it ships to the UK and the on-hand shipping calculator will work out from the start whether it's worth just browsing the rest of the site or whether you should just pop to Boots. You do need to know the US exchange rate for a clearer idea of the deals on offer.

The Garden Pharmacy
www.garden.co.uk

Another Annick Goutal stockist, with a good range of her sought-after scents, this Covent Garden-based business has all the big-name fragrances at reasonable prices. It also has a neat line in Tisserand aromatherapy products, and, oh joy, stocks the increasingly hard-to-get Kneipp Bath Botanics, which simply define fragrances like Lavender, Spruce and Pine. The site looks gruesome, but don't be put off. Shipping takes three days and costs from £2.95.

Opal is a gem of a site if you have a particular passion for loofahs and for items smelling of tangerines or water melons

Opal
www.opal-london.com

Short and sweet, Opal of London has a particular passion for loofahs, and for stuff smelling of tangerines, watermelons and limes. If you plan to smell like a fruit bowl the buying process is cute, concise and cheap, with prices from £1 to £3 for travel soap to hand scrubs.

Perfuma
www.perfuma.com

Perfuma's clean, clinical-looking site offers make-up, skincare and hair care products, as well as eau de toilette. The extensive list is marred only by a lack of recognisable brands, though the pupa range is worth checking out if only for science-fiction style packaging. Diesel, Comme des Garçons and Ted Baker are among the safer choices. Delivery is free and orders are dispatched in three days. If you don't like the products the site also raises such philosophical questions as, "what is beauty for real people?"

Beer

Time gentleman please! That's not a shout you ever hear in cyberspace where it's never too late to order a sour red beer, set up your own brewery or snap up a few bar towels at bargain prices

Beerparadise

www.beerparadise.ltd.uk/

The ultimate site for beer snobs although, slightly confusingly, if you want to order some of the manifold ales on display you go through to a linked site, www.beerritz.co.uk/system/index.html. Here, the button marked "bargain bins" turned out to be a bin without bargains. If you do order online, you may have to wait 14 days for your favourite brand of amber nectar to arrive.

Belgian beers

www.belgianshop.com/en/

With Stella Artois cropping up so frequently as the last guess of the desperate in the perennial "name five famous Belgians" pub quiz question, this site should do a reasonable trade – especially because, as it constantly reminds you, "we ship globally!!!". With eight sour red beers, 17 Trappist beers and 20 white beers, this site is well-stocked too, which makes it even more of a shame that the order online feature is so temperamental.

Breweriana

www.breweriana.co.uk/home.htm

If you've drunk enough beer or have decided that you're supping so much that you might as well turn your front room into a full-scale replica of the Rovers Return, you can order bar towels (a snip at £1.75) here or even a lapel badge bearing the legend "Lager reaches the prats other beer cannot reach". But you do have to print out the order form and fax it to them.

Drinkshop

www.thedrinkshop.com/main.php3

The largest selection of beer online and that's official! Actually, it's only official as far as this site is concerned and then only if you accept that cider is a beer, thereby running the risk of awakening the wrath of the Wurzels. You will find

The Felinfoel Brewery site eschews clever gizmos for a traditional Welsh dragon

most of the household names here but it's not quite as impressive when it comes to the more esoteric brews. Still, next day delivery is good.

Home brew shop
www.homebrewshop.co.uk/
Will home brewing be the latest 1970s craze to make a comeback? Probably not, but home-brew devotees may want to visit this site which cut the prices on 73 DIY products in one month. There are also special offers on a few beers.

Lastorders
http://www.lastorders.com/html/home.asp
This online off licence may have been dreamed up over a pint but the site was clearly designed by someone who didn't indulge. It's easy to follow, informative and sells most of the beers you'd expect with the odd regional novelty thrown in. Refreshments are delivered next day but most are lagers rather than beer.

Dcotland's Craft Brewers Co-operative
www.lugton.co.uk/
Ideologically sound collective who will deliver their range of traditional "hand-crafted" beers anywhere in the UK within 72 hours of receiving the order. Don't be put off by the fact that most of their brews have Tartan-waving names like Loch Lomond and Bannockburn. For sheer commercial cynicism, the launch of "e-beer – the ale of the Internet" takes some beating.

You can also order your favourite tipple online from the following breweries:

www.blacksheep.co.uk/	Blacksheep
www.caledonian-brewery.co.uk/Home/home.html	Caledonian
www.carlsberg.co.uk/	Carlsberg
www.charleswells.co.uk/	Charleswells
www.felinfoel-brewery.co.uk/	Felinfoel
www.bdksol.co.uk/hesket	Only in nine-gallon barrels
www.tanglefoot.co.uk/	Tanglefoot

Bikes

Cut a swathe through
incomprehensible jargon,
make sense of your inside leg
measurement and find out how
often a cyclist gets almost
as wet as a drowned rat.
The power of the Internet!

Bicycle Net

www.bicyclenet.co.uk

This site is "proud to belong to the Which? Web Trader" code of practice.
Sadly, the code does not insist that you design a decent homepage. But stick
with it because this is actually quite a decent site. There's a glossary for
beginners and tips on what model you need according to your inside leg measurement. Delivery charges are calculated for you right at the start of the
checkout process (normally £6.50 will ensure your bike arrives within four
working days). Unlike many of the sites featured here, Bicycle Net only retails
online and they are happy to be compared with the high street on price. Their
stock ranges from kids' bikes to BMX to folding bikes,

Bike Park

www.bikepark.co.uk

A decent site which, while it isn't as sophisticated as some e-stores on the
Web, looks and feels as if it has been put together by enthusiasts. The
personal approach even extends to the links which point you to other 'fan'
pages. The shop sells a fair range of bikes (including the ubiquitous micro
scooters) as well as accessories and clothing. Another Which? Web Trader,
Bikepark also offers free delivery on all bikes within the UK and there's a nice
section for beginners which declares, among other things, that the keen
cyclist will get thoroughly soaked 12 times a year "and we know because
we've counted" say founders Julian Wall and Phil Cavell.

Cycle Centre Online

www.cyclestore.co.uk/

This site comes with more security guarantees than Fort Knox. A member of
Which? Web Trader, it also has a Verisign gold seal on its home page, just

below the link to the innards of the site. Down the left you'll find a long list of topics and brand names from bottom brackets (an essential item which start at £15) to Vredestein bikes. Delivery is £5 on orders up to £50 within the UK and there's a good range of bikes to choose from here, just don't be put off by the cheesy picture of "the team" on the homepage.

CycleXpress
www.cyclexpress.co.uk
There is a good range of categories on the toolbar here and the site looks great. They only stock three brands of bikes (Diamond Back, Fisher and GT) so the range is a little limited, but there are plenty of accessories. The downsides are the fact that you have to choose products by brand and not style, and the product descriptions are too brief. The major plus point is the upgrade advice service, which helps you improve your bike bit by bit.

RBM Sports
www.rbmsports.com
RBM claims to "take playtime seriously" whether you're into cross country, dual slalom or BMX. The site doesn't take its own technical architecture quite as seriously as what looks like a link to product reviews written by bikers (an excellent idea) doesn't link anywhere. This is a US site and although they do deliver to the UK you can't find out about shipping charges until after you've ordered.

ON YER BIKE!

The biking world is one of the worst offenders for unintelligible jargon and technical lingo.

Whilst looking through any bike magazine or website you can easily get lost in custom bro built pedal spindles and LX5 Bolt cranks or 44/32/22 removable spider and 4 arm cranks.

Very few people can cope with a mass of cantilever beam problems or older MTB triple drive trains.

Some bike manufacturers might follow Cove Bikes' lead. When buying their bikes you can choose between a stiffy, G-Spot, or quickie. Makes you pine for custom bro built pedal spindles, doesn't it?

Single Track Bikes
www.singletrack.co.uk
Skip the intro to this site which can take a while to load and go straight to the home page. The site comes complete with its own incoherent soundtrack and a chat room called the Graffiti Room. There's a wide range of stock and Single Track is another Which? Web Trader. Delivery is normally within 48 hours by Royal Mail. The site doesn't specify how much you might pay before you buy.

Ultimate bikes
www.ultimatebikes.co.uk
The welcome page and the online shop don't feel like they're part of the same site. Indeed, one of the few visual clues that they are related is the logo of a crumpled bike. The online catalogue looks fact packed and extensive but if you click on some of the accessories for info you may find yourself greeted with an apology and a promise that the catalogue is being continually updated.

Boats

Build your own,
buy your own and
earn the right to
say "hello sailor!"

Boat Hunter

www.boathunter.com

Online yacht brokers with listings of boats from all over the world. Email the details of the exact boat you are looking for, or just browse the site and imagine yourself sailing away on the deck of an $80,000 sloop. The site will check title and registration documents, and ensure money changes hands smoothly.

Marine Online

www.marineonline.co.uk – secure

There's enough kit here to build a boat from scratch. Galley equipment and deck fittings line up alongside thoughtful items like plastic glasses for when Hurricane Charlie upsets your gin and tonic. All prices include delivery but not VAT, and orders received before 11am are sent out the same day.

Southwater Marine

www.southwater.com

Sleek site for new and secondhand powerboats to add that touch of James Bond to your seaside break. Book a viewing appointment or offer your boat for sale. Finance packages and insurance may be available by now.

Virginia Currer Marine

www.vcmarine.co.uk

This is the place to come if you've always fancied river life. Narrow boats, Dutch barges and even restaurant boats are available, some complete with residential moorings. There are photos and deck plans for most listings and you can email for further details or to appoint the site as your sales broker.

Yacht People

www.yachtpeople.com – secure

Okay, so you can't actually buy a yacht, but the chandlery pages of this large sailing site have pretty much everything else you might need for some serious messing about in boats, right down to bilge pumps and outboard motors. There are special offers on larger items such as inflatable dinghies or an ORC Offshore Liferaft. Shipping costs depend on the weight of your order.

Books

They're the most popular item to be bought over the Net, so it's odd how many sites have badly designed home pages or don't allow you to order online. Here are some of the best and weirdest

General The big names and biggest stocks

Amazon
www.amazon.co.uk

Amazon is the most famous name in online shopping, having branched out way beyond its original niche. It's worth searching both the UK and the US (www.amazon.com) sites because the American one has an easy-to-track-down bargain basement where, if you don't mind waiting, you could save a lot of money. The UK site's "three for £10" offer is a bit more limited. The search mechanism is quick and simple, although you sometimes get different results depending on which page you access it from. As you would expect, Amazon offers secure ordering and is generally very good at letting you know what's happened to your order. The user reviews are often worth reading.

Bol
www.uk.bol.com

As the world's largest book publisher, it was only a matter of time before Bertelsmann started selling books online. Their site is a professional effort with a hefty stock of titles, including some pretty obscure stuff. However, it doesn't always make it easy for you get enough info to make an informed choice. For example, if you buy Ross Macdonald's third Lew Archer omnibus from Amazon, it tells you which novels are included; Bol.com doesn't. Www.barnesandnoble.com is part of the same network.

Bookzone
www.bookzone.com

Bookzone is not just an online bookstore, it's an online book community where you can rub virtual shoulders with the literati. This site also acts as a gateway to publishers who will sell direct to you, but often only if you're in North America. (So it's time to set aside your dream of owning that book of Princess Diana's celestial love, as told to a Norwegian medium.)

Borders
www.borders.com

A useful place for fans of obscure American authors who aren't always well represented on some of the bigger sites. Shipping costs are clearly identified and vary according to how fast you want to get your hands on the book. Borders is worth keeping as a bookmark or favourite because it reaches parts of the book world that some of its bigger rivals don't.

Country Bookstore
www.countrybookstore.co.uk

Decorated with soft, presumably rural, shades of blue and green, this site has a certain sedative effect if you've been surfing too long. But it's good to see an independent bookshop competing on the Web, and with a million page views a month, competing is the word. You can even buy books from this company over your WAP phone.

The Good Book Guide
www.titlefinder.com

This British site promises to find the book you want as well as offering a decent selection of current titles. Put to the test with some obscure requests, it came up trumps most of the time. Comes with the *Which?* seal of approval and a *soupçon* of decent copy about books and writers.

Iron Kettle Books
www.ironkettle.com

No Barnes and Noble nor Amazon, as it's the first to admit, Iron Kettle started off selling remaindered books to American schools. It now delivers to individuals and outside the US, and often sells its small, but interesting, stock for a third of the listed price. Among the bargains in its spring sale were a dictionary of cricket and a book on a man who'd had his memory surgically removed.

Ottakar's
http://ottakars.co.uk

The real star of this site is the search engine, which works swiftly and accurately to reinforce the point

FIVE FOR UNDER A FIVER*
* Before postage

Facts and Figures of Leeds United, 1980 edition, 95p, from Soccer Books Limited

Steps Published by Paragon, this book is without an accredited author. £1.79 from Bol

The Unauthorized Teenage Mutant Ninja Turtles Quiz Book (US edition), £2.12, from WH Smith

Alan Judd's biography of Ford Madox Ford, £3.44, from Iron Kettle

Pam Ayers' *Jilly Cooper The Works* includes her immortal ode 'Ooh I Wish I'd Looked After Me Teeth'. A mere £4.79 from Amazon UK

You don't have to be a big chain to
have a huge online catalogue as
independent shop Ottakar's proves

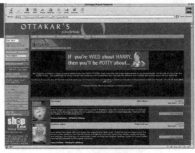

that this independent bookshop has access to a comprehensive stock of
titles. There is also a link to the site Fired Up, where Ottakars puts signed
books up for auction. The discounts on offer are pretty reasonable too.

Waterstones
www.waterstones.co.uk
As you might expect, this site has a more erudite, upmarket ambience than
either Bol or Amazon. If there is a criticism to be made, it's that sometimes it
just packs too much in, so the screen can seem a little too full. Otherwise, it's
pretty much what you would expect from this chain: encrypted, well-stocked
and thorough. Its search mechanism is extremely slick and easy to use, too.

WHSmith
www.whsmith.co.uk
WHSmith boasts that its site offers every British book still in print, a claim
this reviewer was unable to disprove after several hours of effort. If you're
searching for a particular author or book, it's worth narrowing down your field
as much as possible. Overall, this is a good, robust site and a role model to
other high-street brands on how not to screw things up on the Internet.

Also worth a mention if you're into that sort of thing:
www.beatbooks.com for Jack Kerouac, Grateful Dead and Charles Manson
www.comedybooks.com for rib-tickling books about professional rib-ticklers
www.hungrygulch.com for lovers of the American West; email orders only
www.okukbooks.com for children's books, with reviews by its audience
www.highlanderweb.co.uk/book/shop for all about the Auld Country
www.alphabetstreet.infront.co.uk for a decent alternative to Amazon etc
www.netcomuk.co.uk/~james_j/Front_page.htm for books about cars
www.stanleyfish.com for books about trains; email ordering only
www.neosoft.com/~bmiller/fiery1.htm for those who like fiery foods

E-books What you can do if things go wrong

That's 'e' as in electronic, not ecstatic, these are books you can usually download off the Internet for a small fee and either read on screen or, more likely, print out. Shorter work. like poems, can be just read on the Internet.

Ebooks for you
www.ebooksforyou.com
Don't let the corny title or the relatively small selection of e-books on this site put you off. Among the intriguing titles are Evel Knievel's memoirs (called, you guessed it, *Evel Ways*) and a smattering of classics from HG Wells' *War of the Worlds* to Stephen Crane's *Red Badge Of Courage*. Typical prices are $5-8.

E-pulp
www.e-pulp.com
Great title and suitably hard-boiled design raise expectations for this electronic store of new mystery and sci-fi writing. Sadly the authors don't quite live up to them. Possibly because crime is such a well-populated genre of fiction, the summaries often tremble on the edge of self-parody. For completists only.

Lee Nolan Childers
http://members.aol.com/Bstseller1/Index.html
Leta Nolan Childers is not a lost Nolan sister but arguably the top-selling e-book author in the world. Her output ranges from private detective stories starring Cat Callahan (who's a woman not a cat) to tales of Gaelic family life. Watch out for low-flying shamrocks.

Universal download
www.udownload.com
Most e-book sites are partial and populated by authors you've never heard of. Not this one. It allows the user to peruse TS Eliot's *The Waste Land*, inspect the Treaty of Versailles or download *War And Peace*. Although the selection on some minor writers is idiosyncratic (no *Blue Guitar* in the Wallace Stevens section but three of his lesser works) this is a thoroughly impressive selection of electronic texts and comes with a friendly, ersatz Yahoo-style home page.

Ye Olde Electronic Book Shoppe
www.ebookshoppe.com
Ye Olde Electronic Book Shoppe panders to quill pen freaks by calling itself Scribbler and offers an apparently impressive selection of genres. However, the fiction category includes an account of living with spinal muscular atrophy which, excellent as it may be, presumably isn't fictional. This is a good site for secret lovers of romantic fiction, but others may find it less diverting.

A WORD IN YOUR EAR...

When buying used books online, do check:

1 Shipping costs and policies. They're not always easy to find.

2 The condition of the books. Good sites have ratings or say if the title is worn or damaged.

3 The book you're buying. When you're scrolling down your umpteenth text page, it's easy to misread the short description of the book you think you're looking for and get an unpleasant shock when it arrives.

4 The policy on returns. For obvious reasons, sellers of used books don't offer the kind of "no quibble guarantee" you get from the bigger stores. If you can't see a policy, ring or email them before you buy.

5 If the site is secure. A disturbing number of smaller US stores seem to expect you to key in your credit card details on unencrypted sites. If in doubt, ask.

Used Out of print but not out of mind

A Book For All Reasons
www.abfar.co.uk
A distinctly middlebrow list of fiction (from Georgette Heyer to Nevil Shute) lets down a site best known for its extensive stock of tomes on military history. You can enquire about the book you want by email and the shop will email you back confirming availability, etc.

Advanced Book Exchange
www.abebooks.com
The Advanced Book Exchange describes itself as the world's largest network of independent booksellers, and its homepage has been designed as a homage to Amazon's. You can search its list of 20 million titles and find some pretty obscure stuff, such as the out-of-print autobiography of Bryan Ferry or the European diary of a wealthy young American called John F Kennedy. Probably the best place to start if you want old, out of print books, even if they're paperbacks.

Bibliofind
www.bibliofind.com
Another site which spans an impressive network of booksellers – it claims to have 10 million titles in its archive. Like the Advanced Books Exchange, Bibliofind uses a secure server for ordering.

Biblion
www.biblion.co.uk
"The home of British antiquarian and remarkable books" is an online network of 1000 dealers which is intended as much for the book trade as for the general punter. Still, there can be few other places on the Web where you could find the 1885 reports on insects injurious to hop plants, corn crops and fruit crops in Great Britain. Whether you can complete your purchase of such highly elusive material online depends largely on the dealer you are referred to.

Dusty Covers
www.dustycovers.com
In the bargain basement you can find Captain Scarlet's 1993 annual beside such unusual tomes as Elisabeth Cooper's *The Love Letters Of A Chinese*

Lady, first published in 1919. Categories include music (which has a decent archive of rock titles), fiction, children's books, and war and espionage. You can order through email and pay by cheque.

Maps And Prints

www.mapsandprints.com/manuscripts.cfm

If you're interested in some rather older used books, why not splash out $200 on a medieval manuscript of a Book of Hours? Art Source International's rather limited stock of old manuscripts sits alongside a more impressive array of maps, globes and such. This site positively encourages you to order online, uses a secure server and is upfront about its shipping costs.

Mr Mac

www.rmcd.demon.co.uk

Mr Mac is an ABE member so you can order books by credit card through that link. A fair range of books is listed by author and you can email requests to Ranald McDonald who is based, rather disappointingly, in Southampton.

It wasn't possible to order books online from the following as this book went to press but they're still worth a look

www.bookshelfuk.com With an email search facility for out of print books, this site seems rather too proud of its "famous soft toys".

www.bookword.com is a decently designed site where it's easy to find what you want. It covers most genres and rates each used book on its condition. Titles can be reserved by email.

www.easternbooks.co.uk As its name suggests, it stocks lots of used books about Eastern Europe, the Middle East and the Orient.

www.edicionesgrial.com This Anglo-Spanish site contains a limited edition facsimile of the *Quest For the Holy Grail* complete with a reproduction of the original binding for £1,495 plus shipping. Ignore the QuickTime plug-in prompt.

www.hrkahnbooks.com This is a Canadian shop which specialises in old books on travel. Stock and prices vary from £15,400 for eight volumes and an atlas of the voyages of Captain Cook down to a more modest £345 for an account of three years in the Sandwich Islands.

 Specialist When you want a site that knows its stuff

Arts

www.arts-books.com

Cleanly designed, simple to navigate, brimming with useful information about how to order stuff safely and, rarest of all, British, this site is a must-visit for anyone interested in the performing arts. You can buy books, music, videos, audio books and Capezio dance belts for men! It's just a shame that so much of the site appeals only to tap dancers and the like.

Business

www.bookstore.mcgraw-hill.com

This is a "real professional bookstore" aimed at outstanding professionals who can't wait to delve into its archive of 35,000 business titles. Although it's owned by a leading business and academic publisher, this store sells titles by all publishers. You can even find a title which tells you how Genghis Khan and Bill Gates made their fortunes, although you suspect competition was a bit less intense when Genghis was pioneering his brand of monopoly capitalism.

Films

www.readthemovie.com

You would think this Amazon-associate site would help you find the book which inspired the movie. Well, you'd be almost right, except that films like *Chopper Chicks in Zombietown* (starring Billy Bob Thornton) obviously didn't require any literary inspiration, although they're still listed here. In fact this site also sells audiobooks, soundtracks, videos, DVDs and laserdiscs of popular movies (plus a few TV series), all at discount prices. There's also a small archive section of certain actors and actresses. Mind you, if you wanted to know how *A Bug's Life* inspired enough titles to outnumber an ant colony this is the place for you. Compelling in an odd sort of way.

The place to go if you want to know just how many spin-off books were 'inspired' by Disney's A Bug's Life. Alas, there is no information on the literary source for Chopper Chicks In Zombietown

Medicine
www.donfer.co.uk/d-commerce
Doctors, vets and hypochondriacs can now order online through a secure server from Donald Ferrier – an Edinburgh medical bookshop which sells tomes on (amongst others) surgery, anaesthetics and psychology. They aim to deliver within 24 hours; the charge for orders under £25 is £2.50; over that is free.

Politics
www.politicos.co.uk
With anything from the latest political blockbuster to memorabilia, this site has almost everything the political buff could desire. Items on offer range from Lydia Miller's heartbreaking hysterical romance about a woman with a schoolgirl crush on George Bush to a ticket to the Senate for the day in 1999 when they voted on Clinton's impeachment (yours for £35). Ordering is secure, although it can take time.

Sport
www.soccer-books.co.uk
A well-stocked specialist site with no frills, this site is particularly valuable for its extensive stock of football videos, including a double bill of coaching tips from Pele and a biography of Eusebio. There's also a small selection of books about non-football sports and music (if that's the right word) CDs about football. With a 10 per cent discount for orders of £60 and over, this is clearly aimed at the serious fan.

Travel
www.mapsworldwide.co.uk
This *Which?* approved site just screams bargain from its home page – 20 per cent off Ordnance Survey maps! A new waterproof map of Snowdonia for £6.33!! Or 15 per cent off a CD ROM which computes the most economical route between any two streets in Britain!!! A must for armchair travellers.

These sites might also be worth considering:
www.deiltak.com for first editions, biographies, US first editions, non-fiction
www.bractonbooks.co.uk for anthropology, ethnography, social science
www.shentonbooks.demon.co.uk for clocks, watches, barometers, etc
www.clique.co.uk/jopplety for science fiction, children's books
www.simonfinch.com for rare books, especially early printed books
www.esotericism.co.uk as the name suggests, this stocks esoteric stuff from neoplatonism and gnosticism to alchemy, mysticism and paganism

---

SHEER BLOODY POETRY

The Internet isn't all about Bill and Monica jokes and Billy Bob's wacky souvenirs. There's an awful lot of poetry in cyberspace too.

Not all of it's that good but *www.footballpoets.org/* is worth a look. Among others, it features Attila the Stockbroker and Stuart Butler – the author of a short ode to the new Sky TV deal which is worth reproducing in full:

"At £375,000 a week/ It gets difficult to suspend belief/ So let's all watch Sunday league/ And play football on the common/ (With coats for a goal/ Equal pay for all/ And asylum seekers welcome.)" It beats Andre Motion's ode to the Queen Mum

Cameras

Whether you want to take better holiday snaps or be the new David Bailey the Net is full of bargains, if you know where to look. You can also find cameras which are even older than Mr Bailey himself

Best Stuff
www.beststuff.co.uk
If the range of choices seems overwhelming, consider heading to Best Stuff. In each category of electrical goods it features only one product, "the best", along with a brief explanation of why it has earned the title. Whether it actually is the best is far from guaranteed. A quick check of leading camera sites suggests that this site's idea of "the best" isn't on offer anywhere else…

Camera Collectors
www.camera-collectors.com
The vintage and collectible cameras on sale here include specialist models from the likes of Rollei, Linhot and Leica. James Bond wannabes can even snap up a miniature Minox CFI for $600. Delivery to the UK is available but – and it's a very big but – it costs a flat $23.50. With the average camera price on this site somewhere between $25 and $50, that almost doubles the cost. But if you want something out of the ordinary, you may just have to stump up.

Cameras Direct
www.camerasdirect.co.uk
A big selection of bargains makes this a must-visit site. Though you have to register to access the Today Only special offers, savings of up to 70 per cent off big brand RRPs are available, and you can expect to save at least £20-£70 on a best-selling model. Three-day delivery costs £4.99, but if you're off on holiday tomorrow, you can get your camera delivered to your door within 24 hours for £9.99. Film is a particularly good buy, with RRP prices slashed by more than 50 per cent. If you're buying a three-pack, that £4.99 delivery charge is more than worthwhile. The site is easy to use, features 360-degree rotating images of most products, and advertises free technical assistance – a rarity for a cut-price web store. One word of warning though: changes to your selection can't be made once you've clicked through to the checkout.

Cut-price seems to apply to design as much as product, but this site is easy to use, offers free technical help and a big selection of bargains

Comet
www.comet.co.uk

Among the PCs, dishwashers and mobile phones, you'll find camcorders and cameras. Well, you'll find a few… Comet doesn't have the biggest camera selection in the world but the site does offer useful buying tips. There are full and friendly explanations of features such as DX Coding, and advice on what to consider when making your choice. The ability to search within a price range is a good idea, let down somewhat by the lack of products to compare.

The Digital Kingdom
www.thedigitalkingdom.com

Eight big name brands of digital camera are on offer on this US site. If you're looking to buy at the more expensive end of the market, you could be in for some very big savings indeed. You have to register and create an account before you buy, but you would do well to make yourself a cup of tea first, as you will be told repeatedly that you have not filled in all the required fields, even when it's quite clear that you have. But it's worth persevering – on a $1000 camera, you could easily save more than $500.

Dixons
www.dixons.co.uk

The photography section of Dixons' e-store is not huge – but some great savings can be made. Choose from around ten products in each category (digital, APS, compact etc), with close-up photos and basic specifications. If you're not sure exactly what you want, go elsewhere for reviews and info and head here only when you have a product name, number and RRP. But there are no cut-price guarantees: you'll find some big-brand cameras available here for a lot less than at rival online stores, but some for quite a bit more. Watch out for special deals on certain models too, such as free film for 12 months. Once you've registered, ordering is straightforward, but note that Dixons will only deliver to the address of the credit card holder, and postage and packing are added at the checkout. Delivery is within three working days.

1st Cameras
www.1stcameras.co.uk

1st Cameras is a dedicated supplier of Fujifilm and Fujifilm cameras, which does tend to colour its online recommendations. Product descriptions are detailed, and there are also a few background pieces (Why go digital? Why Fujifilm? etc) There's even a message board, where you can post your views on the Fujifilm range. (When we checked, the only contribution was from the moderator.) Shipping costs are according to Royal Mail rates and delivery takes between one and five days, but exercise caution when buying: the advertised prices do not include VAT, which is added at the checkout.

CAMERA OBSCURA

Andrews Cameras at www.andrewscameras.co.uk offers a different kind of camera, the collectable kind.

Prices vary from less than you'd pay for a new high street camera to £2250 for a Zeiss 180mm fz 8 Olympia Sonner and grip for Contarex 3-D.

If that's Greek to you, you're better off heading somewhere more mainstream, but hard core devotees will want to linger here a while even if they do find the site's rather crude design a bit frustrating. A treat for nostalgia freaks.

iGadget
www.igadget.com

This US site has a pretty big selection of cut-price cameras – you can make savings on big brand names from $20 to more than $200. This makes it well worth a look, especially if you're after the latest digital model. The site does offer delivery to the UK and most products are dispatched within 24 hours, but you have to email the company first to get a quote for the shipping charges.

Miller Brothers Electrical and Gas Appliance Superstore
www.millerbros.co.uk

This is a no-frills site with a reasonable selection of cameras and accessories for delivery anywhere within the UK mainland. You won't save a lot here – on average around £20 – and there's a £10 per order delivery charge. But still, that's £10 less than you'd pay if you walked to your high-street camera dealer and paid full whack. Before you buy, just make sure you check that Cameras Direct or Dixons doesn't have the same model for less.

Quality Direct
www.qed-uk.com

The cheap, bold, unattractive homepage gives the impression of an online industrial estate. Quality Direct isn't flash, but it does offer free delivery

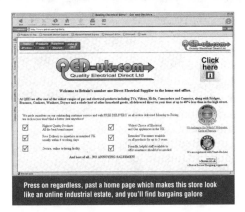

Press on regardless, past a home page which makes this store look like an online industrial estate, and you'll find bargains galore

within four working days and reductions of up to 40 per cent on high street prices. You'll find a huge range of cameras on offer, often at much cheaper prices than those offered by some of its more upmarket competitors, and more detailed product descriptions. But if it's a best-selling brand you're after, you'd be best advised to shop around before you think of heading here.

Tempo
www.tempo.co.uk
The products at this relatively new high-street discount operation are laid out by brand (all the big ones) or by category, but the selection of what it quaintly calls 'photographic' and digital, cameras is fairly small. It's worth checking, but with delivery at a flat charge of £4.99 and savings averaging around £5 off the RRP, you're not likely to get that great a deal. But if you do find something you like, you can choose a delivery date that suits you – a consideration for the customer that other e-businesses would do well to emulate.

Yahoo Shopping – Photography
http://shopping.yahoo.com/electronics/photography
There is a huge selection of brands on offer in this online market of several e-stores but beware: most are US-based, and most will not deliver to the UK. However, the site is a fantastic resource, with vast amounts of background information and facts. You will find very thorough camera specs, lots of detail on image quality and model features, and even a Consumer Consensus, taken from submissions to the consumer reviews section. Presuming you do find something that you like, the odds are that you probably will be able to order it for UK delivery if you spend a bit of time checking through the stores.

Cars

If you're keen to get a new set of wheels and are more worried about saving money than test driving, give the showroom salesmanship a miss and check these sites out

 **Buy cheap, buy abroad**

Auto Europ
www.autoeurop.co.uk
Auto Europ is a pretty basic site, but they do quote offers they can currently promise, like £10,000 for a Ford Focus with extras, VAT, delivery and 12 months road tax included. Simply email the enquiry form with your request.

Carbusters
www.carbusters.com
Who you gonna call? Well *Which?* thinks you'll phone them. With deals like a VW Golf VS5 door for £17,000 on the road (fee inclusive) they may be right.

Discount Imports
www.discountimports.co.uk
The Ferrari red backdrop sets the scene for this sporty offering from abroad. The simple design remains difficult to navigate with no clear indication at first of the service that they actually offer. As it turns out you can search for cars and make the usual online request for information. Prices include shipping fees, UK transportation, VAT and the fee the company charges for its search.

Go Brussels
www.gobrussels.com
Go Brussels will contact dealers in Belgium about the make of car you're interested in buying. You email your request and once you've made your choice you travel to Brussels, are taken to the dealer and drive away in your new European-priced car. There are no typical price quotes for comparison.

 **Brand names which sell online**

Peugeot
www.peugeot.co.uk
The popular online deal which manufacturers are offering is to allow you to sort out all the fiddling details before you get to the garage. You select a model, make your specifications and once you find one to suit you can break down your financing preferences, including part-exchange. From here you can arrange a test drive and meeting to finalise the details with a dealer in your area. Takes the hassle out of car buying.

Renault
www.renault.co.uk
Renault To Go allows you to make an online 24-hour reservation to buy nearly new Renault cars. Select an area or enter your postcode for local dealers, pick the make, model, engine size, preferred fuel, and even cancel the car colours you won't be seen dead in and see what they can offer. No dosh changes hands so you don't *have* to turn up. Every car is less than 18 months old and comes complete with history and mileage guaranteed by Renault.

Vauxhall
http://buying.vauxhall.co.uk
Vauxhall were the first manufacturer to harness the benefits of e-commerce, producing their own .com version of brand models the Tigra, Astra and Corsa. All these are available to view, each working out around a few thousands pounds cheaper than their sister models. How to buy, however, remains a complete mystery. Sort it out boys.

Not every manufacturer is keen to offer the same discount deals and ease of buying as the above but Audi, Ford and Saab will help you find a local dealer. With both Jaguar and Saab you can request a test drive.

Audi
www.audi.co.uk
Click on non-Flash for one of the worst customer interfaces on the Web.

Ford
www.ford.co.uk
Get the past the marketing guff and this is slick, useful and easy to navigate.

Saab
www.saab.co.uk
This site is so understated it's almost apologetic. You can't dream build your own Saab but you can find used cars and, hmm, download Saab wallpaper.

Cars

 Just one careful lady owner. . .

AutoBytel
www.autobytel.co.uk
The bustling homepage can be quite intimidating if you're new to all this car and Internet technology, but the Research section should help to put your mind at rest. From here you can compare up to three cars, focus on one particular model to judge if it's the one for you, read expert reviews and find out what your current trade-in may be worth. But once you've been through all this you're not much closer to owning the model of your dreams. All you can do is make your request and wait for the dealer to contact you.

Autotrader
www.autotrader.co.uk
No online sales but the comprehensive and frequently changing database of new and used vehicles which *Autotrader* boasts is worth a mention. Focus on the menu buttons to the right, select a category and make your search as advanced as you like, bearing in mind how far you're willing to travel. On each occasion they managed to come up with brief details of the make, model and price, and where to go from there. After making your selection you are automatically linked to insurance and finance sites.

Car Shop
www.carshop.co.uk
Simple name for a simple system. The Buy & Go section sticks out but I didn't expect it to be as easy as it is. Search for the make and model of the car you wish to buy, view specs and images of the cars on offer, choose one and put down your deposit on your credit card. The most complicated bit is deciding whether you want insurance, part-exchange or financing. Special offers include a Volkswagen Polo for £6000. Easy as one, two, three.

Exchange & Mart
www.exchangeandmart.co.uk
You may not be able buy online but the *Mart* is still at the pinnacle used car directories. Make your search as simple or complex as you choose, even down to whether you want central locking and an in-car CD player. Each discovery comes complete with a price guide to make sure you're not being ripped

---

DO DO THAT JOU JOU
www.joujou.co.uk
Cars are like fashion, everyone buys the latest styles and eventually it becomes passé. Looking to stand out from the crowd, Jou Jou is the smallest car in the world and is only available online. It resembles a glorified golf cart, and the colour choice of lemon, sky blue, mint and Alpine rose leaves something to be desired, but no one will ever criticise you for being old hat. Simply fill in the order form to reserve your model, confirm it and pay your deposit, paying the reminder when they deliver. Priced at a paltry £11,200 for the Turbo.

off, insurance quotes and car reviews. From here do the usual and ring for that car.

One Swoop

www.oneswoop.com

This brilliant site offers discounted vehicles and express shopping. Search by your chosen make, model or price range and you'll find a long list of options. Take your pick and email your order, which they will then follow through on. Each list includes their price compared to standard UK prices, and many offers include discounts of up to £4,000. Keen to keep you

Autobytel shows you a list of vehicles to compare and how far the cars are from your post code. Helpful devils

informed they advise you to print out every stage of the process for your own records and state exactly how long delivery will take, ranging from anywhere between two and twenty-two weeks.

What Car?

www.whatcar.co.uk/

Like *Exchange & Mart*, a good price guide for used cars, and a sophisticated search engine as well as the chance to sell your old car for less than a fiver.

Parts

Where to go when they're not all in working order

Find A Part

www.find-a-part.com

Find A Part does exactly that. The site itself is easy to follow, but you will need to know the ins and outs of your car for them to be able to help. The basic vehicle information was relatively simple – make, model, and engine size, but if it's a body part they need to know colour codes and for engine parts, you'd better know everything there is to know about your gearbox. If you can cope with this click away and wait for them to return with help.

World Parts

www.world-parts.com

World Parts can save you the time and energy it takes to find a garage with the parts to suit your particular vehicle. Whether it's a gearbox or an entire engine you're missing, simply select the make, model, country you live in and they'll list the garages you need to contact, complete with what they have and contact details.

Celebrities

Whether you're after an autograph, birth certificate, vintage movie poster or an Elvis fridge magnet, the Internet is your friend

Art Rock Online

www.artrock.com

Online utopia for rock and pop fans, selling posters, t-shirts and other items from a huge range of musicians and bands. Lots of unusual items, such as an original backstage pass for The Mothers of Invention ($100), or a photo of the Rolling Stones signed by each member ($2000). They ship internationally for between $20 and $43 on top of your order, and if you subscribe to their newsletter, you'll be notified when they get any interesting new arrivals.

Arundel Autograph Gallery

www.autographs.co.uk

This site offers signed photos and letters from public figures, including movie stars, sportsmen and politicians. Everyone from Caprice to Winston Churchill is here, and there's even a letter signed by Diana Spencer just before she married Prince Charles. There's no secure ordering, despite an online form, but you can email for more information or to subscribe to a newsletter update.

Celebrity Birth Certificates

www.online-homesales.co.uk

Actresses who fudge their ages beware. This site sells copies of genuine birth certificates from celebrities in the world of film, television sport and public life, as long as they were born in the UK. An unframed copy will cost you £25, or a framed one will set you back £49, although they do offer discounts if you want to buy a set like all The Beatles. Marriage certificates are also available.

Elvis! Elvis! Elvis!

www.elvisproducts.com

The King gets plenty of memorabilia sites all of his own, but this is one of the better ones, despite having little in the way of original items. The kitsch value of the fridge magnets and guitar-shaped music boxes speak for themselves, but there are also DVDs and videos of his movies and live performances up for grabs. Shipping is via airmail and depends on the weight of your order.

Exclusive Rock and Pop Memorabilia
www.azalmax.demon.co.uk
This site sells high quality posters, cards, magazines, tickets and, in the case of The Beautiful South, beer mats. If your life is not complete without a 1996 Prodigy calendar, you can put that right for just £2. You can reserve an item by email, but they request cheques for orders which are sent out on receipt.

Novelty Togs
www.noveltytogs.com
Jazz up a staid wardrobe with some classy items like Bart Simpson socks or Cartman slippers. There's *Simpsons*, *South Park* and *Mr Men* merchandise, plus a range of socks featuring characters like Winnie the Pooh and Tweetie Pie for adults and kids. Prices exclude VAT but delivery is free within the UK.

Recollections
www.recollections.co.uk
Lots of autographed concert programmes and ticket stubs, along with a variety of old and new items of rock memorabilia, many at very good prices. A 1983 Culture Club tour programme autographed by Boy George will set you back £15. All items have a seven-day money-back guarantee and the site promises to ship either the same or the next day.

S&P Parker's Movie Market
http://parkermovies.com
Vintage film posters rub shoulders with photos of up and coming Hollywood stars on this well-designed site. A number of items lack pictures to browse, but on the whole the ordering process is fast and straightforward with the very considerable stock list arranged in alphabetical order. You have to get quite a way through the ordering process before it tells you that delivery is £1.50 within the UK (there's no help facility on the homepage), but otherwise, it's an excellent site.

Starstore
www.starstore.com
More than 13,000 items of movie and TV memorabilia, searchable by name, show or even catchphrase. Postage costs 20 per cent of the order (maximum £5) unless you're ordering something like a life-size cardboard cutout of Buffy the Vampire Slayer, in which case they'll email you with the full shipping costs.

Sadly the picture format doesn't do justice to the fridge magnets in all their glory. Here's the home page instead

Chocolates & sweets

Bars, fudge and humbug!
Is this the Internet or
the House of Commons?

Chocolate The world's favourite stress-relieving drug

Choc Express
www.chocexpress.com
Browsing according to the personality of the recipient may not always be that useful (eg boiled sweets for the cool teenager) but it's fun. The images are small but it does offer useful info including the exact number of chocolates in a box rather than the weight, making it far easier to determine value for money. Items are pricey but the site offers free delivery and a vast selection.

Chocolate Store
www.chocolatestore.com
To shop here you just need to decide whether you prefer Swiss, Belgian or English truffles and chocolate. With pictures of most products and a brief description of each, you at least know what you get for your £18 and 500g of chocolate. It would be nice to know shipping costs before you order, however.

Cromwells Chocolates
www.cromwellschocolates.co.uk
You won't be dazzled by the selection of fine English chocolates sold here, but it only takes a few clicks to buy a box. Each contains chocolate creams, truffles and pralines, with prices from £5.95 to £24.95. File under adequate.

Thorntons
www.thorntons.co.uk
A disappointing effort. The site is quite sparse and the keyword search comes up with few items. They remain value for money, however, with 80 delicious continental chocolates for £20, but delivery is charged at £3.95.

The kind that isn't "full of Cadbury goodness"

Cotswold Fudge
www.cotswoldfudge.co.uk
This no-nonsense site has obviously put all its cash into the product rather than the graphics. With unusual fudge varieties including lemon meringue at £5.95 for a 400g box including post and packing, it'll take you a few minutes to settle on a gift, and Cotswold will post to whatever address you want.

San Francisco Fudge
www.sanfranciscofudge.co.uk
The URL betrays the fact that this fudge factory is not based in Bath, not San Francisco. Luxury items include Rocky Road and Baileys fudge and chocolate chip cookies. All items are priced at just over £3 for a half-pound or 250g.

 **If you still want candy...**

Candy Capers
www.sweets-candy-direct.com
A tempting site. Admittedly the homepage displays an off-putting picture of a middle-aged couple surrounded by mint humbugs, but the shelves are stocked with all your favourite childhood sweets. But at only £1.80 for a quarter kg bag, it may prove detrimental to your teeth if you buy the required £10 worth of sweets.

Chambers Candy Store
www.chamberscandy.co.uk
This quaint site offers such traditional sweets as Elizabethan comfits in tiny tins and unusual items like dusted chocolate-covered blueberry raisins in Fabergé-style eggs. With delivery charges not listed until you've keyed in your credit card details, it's best to contact the company before you buy.

Daisy's Sweet Emporium
www.daisyssweetemporium.com
Daisy's store includes jelly sweets, boiled sweets, candy rock and your classic school tuck shop items like sour apples and foam shrimps. For value for money and range, this site is hard to beat.

CYBER CANDY

If you're tired of your average Mars bar, Snickers or Dairy Milk, and are looking for something a little bit different in the sweetie department, Cyber Candy sell a huge range of sweets and candy usually only found in America and Australia.

America's favourites – Hershey bars, Reeses Pieces and Baby Ruths – are all included plus items for the more adventurous, such as Australia's Ovalteenies (they're tablets of Ovaltine), and musk-flavoured Lifesavers. Each sweetie costs under £1, with first or second class postage extra.

Cyber Candy –
www.cybercandy.co.uk

Clothes & fashion

Desperate for a new pair of wellies?
A Crombie outfit to up the cred level
with the lads on your manor?
A sequinned basque? Size up the
Web – it's tailor made for top threads

General Where to go for advice, Oz gear and big glamour

The Australian Clothing Company
www.ozclothingco.com
Heavy-duty oiled cotton coats and jackets as well as hats and boots for those
anticipating very rough weather or spending a lot of time out in the open. The
kit is as worn by Aussie stockmen for years and should last you a lifetime.
There's an online order form to complete, although part of it was still under
construction when we looked and delivery details were not available.

Ready 2 Shop
www.ready2shop.com
Nothing to buy but loads of fun to be had at this interactive women's fashion
advice site. You say which bits of your body you love or hate and online gurus
will give you an instant list of outfits that might suit you and tell you where you
can buy them. There's also a section on cool kids' clothing, but nothing for
the menfolk yet. Save time, money and a few fashion disasters.

Sixteen 47
www.sixteen47.com
A stylish and fun range of clothes for women over size 16, created by Dawn
French and Helen Teague. The clothes would probably look better if they
were modelled on people rather than mannequins, but this is an attractive and
easy-to-use site. Full online ordering wasn't yet up and running when we
visited, but fill in the detailed enquiry form and the company will contact you.

Accessories

The bag, shoes and belt make the outfit

Accessorize

www.accessorize.co.uk

This jazzy site ties in well with the jewellery and accessories on offer. They can't show every piece of their collection, but every category contains around 10 items with clear pictures. No cheaper than the high street (between £3 and £10 for bracelets) and at £3 delivery, it's better to buy in bulk. If you decide you don't like the items once they're delivered, take them back to the shop.

Pink Ice

www.pink-ice.com

Pink name, pink site and pink accessories. Ignore the limited range – what they have is straight from the catwalk at more affordable prices. Some of the more unusual items include body jewellery add-ons to make your pierced navel even more ravishing, with prices from £12 to £60 depending on the metal and design. Designer bags for around £50 include the Billy Bag and Kimi beaded bags, and if you're bored with your old pastel pashmina, try an embroidered design for £200.

Sunglasses 2000

www.sunglasses2000.com

Based in the US, this is the ultimate sunglasses warehouse. Designer ranges include Gucci, Ray Ban, Fendi and Nike, at more affordable prices, generally between $50 and $100. Each brand holds 40 to 50 different designs, with clear images, a choice of colours and precise measurements so you can find the perfect fit. Shipping to the UK is an extra $15, taking up to 14 days. Even so, prices are cheaper than this side of the Atlantic.

The Red Hand

www.theredhand.com

Easy-to-navigate site selling original accessories from hot young designers, including jewellery, bags and wraps. Particularly clever is the PVC bucket-shape handbag with matching spade-shape purse. A vintage accessories section is promised soon. Prices are inclusive of delivery, although delivery time isn't specified.

TIES

Airport favourite Tie Rack offers a comprehensive site with silk, printed, fun and classic ties in a variety of colours. Click on the image to see your chosen tie matched with a suitable shirt. Prices start from £12.

www.tie-rack.com

Limited selection of woven and printed ties. Annoyingly there is no direct link to the order form, so get a pen and paper ready.

www.fox andchave. co.uk

Decide what you want your tie to say about you – high flyer, fashion victim, or smooth operator. Discounts available if you buy in bulk!

www.saxdesign.com

If it's Versace, sweetie, it's here

Brown Bag Clothing
www.bbclothing.co.uk
Armani, Moschino and Versace are among the designers with ranges on this chi-chi clothes site for men and women. They promise to have the latest styles at discount prices, not just last year's overstocks, and certainly some of the special-offer clothes were on sale at almost 60 per cent off the RRP. You can search by designer or by the item of clothing you're looking for and there's a 14-day no-quibble refund on all orders.

Designer Discount
www.designerdiscount.co.uk
Don't be put off by the tacky opening page which has Brad Pitt peering from the screen. Once inside, you can search this professionally organised site by designer or simply browse the thumbnail images of their entire catalogue. If you don't usually go in for such glamour names as Versace, Valentino and YSL, the discounts could change your mind – the £40 and £50 reductions on many items reduce designer clothes to high-street prices.

Dressmart
www.dressmart.co.uk
Stock site selling mainstream menswear, including Mulberry, Van Heusen and Pierre Cardin. Useful if you work in the centre of London and run short of clean shirts as they guarantee a two-hour shirt-and-tie delivery. Only certain postcodes qualify for the Express service and prices range from £45 to £75, depending on the designer you choose.

Into Fashion
www.intofashion.com
One for the girls with clothing, jewellery and accessories. This jazzy site wins hands down in the shopping confidence stakes, offering five different angles of every item for you to browse. The designer names include trend-setters Johnny Loves Rosie, Jasper Conran and Frost French, all with 33 per cent discounts and free delivery.

Metropolis Clothing
www.metropolis-clothing.com
This Newcastle-based company offers a huge list of top designer names to choose from – Katherine Hamnett, Scott and Vivienne Westwood to name a few, all at discount prices with free delivery. Once you get down to details, however, only a few items are available under each heading and the majority appear to be ordinary over-sized t-shirts with the designer's name printed on. Not as exciting as it first promises but worth a quick look.

Into Fashion's site is the female fashion-shopper's best friend with five different angles of each item on offer

UK Designer Shop

www.ukdesignershop.com

With its confusing navigation system, malfunctioning links and extremely limited range (Pierre Cardin seems to feature very heavily amid some very high-street names), this site is only worth the time and effort of browsing if you're a man who can't say no to designer names, but also can't really afford to say yes. Up to 50 per cent off and two-for-one deals say it all.

Zercon

www.zercon.com

This site offers unisex clothes, so don't bother searching both the men's and women's sections as only sizes differ in most cases. Dull and grey, the visuals are a good reflection of the clothes on offer and only the brand labels stand out. Top names include Dolce & Gabbana, Ralph Lauren and Tommy Hilfiger. On the plus side, they are cheaper than the high street and if you take the time to join, you can enjoy an extra five per cent discount.

 **Affordable, dependable and fun**

Brooks Brothers

www.brooksbrothers.com

In the UK Brooks are one of the first ports of call if you want to rent a tux, but they only sell online from their US site. Consequently you'll need to calculate the import duties and taxes for yourself, and shipping charges start at $35. Prices for their bland, play-safe men's suits begin at $329, so you may find it cheaper to stick to shopping in UK stores. At these prices one would expect to be able to either see or read about what each item is made from, but even the enlarged images are not great quality.

French Connection
www.frenchconnection.com
Unfortunately the arty opening page and a 15-page catalogue of their summer collection gave a false impression, as this visitor wasn't able to buy all the luscious items which had just been displayed. Whether French Connection were just testing the Internet waters only they know. It was possible to view the catalogue and buy either a sample from their perfume range or an FC branded t-shirt – neither of which was particularly impressive. The site was a big disappointment, but FCUK is only one of a number of high-street names which has yet to fully embrace the Net and its technology.

The following also had websites but no online ordering when we visited…
www.benetton.com
www.kookai.com
www.oasis-stores.co.uk
www.riverisland.com

Monsoon
www.monsoon.co.uk
The bright Mediterranean backdrop links well with the clothes and homewares featured. You can search by product or the look you're after – Bohemian chic, Paradise and so on. Click on the image provided to view a larger picture,

Zoom.co.uk The Internet's favourite high-street mall

The high street wouldn't be the same without such Arcadia names as Top Shop, Dorothy Perkins and Principles, and, under the stripy orange livery of the Zoom.co.uk portal, they're now embracing the Net. Each store has its own site but all follow a similar set-up: vibrant, colourful and easy-to-follow. There are multiple ways to shop including casual browsing and quick shopping, online magazines with news, reviews and competitions, and specialist sections, including maternity wear and larger sizes. The descriptions and images could be better, but they do offer washing guidelines, fitting-room help and packed sale sections. Most of all, they make you want to buy online.

www.burtonmenswear.co.uk
www.dorothyperkins.co.uk
www.evans.ltd.co.uk
www.hawkshead.co.uk
www.principles.co.uk
www.su214.co.uk
www.topman.co.uk
www.tops.co.uk
www.wadesmith.co.uk

which comes complete with washing instructions, size guide and alternative recommendations – all thoughtful touches. High-street prices apply and delivery is fixed at £3, irrespective of the size of your order. This is a good, comprehensive site that actually makes you want to shop there.

Next

www.next.co.uk

The simple, clean homepage seems to provide everything you need to know. You can browse or use the quick-shop facility to shop for men's, women's or children's clothes and housewares. Use the next-day delivery facility and you can benefit from free returns. Sounds too good to be true? It is. You can only buy if you're an account holder and the online registration doesn't recognise all postcodes. If you do decide to register, don't think you can make up time by using the quick-shop facility as you need the codes provided in the Next Directory to make a search. The directory costs £3. If none of this has put you off, they do provide a comprehensive directory with clear and enlarged images, fabric details and easy ordering once you're in.

 Serious streetwear for the hipster in you

Abercrombie & Fitch

www.abercrombie.com

Having been eulogised in many an American rap song, Abercrombie & Fitch clothes have become a must-have with those in the know. Skate and urban wear dominates but, being American, everything is slightly toned down compared to their UK competitors. Inexpensive compared to the UK market, jeans and fleeces are priced at around $50 with t-shirts for $19, though you should always bear in mind the added costs of importing. For international deliveries add an extra $25 and allow for 2-4 weeks' wait. You'll also need to sort out any duties and taxes yourself, but it's worth it for something a little more original than a pair of Levi's and a Gap fleece.

A.W. Rust

www.awrust.co.uk

A fresh and simple amateur site selling popular favourites with the boys – Sonneti, Rockport, Gas and Fred Perry. It won't take you long to browse with only a few items under each brand, but discounts at up to 50 per cent off make up for it. Similar discounts apply to the leather section with snakeskin leather jackets for under £130 and leather tops at around £40.

Boxfresh

www.boxfresh.co.uk

If you don't care for the jungle that plays whilst you browse this site, then this up-and-coming brand probably isn't for you. But even if said music does

Full marks go to Diesel for their stylishly designed site – this is the 'cover' of their catalogue – but even their speed-shopper takes time

appeal, this site offers only a limited selection, poor images and tiny swatches of the available colours. Surely such a premium brand could do better, even for those who know what they're getting? On the plus side, some prices work out cheaper than those bumped up by department stores, and delivery is free.

Designer Heaven
www.designerheaven.com
Labels for boys rather than designers for men – the brands include Full Circle, Henri Lloyd, John Smedley and Cabourn. It's a pricey and limited range too – t-shirts begin around the £50 mark and jackets around £100. The descriptions and images are adequate and ordering is simple.

Diesel
www.diesel.co.uk
The trendy place to get your denims, Diesel has produced an equally stylish online shop. Select a Flash or non-Flash version and meander through virtual racks of clothes, accessories and fragrances, or use their speed-shopper. This term, however, is misleading, as unless you know what a Huppo jacket or a Doppi top looks like, shopping could take you some time. High-street prices apply but you may pick up something out of the ordinary.

Fat Face
www.fatface.co.uk
Surfer bods fill the homepage, so it's not difficult to recognise the young, fit and funky target audience. Despite their swank status, the clothes are relatively inexpensive, with most items under £35. The extensive online

catalogue sells men's, women's and kids' clothes, plus accessories, but when it comes to sizes Fat Face fares poorly, with many women's items only going up to a size 12 or 14. They also lose marks for requiring registration.

Iikon
http://shop.iikon.com

Skaters' heaven. Rare and collectible skateboards are sold alongside the only skate footwear to be seen in, Northwave trainers. The fat-soled street trainers are sold at cheaper than average prices, £35 – £50, but they do insist you register before you can buy. Converting the various foreign sizes is also too much like hard work unless you use the calculator.

LondonWide
www.londonwide.co.uk

The essence of London streetwear is on offer here, so you can stand out from the crowd with very latest and best in retro chic. Soochi, Burro and Battery Organic are just three of the bizarrely named designers. You pay a price for original designs – £68 for aei:kei's revealing Spider breast top – but they do sell lower-range t-shirts for men and women, with typical prices around £20. This may seem a lot for a bit of cotton with a stencilled print, but the adulation from your peers will make up for it.

Rubens
www.rubensmenswear.com

Amateurish graphics and pictures let down this otherwise adequate site, which sells everything from the skaters' must-have label O'Neill to trendy Base footwear and Ben Sherman shirts. Discount prices are available on some stock, but otherwise standard high-street prices apply: £60 – £80 for Base footwear, £25 for O'Neill t-shirts.

Surf On The Net
www.surfonthenet.co.uk

As the name suggests, this label superstore is dedicated to those who ride the waves, with shirts, dresses and fleeces on sale as well as swimwear. Top brands include Mambo, Rip Curl, Vans and Kangaroo, and there are men's, women's and kiddie sizes. Prices match the high street, delivery is free and you get the added bonus of Surfzine with news, views, schools and cams.

Ted Baker
www.tedbaker.co.uk

This annoying and badly organised site is not for those new to Ted's line of urban wear, or for those in a hurry. Standard men's and women's clothing categories apply but it's a mystery why Lentil and Danish are used as names for skirts, or why Kiwi should be used to refer to a stone pair of trousers. You're also required to register before you can purchase, so casual browsers and the impulsive buyers are not catered for either.

Underwear
Pose in silly frillies or chill in thermals

Agent Provocateur
www.agentprovocateur.com

If the current Agent Provocateur range at your local Marks & Spencer is a little safe for you, you can buy the real thing from this site. Both the lingerie and the site are stylish and risqué. Select a complete image and then view each item in the collection individually before you buy. It's pricier than M & S, though – generally anywhere between £30 and £60 for a single item.

> ## EASY SHOP
>
> Easy Shop is exactly as its name suggests, with a choice of searching by brand or lingerie item. Brands include Sloggi for men, Gossard for women and a host of designers ranges for anyone: Dolce & Gabbana, Moschino and French Connection.
>
> ----
>
> The faster option is to select the item category. Answer four questions – size, occasion, style and price range – and they'll come up with a selection.
>
> ----
>
> The step-by-step ordering process helps to avoid confusion, and though prices will vary according to the label you choose, many of the items are discounted.
>
> ----
>
> www.easy shop.co.uk

Amazing Undies
www.amazingundies.co.uk

High-street names such as Gossard and Pretty Polly rub shoulders with more specialised items on this easy-to-navigate site – underwear for the fuller figure, Shock Absorber sports bras and that revolutionary underwear item for those feeling a bit flat, the Gel Bra, a natural-looking alternative to the padded bra. You can search by brand to see thumbnail images which can be enlarged. Standard prices apply even for the more specialised items, so this is a good site to visit if you don't fall into average categories.

Ann Summers
www.annsummers.co.uk

Don't be put off by the tacky-looking site – the Ann Summers' site holds an extensive online catalogue with something for every taste. Scroll along, read (if you can) the adequate descriptions and view enlarged images if need be. Only slightly pricier than the high street – £18 for bras – this is a useful site for lingerie that's little bit different but not beyond the average budget. No three-pack knickers available, however.

Brief Look Lingerie
www.brieflook.co.uk

To save time, Brief Look allow you to browse their extensive catalogue according to your own size needs, rather than searching through reams of styles that are never going to fit. Encouragingly, they also appreciate that not all women wear a 34B bra – their sizes range from a 30A all the way to a

You can certainly see why they call the site Direct Male.
That's 'Charmer' above with 'Jungle' below, from Kiniki

50F. The designs themselves are up-to-date, and prices vary from £3 to £20 for knickers and £10 to £50 for bras. If, like the majority of women, you're wearing the wrong-size bra, the site also offers free advice and tips for a better fit. The site also stocks menswear and offers a wide range of fits.

Kiniki Direct Male
www.kiniki.com
If you're a man or someone looking to improve the state of a (male) partner's underwear, this may not necessarily be for you. Search boxers, briefs, thongs or swimwear and you may be somewhat intimidated. Tamer items include the 'Charmer' boxers in black satin, or for the more adventurous, 'Jungle' boxers in stylish leopard print – and there's a matching short satin robe. In shopping terms, the site is easy to use and you can enjoy a 20 per cent discount if you buy online. Not for the faint-hearted but sure to draw a big gay following.

Nile Trading
www.nile.co.uk
Not exactly sexy, but doubtless a Godsend in the deep midwinter: a complete range of lightweight thermal underwear, available from a Leicester-based company. All the tights, vests, and pants are made in Britain and since you're buying direct from the manufacturer, prices are excellent. There's no need to shiver ever again. Delivery is calculated at the checkout and your long-johns will be keeping you warm within the week.

Toe Rags
www.toerags.com
If your sock drawer is a black hole, fill it up again with a selection of these hardwearing cotton socks in a wide range of colours. Single pairs are £4.99

or invest £6.99 in a twin pack. The site has recently expanded to sell men's and women's clothes as well, with an emphasis on comfortable outdoor style. You have to register in order to shop and there's no online information about delivery costs, but it's certainly a nice site to look at.

Victoria's Secret

www.victoriassecret.com

Victoria's underwear is so popular she can afford to have supermodels promoting it on her website. Aside from the standard semi-naked women, the site itself is plain, making it simple to navigate. Get your indulgence fix with Deluxe and even Miracle bras or search for wardrobe essentials in the Bra Salon. Once converted, prices are average for the UK market, but you do need to take into account shipping fees, $14.95 for the first $75 spent and so on. They also offer a useful information section on international duties and an e-zine section on what's happening in the bra world.

 **From Thomas Pink to Linda Lusardi**

Café Coton

www.cafecoton.co.uk

Don't be put off by your grandad's favourite checked shirts displayed on the opening page: this site promises French flair. Choose from soft collar, button-down, double cuff, French and Italian style collar shirts, all priced at £33 with free delivery in two working days. Unfortunately you can only look at images of folded shirts, making it difficult to imagine what they'll look like on.

Crombie, outfitters to royalty, is the place to go if you have an eye for a sharp whistle and a taste for the finer things in life

Crombie

www.crombie.co.uk

Crombie has been in business for nearly 200 years, and the company shows the attention to detail that has kept them in business so long with this speedy and efficient website. Sadly you can't buy a Crombie coat online, but a good range of shirts, ties, knitwear and accessories are available for the discerning traditional male. Delivery charges are calculated at the checkout and since they ship overseas, everything is sent via UPS.

Edward Teach

www.edward-teach.com

Before you go past the homepage, make sure you know all your shirt measurements. Choose from a selection of 50 different colours, 10 collar and six cuff styles and design your own handmade shirt. For £79.95, including postage, ET will make and deliver your new shirt in 18 days. Costly but unique.

Hector Russell

www.hector-russell.com

A Highland fling can be yours at this kilt supplier's site. Since kilt-making is a serious business, you can't just click and have one sent out, but you can email for further details and there are excellent photos and guidelines to the different styles on the site. Secure shopping using an order form is available for accessories like sporrans and clan ties.

Menswear Direct

www.menswear-direct.com

Linda Lusardi has recently launched this online men's clothing store, but don't be put off by the cheap and cheerful design and slightly clumsy text – there are quality items to be found here at excellent prices. Suits, shirts, ties and other accessories are available and there's a useful sizing guide if you're confused about what to buy. Delivery information was not available when we looked at the site, but you can email them for P&P charges.

Shirt Press

www.shirt-press.co.uk

The answer to all our prayers: shirts that never need to be ironed. Add to this a well thought-out website with button cuffs, double cuffs, dress shirts and ties to choose from in every possible colour. You do pay a price for the luxury of an empty ironing basket, however – usually £70, or £100 for two shirts. There are no full-length shots on the site but the close-up pictures do let you see the quality of what you're buying.

Thomas Pink

www.thomaspink.co.uk

Yet another shirt shop. Mr. Pink sells tailored men's, and a limited range of women's, shirts. Thankfully the shirts are slightly more interesting than the site itself, but only just. Shirts, ties and cufflinks are each priced at around the £50 mark, but you can only look at enlarged images of the shirt collar and tie, so you'll need to use a little more imagination than the site has.

4XL

www.forxl.co.uk

If you're over six feet tall, you'll be familiar with the problem of trousers that only reach your ankles. 4XL offers a range of jeans from known manufacturers such as Wrangler, as well as more formal trousers to cover even the longest shanks. Some of the photos don't show the merchandise to best effect, but the quality is guaranteed and all prices include delivery.

 **The original mail-order concept, updated**

Bluebelle

www.bluebelle.co.uk

If revealing eveningwear is your thing, you could find something you like on this independent womenswear site, with swimwear and leisurewear also on offer. Prices are very reasonable, although styling the models as nightclub pole dancers does not raise the site's class factor. Delivery is calculated when you check out and your slinky number should reach you within 7 days.

Boden

www.boden.co.uk

Online version of the hugely successful catalogue selling upmarket family clothes in contemporary designs. The range spans sturdy trousers for busy fathers to pretty velvet cardigans for women looking for a little glamour. The Mini Boden section has kids' styles you'll find irresistible, no matter how grubby they're likely to get. Prices online are 10 per cent cheaper than through the catalogue. There are various delivery choices, starting at £3, and if you live in London you can even request a same-day courier service for £10.

Brora

www.brora.co.uk

There's nothing like the feel of cashmere and this site will tempt you to feel it just a little more often. There are gorgeous and colourful cashmere designs for men, women and kids (who, quite frankly, don't deserve it) and although the prices are about average, there are some bargains to be had in the Sale section. Delivery starts at £6 and is free on orders over £300.

Cotton Traders

www.cotton-traders.co.uk

If you live in your rugby shirt, you'll know this name. Online shopping wasn't fully up and running when we visited, but you can email for a catalogue or

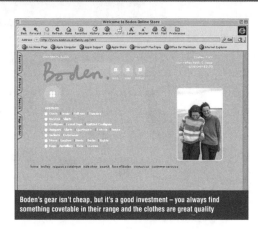

Boden's gear isn't cheap, but it's a good investment – you always find something covetable in their range and the clothes are great quality

phone your order to the number on the site. Specialists in super-tough sporty shirts, CTs also stock a range of other quality cotton gear at excellent prices.

Freemans
www.freemans.com
The trusted catalogue has had a style overhaul in recent years and now features wearable and affordable ranges from labels like Whistles and Betty Jackson. The menswear section has clothes ranging from Pierre Cardin to Red or Dead, and the whole site is beautifully laid out and a joy to use. Delivery and returns are free and take two to three days.

James Meade
www.jamesmeade.com
High quality, conservative classic clothes from a company owned by an ex-Coldstream Guardsman. There's an alteration service on trouser and skirt lengths and they will even monogram and recuff and collar your shirts for you.

Kays
www.kaysnet.com
You're unlikely to set the world on fire with these clothes, but the selection is good and the prices are keen. Kays still offers the option to spread your payments over 20 weeks to make budgeting easier. The site is easy to use with an informative welcome section for new shoppers and if you get your order in before 10am it will be delivered free within 48 hours.

If you buy this stuff it'll make you look like a pouty French actress. Well, not really, but it sure is cute, and there's designer gear at les prix très bon marché

Lands' End

www.landsend.co.uk

UK website for the US clothing catalogue giant. You're unlikely to see Madonna wearing Lands' End as they stick firmly to the middle of the road in terms of design, but if you're looking for long-lasting cotton t-shirts and wrinkle-resistant chinos, you'll find them here. The stock is all good value for money, with regular sales and special offers. Delivery is speedy and efficient, and costs £3.50 no matter what the size of your order.

La Redoute

www.redoute.co.uk

Even catalogue shopping is more chic in France. Given the design and quality of the clothes, this site is excellent value for money. Women, men, and kids can all get a fix of French style, and if you don't like what you've chosen, send it back Freepost for a full refund. Post and packing costs £2.45 on all orders and your clothes should reach you within five days.

Long Tall Sally

www.longtallsally.co.uk

Wide range of stylish clothes for women over 5ft 8in from leather skirts or a formal worksuit. There's also a swimwear section for the long-bodied and maternity wear for high-held bumps. The Special Occasion wear could be a bit more special, however. Orders are usually dispatched within 24 hours, and there's a charge of £2 if you spend less than £30 or £3 for larger orders.

Lounge Lizard

www.eclipse.co.uk/pens/lizard/

This site shows details of the Lounge Lizard clothing range from Australia and it's vehemently anti-fit. If it's baggy you're looking for, you'll get it here, although some of the drawings are less flattering that they could be. There's no online ordering yet, just a form to print out and fax through, but prices are competitive and there's a good choice of colours and styles.

Racing Green

www.racinggreen.co.uk

A good, clear version of the men's and women's casual clothing catalogue, this features high quality products, good clearance offers (available only online) and a Fast Find service to avoid downloading items that you're not interested in. The site is linked to the warehouse system so you will know immediately if an item is out of stock, and there is privilege shopping for registered regular customers. Delivery is only £1.95 and orders over £100 are carriage free.

Sweaty Betty

www.sweatybetty.com

Dance and sport inspired streetwear for hard-bodied young things. There's a limited range on the website, but the snow-wear range is on its way. Make Lycra your friend with greatly desirable crop tops, halter tops and mesh dresses, all shown off to perfection on this hugely impressive animated site. The shopping service was not fully launched when we looked, but they promise speedy service and a fully secure shopping experience.

Usisi Ltd.

www.usisidirect.com

Brightly coloured, 100 per cent cotton clothing direct from South Africa. Adult clothing includes generously sized sweatshirts and polo shirts with often lurid animal and vegetable designs (we liked the zebra). Take a look at the blue pin-striped t-shirts for something less hectic. In the children's range we loved the padded jacket printed with safari animals. Prices are very reasonable, given the originality of the garments and the fact that prices include delivery.

 Children How to keep them hip and happy from 0-16

Baby Planet

www.babyplanet.co.uk

Kids of up to six years old are catered for by this tie-dye emporium selling brightly coloured hippy hooded sweatshirts, romper suits and t-shirts in 100 per cent cotton and fully washable. Your mother-in-law will be outraged – a good enough reason to buy one in itself. Shopping is not secure, but once you send your e-mail order form, they will call you for your credit card details.

Gatefish
www.gatefish.com
Fleeces, sweatshirt and t-shirts for kids over three with the emphasis on practicality. All items are easily washable and hardwearing: some even have reflective motifs to help make your kids more visible. There's also a section of very cute fancy dress. Prices are higher than average, but the quality probably makes up for that. Delivery is calculated on site.

Flowerpot Clothing
www.flowerpotclothing.com
Sweet embroidered and appliquéd Aran sweaters, fleeces and sweatshirts from this small company in Loughborough. Prices are good (£19 for the pure wool Arans), given the craft that goes into each one, and the site is a cinch to surf. They also stock women's versions of some of the products.

Giant Peach
www.giantpeach.co.uk
Truly adorable kidswear ranging from the traditional to the very funky indeed for little people up to the age of eight. Packed with good ideas like laminated paint smocks for messy young artists, and they also stock a range of gifts and nursery accessories. You have to register with the site in order to shop, but orders within the UK are shipped free.

Patricia Smith
www.psdesigns.demon.co.uk
Cornish clothing company making and selling traditional children's garb for well-brought up little people. Lots of smocked party dresses in cotton, and there's even a sailor suit if you really want to torture your son, although there are more up to date fleece sweatshirts as well. Despite the care that has gone into designing this site, there is no shopping basket, so you have to print out a form to order. Delivery costs £3 and can take 28 days.

Poppy
www.poppy-children.co.uk
Bright and pretty crease-resistant cotton dresses, with jackets and hats to match, for little girls who want to impress. The printed fabrics are designed by local artists so you won't find the fabric being used elsewhere. The prices are not cheap but

LABELLED WITH LOVE

All the groovy kid's clothing in the world is no good if your little loves have a habit of leaving them lying around. Solve the problem in time-honoured fashion by labelling every item you can. The following sites can help:

Woven or iron-on tapes, cut and ready for use. Penmark also makes woven luggage straps.

Penmark Name Tapes
www.nametapesdirect.com

Woven tapes, plain or with embroidered logos.

Premier Name Tapes
www.premierservices.co.uk

Clothes & fashion

Children's Warehouse: hard-wearing and colourful, the clothes have a designer twist at sensible prices that will win them fans

the quality is good, and there's little in the high street to match the designs. Deliveries should take no more than five days and charges start at £2.99.

SolSafe
www.solsafe.com
Useful t-shirts and hats guaranteed to keep the sun's rays away from delicate skin. All fabric is treated so that it offers a 30+ SPF compared to regular clothes which offer little protection. The t-shirts come in lots of colours and cost £10, while the hats cost £5. You can email your order to them, or phone through your card details separately.

School Uniforms Online
www.schooluniformsonline.co.uk
Standard school uniform items like duffel coats and polo shirts are available on this straightforward site at much lower prices than on the high street, plus you don't have to depress the kids by taking them to the school outfitter while they're still on summer holidays. They also stock a range of Scout and Guide uniforms, and dance clothes. Five-day delivery costs £2.95 on all UK orders.

Children's Warehouse
www.childrens-warehouse.com
Once you've found Caroline Bunting's neat, West London-based site you'll find yourself returning again and again. Her kids' clothes are well designed and great quality, there's every item you could want, in sizes from babies' to 12-year olds' and from cuddly fleeces to cute pyjamas, and they're just hip enough to silence your little darlings' pleas for Karan and Hilfiger (for ten minutes). Delivery costs £3, returns are free and prices not outrageous.

Coffee and tea

Caffeine is one of the few addictive drugs you really can buy over the Internet. And the choice is all yours: you can buy it from Baltimore, Chelsea or the island of St Helena

Baltimore Coffee Company
www.baltcoffee.com
According to the rather dull home page this is the most comprehensive tea and coffee site on the web. They might well be right as the range of products is vast and each comes with no less than six different types of grind. Although the payment screen is untidy you are soon assured that it's safe and can choose to have your order confirmed by email if you so desire.

Barnie Coffee
www.barniescoffee.com
This is a mercifully simple site that doesn't bother with fancy graphics. The products are listed on a side bar and Barnie's featured choice is described in detail in the middle. Navigation is clear and easy, and it all looks great. Then everything falls apart during registration. This takes ages, is way too complex and once you are through, it hits you with international delivery at $50!

Clipper Teas
www.clipper-teas.com
Masses of information on the company, and tea in general but the store is not immediately evident on the amateurish home page and some text is obscured by pictures on the rest of the site so no gold star for graphics. The selection is good with a definite ethical bias in favour of fair trade and organic teas. There's some intriguing product info and you can request free samples.

Coffee, Tea and Spice
www.coffeecoffee.com
Coffee, Tea and Spice is a small firm operating out of one shop. There is no mention of a secure server and the request to log in seems a bit unnecessary.

However, when you know that Myrna Blaine is preparing your coffee herself, who cares? The purchase process itself is clear and logical and delivery charges are ridiculously low, easily eclipsing most of the big players.

Flying Saucers

www.flyingsaucers.com

There is no UK delivery but this site is a must for sci-fi loving coffee drinkers. Technically it's poor with a single scrolling list for all products and text obscured by graphics, but somehow you don't really care as there are "70 flavors and varieties of coffee (in space ship packaging)". Along with this the selection of alien merchandise is unrivalled… in this solar system anyway.

Java Johns

www.javajohns.com/home.htm

They gain some credit for not blaring about the Ink Spots' Java Jive as you access the rather spartan home page. But they haven't skimped on product range. They do deliver to the UK, but there's nothing to confirm that you are on a secure server. If you go to www.javajohns.com you find a link to the espresso top 50, a site network coffee addicts may not be able to live without.

Starbucks

www.starbucks.com

Starbucks is one of the best known names in coffee but the closest they get to delivering to the UK is shipping to Canada which isn't really that close at all. Pity because the product range on display is quite impressive.

St Helena

www.st-helena-coffee.sh

The Island of St Helena coffee company site doesn't seem like much from the home page but delving further reveals some stunning images of the island. If you can draw yourself away, there is a simple navigation system and secure server but a limited range. World wide delivery is included in the price.

Whittard

www.whittard.co.uk

The coffee and tea shop for people who know which finger to raise when they're having a cuppa has a decent online store with an impressive range of products, extremely clear advice on how to buy through the site (including reassurance that you're on a secure server) and an exhaustive FAQ to reassure first time buyers. There is even free advice of the "how to make a perfect cuppa" variety which concludes with the slightly baffling advice: "Teapots should never be bleached." Ah, so that's what… The customer testimonials have to be read to be believed: one satisfied shopper compares a member of staff to a "modern day ship captain", others fall into raptures over the packaging, while one visitor rhapsodises over the "incredibly beautiful" web site. It's true, some Netheads really should get out more.

Collectibles

That's collectibles as in shark's teeth, corkscrews, Star Trek medals... oh, and a few old coins and stamps

General   Including one Eastern Airlines coffee pot

Acubid
www.acubid.com
A rather respectable homepage doesn't quite conceal the sheer gaudiness and oddness of many of the goods up for grabs on this auction site. Among the bizarre range of collectibles on offer when the site was inspected were a figure of Barbie's Ken as the Tin Man from the *Wizard of Oz* (probably a shrewd investment at $50) and an APC Smart UPS 420 uninterruptable power supply for your computer at $25. Stronger on stamps than coins and stronger on sports memorabilia than stamps. As a well established site, you will have few security worries when bidding here,

Christies
www.christies.com
Ever since Christies bought Spink, the world's oldest coin dealer in 1993, it's been impossible for serious numismatists to give this site a miss. Spink still has its own site www.spink-online.com but Christies is also worth visiting if you're collecting anything from sports memorabilia to corkscrews (it's no joke - a good corkscrew can fetch £5,000 these days). Given the company's policy of only accepting bids in person or over the phone, this is strictly window shopping, but it's one hell of a window.

Dibit
www.dibit.com
Exonumists may be somewhat disappointed by this site (to you and me that's people who collect tokens and medals which resemble currency but were not intended to act as currency, got that?) It doesn't always have the range of bigger auction houses like eBay, but the search facility is pretty nifty and it's a bit like going through a January sale. Amid all the tat you'll probably find something to reward your patience.

eBay

www.ebay.com

The best known online auctioneer has an extensive range of coins, along with banknotes, stamps and autographs on offer. You may want to avoid the registration process if you're just browsing both on principle (why should you have to bother?) and because it takes a while. Besides, all that form filling is an unnecessary distraction from searching the site which can contain such curiosities as an Eastern Airlines coffee pot ($9.99) or a selection of rare condom tins (on which bids swiftly rose above $200). And, as at an offline auction, you have to know what you are doing before you buy.

QXL

www.qxl.com

Few sites more effectively contradict the stereotypical image of online auctions than QXL. Far from being cyberspace's answer to a smoky back room in which items of dubious origin are traded, this site is packed with clear, in-depth information about each lot. One of the best auction sites for coins and tokens, QXL also has a fair range of stamps and memorabilia. Every so often you come across something like an *Eighth Army News* issue for £1, which is so cheap and so odd you just want to snap it up there and then.

Sotheby's Collectibles

http://search.sothebys.com/search/collArea/collArea.jsp?code=ca004&t
ype=C

This is the direct address for the collectibles section of Sotheby's site, worth knowing because, on a bad day, the journey to here from the .com page (which ought to be the cyberspace equivalent of a walk in the park) can take eons.

Coins & stamps   "Buy them while they're hot"

Franklin Mint

www.franklinmint.com

This is a specialist collectors site that seems dedicated to tack. It's not that fast to navigate and you have to register to buy but there is a guide to what is selling best. International orders are only accepted by phone and mail which is a disadvantage, but the amount of top notch Elvis merchandise could make up for your disappointment. For a company with Mint in its title, there isn't a lot for coin collectors here. At best you'll find a Princess Diana coin set; at worst, the *Star Trek* calendar medal, naff as it sounds, will cost £135.

Harlan J Berk

www.harlanjberk.com

This is probably the most professional site for numismatists on the Web, but given the homemade nature of some of the other sites out there, that's not saying much. The range of coins available covers a huge period of history and spans the globe (they even list Alaska as a country) and tends towards the very expensive. But be warned: if you want to actually view a coin online, the process of clicking for an image sends the company an email.

Ice-coin
www.smart.is/ice-coin/ice.html

A site dedicated to the coinage and coin-based merchandise of Iceland. The product range is therefore a little limited. The shop is simple to use and is relatively inexpensive, but as the slightly questionable English proclaims, perhaps with unintentional candour, "discount is a question about quantity". To make the site still more specialist, it lapses into Icelandic without warning.

Online Coins
www.onlinecoins.com

Backed by a network of US dealers, this site has a searchable archive of coins in various categories from nickel to gold and silver bullion. Once you search for an item you are presented with a list of what's in stock and a phone number and email address for the dealer. That is the theory but the search engine has its temperamental moments when you can almost hear it shrieking "Coins? You want coins? And what makes you think I've got any of those?".

Princess Diana stamps
www.princess-diana-stamps.com

URLs don't come much more descriptive than this. The site is, unsurprisingly, American and very amateur in terms of both design and navigation. The saving grace is the extensive product range. The shipping form is quite complex but there is a choice of secure or non-secure servers, depending on your browser.

Royal Mint
www.royalmint.com

Clean, well-structured site (although you need to tell the site which country you are browsing from before you can go any farther) with an impressive and well-presented stock of coins on offer. The gold bullion sovereign and half-sovereign, produced to commemorate (what else?) the millennium, at £69 and £35 respectively (with free delivery in the UK), seem like a good investment.

Tucson Coin & Autographs
www.tucsoncoinandautograph.com

The website of a small US store which has set up an online shopping facility. There's a secure ordering system which, if you're ordering from the UK, calculates how much shipping costs add up to before you buy. With all that in its favour, the site is let down by a confusing design. If you view the online catalogue and click on "coins" as a category you get one item coming up yet if you click on the coins button on the navigation bar on the left of the home page, you scroll through a long list of rare and valuable coins. It's not immediately apparent (ie after 10 minutes of careful study) whether you can buy these items online or have no recourse but to email the company.

Memorabilia No such thing as a free lunch box

Fun45s

www.fun45s.com

You can find records for your next *National Lampoon Animal House* "Toga! Toga!" tribute party (go ahead and organise one, you know you owe it to yourself) at this site which, with perhaps a dash of hyperbole, calls itself "the internet source for classic vinyl". The invitation to search the archive by "fun category" may sound inappropriate for those who think that the words "fun" and "category" should never be that close together but it's hard not to smile when you scroll down to see categories like "Caution! Power ballads ahead." International shipping costs are available on application by email. There is one slight drawback: the site's no returns policy. Pricing is wonderfully simple: "all records cost $3 each everyday". An unpretentious site which also sells accessories like a record player, white single sleeves, and (back by popular demand, at least that's what the site says) those classic red blank jukebox title strips. And there's secure ordering direct from the site on your credit card. So what are you waiting for?

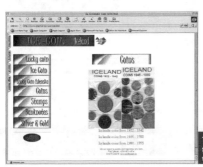

The ice men collecteth: a very specialist site for people who collect Icelandic coins

Prince! The artist formally known as HRH on the Web

Children's video
www.checkout.com
This video of *The Old Man of Lochnagar*, written and narrated by the proper Charlie. Available on video (all 20 minutes of it) from this site for just $8.97 plus shipping. But don't buy anything by Prince Charles and the City Beat, the American 1980s funk artist available from the same store.

Clematis
www.waysidegardens.pointshop.com
The new Prince Charles clematis could be yours for only $7.95 apiece if you order a dozen from US online garden supplies store Wayside. Alas and alack, Wayside does not deliver outside North America.

Die cast model
www.qxl.com
Formally entitled the "Lledo Days Gone HRH Prince Charles 50th birthday" this die cast model went up on QXL last summer for a reserve price of £3.

Fridge magnet
www.politicos.co.uk
Impress your republican *Observer*-reading friends by ordering a *Spitting Image* fridge magnet of the heir to the throne, available for just £2.99.

Paper doll
www.altavista.com
Even that loses out in the kitsch stakes to the pair of Princess Diana and Prince Charles "full colour fashion paper dolls" up for grabs on Alta Vista's auction area for just $5 this summer.

Toasting goblets
www.ebay.com
These souvenirs from the Prince's 1977 visit to our colonial cousins were $79 on eBay, along with 157 other items linked to the heir to the throne.

"It really is appalling..." that the Prince Charles clematis from Wayside Gardens is only sold Stateside

Lunch Box Bonanza

www.cassidyframes.com/box

A genuinely weird site by an American called Jim Cassidy who has never got over his school/golden rule days. You click on the lunch box in the picture to enter a site which, judging from the variety of colour type, is run by someone who, as a kid, would use every crayon in the set to draw. Just when you are about to conclude that this kind of insanity can only happen in America, you scroll down the list of lots for sale and see that one item is quoted at over £100. Time to send Dad into the attic.

Monkees Collection

www.themonkees.com

Here they come, still getting the funniest looks even in cyberspace. The manufactured pop group whose reputation has outlived many of the genuine ones from the 1960s have their own collectors page where, after an electronic rendition of *A Little Bit Me, A Little Bit You*, you are invited to inspect a little bit of Monkees memorabilia. Sadly, the only item of Monkees memorabilia most fans really want (Mike Nesmith's woolly bobble hat) isn't here but you can console yourself by perusing the list of rare bootlegs, books and comics.

Paper Antiques

www.paperantiques.co.uk/forsale/postcardcig.htm

No Flash plug-ins, no animated graphics, not even a home page with a bogus corporate message on it, this Amazon-associated site devoted to all kinds of paper antiques just cuts straight to the chase with an invitation to search its archive of cigarette cards, magazines, Acts of Parliament etc. This approach doesn't seem to pay off as the site had a "For sale" sign posted.

Sharks Teeth

www.sharksteethforsale.com

Captain Al Williams doesn't actually extract the teeth from live sharks you understand (although that sounds like a suitable punishment for errant dentists) - he waits until they have been dead a few thousand years and picks them up off the sea bed. An odd way to make a living but a good tooth (from the extinct Carcharocles Angustidens or giant white shark to you and me) can fetch $250. You can order online and phone in your credit card number.

World War II stamps, coins, propaganda, posters

www.wwii-collectibles.com

As the title suggests this site is dedicated to WWII. The site layout is not that brilliant but if you look hard enough you can find real treasure. Coins, stamps and memorabilia are all present. The site has a unique 'secure' ordering system: you send one email in which you list the usual details and all but the last four numbers on your credit card. Then send a second email with those four numbers, the expiry date, and the key words "I am the authorised card holder for this account". It's ingenuity like this which won the war.

Comics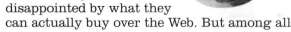

They may be
very collectible
but fans may be
disappointed by what they
can actually buy over the Web. But among all
the sites which have a "look but don't buy"
policy, you can find a few bizarre curios

Bargain Treasures
www.bargaintreasures.com
Typography so lurid it would have been evicted from a progressive rock album
sleeve circa 1973 should not put you off this US-based site, which includes
such goodies as a warrior nun statue and a decent, if not massive, selection
of back issues. The home page is so bright you gotta wear shades and it's a
shame it isn't a tad easier to find your way around, but at least it gives you all
the small print (especially shipping costs) you need to decide whether to buy.

Books'n'comics
www.booksncomics.co.uk
This is one site where you can order online, over a secure server, and which
spells out its terms and conditions very clearly indeed. All that said, you're
more likely to find comic books here (everything from Buffy to the Simpsons'
seminal tomes and 2000AD) than issues of yer actual favourite comics.

Comics International
www.comics-international.com
A useful gateway site offering a virtually definitive directory of UK stockists,
rated hyperlinks to great comic sites, reviews of hundreds of comics and a
FAQ on comic trivia which, among other interesting things, tells you which
sets of Marvel Comics are almost worthless.

Comics Unlimited
www.comicsunlimited.com
A site which almost lives up to its title, with an impressive array of products
from Marvel, DC and Chaos, a resumé of the latest comic news and even
an issue of a psycho circus magazine based on the rock band Kiss. And,
by God, it even delivers outside the good ol' US of A.

Compal Comics
www.compalcomics.com
Auction site that's a must for serious collectors. It allows punters to bid online on a secure server and sells such fascinating items as the original model for the Dan Dare rocket ship, made in 1951 and used by the illustrators, gone for a measly £3,080. Only flaw: the auctions aren't held often enough.

English Magazines
www.englishmagazines.com
This site comes with good word-of-mouth and enables you to subscribe to a range of comics including such immortal works as the *Beano* and *Sabrina The Teenage Witch*. Not for the collector because it focuses on the here and now rather than classic titles and issues of yesteryear.

Vintage Magazines
www.vinmag.com/vintage.htm
The Vintage Magazines Company has a fantastic selection of classic comics in its online back catalogue. It's just a pity that, as this review went to press, the one thing you couldn't order over the Internet was, er, a vintage magazine. The closest you can get to instant shopping gratification is to email them about an issue's availability.

Other sites for you to consider:
www.acmecomics.com runs auctions on e-bay and is in the process of adding an electronic archive of issues

www.comicshack.uk.com is a good British site with a strong archive but, as yet, no online ordering

www.comic-store.com for persistent DC Comic fans only. If you're not ordering from the US you have to email details of the DC title or issue you want and send a money order

www.amazon.co.uk has a significant stock of books about comics

www.whsmith.co.uk has a fund of the same and you get the chance to reserve the latest issue of the *Beano*, *Dandy* etc. If you're always on the look out for comics, it's worth just keying the magic c-word into your favourite search engine(s) as there always seems to be a weird car boot fair or auction somewhere where a collector is selling their complete Dan Dare back catalogue.

Through Internet auctions, rare comics are changing hands at £2,750 a throw. Time to ransack the attic?

Computers

So can you get good deals on a PC online? Is software soft? The Internet positively hums with them, and we're here to help you carve a path through the maze of conflicting

General

Where do you start?

DABS

www.dabs.com

Dabs is the name on every aficionado's lips when it comes to online computer buying. This Bolton-based site can offer the goods more cheaply than most because it takes less profit than competitors, and therefore shifts them in greater volumes. No proper-beige-computers-only attitude, either – Dabs sells Macs as well as PCs, and at £910 for an iMac DVD SE G3 with a 13GB hard drive and 128MB RAM, it undercut Mac Warehouse the last time we looked. All the big PC brands are there, plus peripherals, software, components and audio-visual gear. Colourful and a wheeze to click round, the site is secure, although it could have more information on delivery times (usually pretty rapid and often next-day) and you have to register to buy.

Insight

www.insight.com

Another little gold mine, though this pure-PC site is stronger on components and peripherals than on complete desktop PC systems – its partners here being Toshiba, Hewlett Packard and Compaq. It's American, but you click through to the UK site with no fuss. The main attraction here is what Insight calls its Stock Blowout – a bargain basement where you could pick up anything from a still-boxed IBM notebook to a slightly scuffed AMD K7 motherboard for a fraction of the original cost. No refunds and no returns here, matey. As with most computer warehouses, (free) delivery depends on whether what you want is in stock, but it's generally within 3-4 days and often next-day. Again, you have to register before you buy. Insight's is an SSL site.

PC World

www.pcworld.co.uk

This is the non-techie end of the online buying spectrum. This well-known real-world warehouse site is for those who just know they want a computer. The friendly design is designed to be particularly friendly to the PC novice. Here, there's no bewildering depth or range, just well-known names and a brief selection of everything, from complete packages to monitors, printers, peripherals and software. First-time shoppers should head to the section of the same name to check delivery details and after-sales care, and future shoppers can read PC World's Guide to Computing – sound advice on taking the plunge into technology. Each product comes with a full spec sheet, images and a competitive price tag.

Tech Direct

www.techdirect.co.uk

The black-and-red livery is loud and the search bar to the left of the page offers more fields than you could ever be bothered filling in. From here you're on your own; there's no help with product descriptions. Most annoyingly, even if you are willing to spend hundred of pounds based on this information you still have to register all your details. Delivery times vary according to whether or not the item you're after is in stock.

 Briefly Sites where the consumer is king

Capital

www.capital.uk.com

Clear and easy to navigate, with a handy side-panel listing all the product categories carried by Capital. Unfortunately, such essential computing items as computers, laptops, handheld devices, monitors and scanners couldn't be found anywhere. Slightly less useful than it seems on first glance, but should get better when they get around to stocking the shop.

Comet Direct

www.comet.co.uk

A limited range of PCs and accessories, as you might expect, but pictures and specs for each product are available and the prices are competitive. Comet offers brief tips with most products – one being the refreshing: "ask yourself whether you actually need that laptop before you buy…"

Dixons

www.dixons.co.uk

Much what you'd expect from Dixons, with top brands, scant information and easy navigation. If you're lucky you may pick up a free gift of a printer or a scanner with your PC. The Best Buys section holds PCs for under £500.

It is _so_ a proper computer

Apple Store
www.apple.com

With products this glossy and seductive, it's no wonder Apple offers its own loan or lease scheme; the temptation factor, heightened by great site design and photography, is enormous. The site is international: choose UK from the pop-down list at the bottom of the page to spend your sterling. If you need the new ruby iMac, spec sheets and lots of helpful advice are available, as with all products. Caveats: Apple is a bit mean with the RAM at the lower end of the range and the RAGE graphics cards need updating. No, we didn't care, either. Delivery can take up to 14 days, but is usually much quicker.

Mac Warehouse
www.macwarehouse.co.uk

Good site for Mac-compatible peripherals, plus you can pick up an iMac SE G3 with 128MB of RAM for less than a grand. Everything comes with a spec sheet and though it isn't a pretty site, it works. You need to go through a registration process before you can buy, but it's useful if you need speed as well as low prices, as it will try to deliver next day if you order before 4pm.

 From the big names to the little guys

Aria
www.aria.co.uk

With no secure credit card server, you can't order online but you can email your order to Aria and have someone call you back. Presumably when they do you can ask any questions you may have before you buy. This may well happen in most cases, as there are only spec sheets full of technical jargon to read here, and even then not for every model. On the plus side, you should at least be able to find a top brand model to suit your price bracket and the helpful quick link to their price directory means you can see what deals they can do before you trawl the site.

Carrera
www.carrera.co.uk

Carrera, PC Plus's Top Manufacturer for 1999, may not be as well known as your Dells and your Compaqs, but its jolly website (which has something of the ambience of a holiday company) is up with the best. The news and reviews section contains reviews of Carrera models from the likes of *PC Plus*. Each model is recommended to a particular type of individual and is accompanied by specifications. A good, no-nonsense site.

Computer Manuals

www.compman.co.uk

If you're going to operate something that contains a 1Ghz processor and the kind of software that something so fast can run, you'll need to RTFM in order to make sure you get the best out of your purchase. Here's where to buy. Particularly good are the O'Reilly manuals – the company probably even publishes one that will help you program your juicer.

Dan

www.dan.co.uk

This oddly constructed homepage gives pride of place to news columns, only one of which is dedicated to the doings of Dan. The machines do indeed have a good reputation, as they claim. The site is easy to navigate, with separate business, home and education user sections, and models specifically tailored to their needs. Pick up a starter family PC for around £850, or customise your own. Delivery should take 5-10 days.

Dell

www.dell.co.uk

Efficient and businesslike, online sales specialists Dell aim to provide you with a desktop, work station or notebook to suit your needs, whether that's home office, small business or large conglomerate. From here you're linked to the specific models to suit, or alternatively, select a basic model and customise it to your heart's content. The site has recently been revamped and a number of defunct links exist, but in most cases there are extensive descriptions, spec sheets and guides to help you buy. Prices obviously aren't bargain basement, but the Dell auction link advertises models for as little as £1.

Gateway

Gateway deserves both praise and criticism for its online shopping venture. It's fine that you can customise your Gateway model to suit your needs (after all, how many of us want to buy an expensive, space-gobbling, business computer for the home?). But it's not quite so great if you don't know the difference between a 3.5 diskette and Superdisk LS120. A better idea would be to cater for both levels of consumer knowledge. The flickering "deal of the week"

For such a familiar consumer name, Gateway's site is surprisingly heavy on jargon. Lovely boxes, though

button gets bloody irritating after a while too. Apparently an Essential 600 CM computer "could turn your child into the school's star pupil." Strangely, this claim is not part of the company's service guarantee. There are so many windows on this site that George Formby could die cleaning them.

Just-PC
www.ishop.co.uk/ishop/413/shopscr1.html
Exemplary site, with great design, fast navigation, excellent and even tasteful visuals and a good, broad selection of top-branded goods from desktops to handhelds. Pitched squarely in between the consumer and techie levels, it's particularly strong on software. Secure, with fast and reliable delivery.

Simply
www.simply.co.uk
East London company selling its own Systemax PCs in desktop-ready, customisable or no-monitor, pre-built versions. At the bottom end of the range a pre-configured K500R with an AMD K6-2 processor and 100MHz SDRAM memory and a 56K modem would set you back a mere £587, with a top-end A1000B-E with a 1Ghz Athlon processor steaming in at £3,742. The odd Lexmark, Canon, Epson printer or scanner is also usually on offer. The site is SSL-secure and you can pay by credit card. Simply will send you the goods postage-free in three days, or next day on request if you order before 6pm.

Watford Electronics
www.watford.co.uk
Watford is named after its company base and has been manufacturing and selling its own-brand Aries PC for nearly 30 years. You should be able to pick up a PC Lite without a monitor for under £300. They sell an extensive range of competitively priced desktops and notebooks, and deliver free within three days. Keep an eye on the B-Grade section for bargains.

This shop may be in East London but it will deliver PCs and systems, pre-built or customised, to your desk top

W Store
www.wstore.co.uk
This site has far too many registration requirements and newsletter offers and not enough information on the products that are actually for sale. Although a "helping businesses to buy smarter" slogan is visible (just) amongst all the security scheme badges jostling for position on the homepage, it is not immediately obvious that you should only

Accessories For the tastefully garnished PC

If you thought the man in your life had finished spending all your mortgage repayment money on his new computer toy, there's bad news to follow. You've got your entry level PC – complete with all the essentials, monitor, keyboard etc – but you're just not satisfied. It looks like everyone else's… A relatively simple way to put your stamp on it is to customise your keyboard. Both Access Keyboards and the Keyboard Company sell customised keyboards to your specs, or you can simply choose one from their range of large, small, waterproof and industrial models. If the South Park mousemat you got free with your PC just doesn't give out the right business message, you can pick up a sophisticated mouse rug from Fuse On for £14.99, or advertise your Irish heritage with religious, historical and legend designs from Casey Designs for £6.99. A must-buy are the wrist-rests for £11.95 and the industrial mice for £69, both from Inspace. Face it – once you're hooked, you can say goodbye to all your spare cash.

Access Keyboards
www.accesskeyboards.co.uk
The Keyboard Company
www.keyboardco.com
Mouse House
www.mouse-house.co.uk
Fuse On
www.fuseon.co.uk
Casey Designs
www.caseydesigns.co.uk/system/index.html

Cover Tec
www.covertec.com
Inspace
www.inspace.com
Technofilter UK
www.antiglare.co.uk
Cartridge Shop
www.cartridgeshop.co.uk

spend serious Internet time here if you are buying for business rather than for personal use, as you need to enter company details to register, and thus to buy. If you can get past all these obstacles, the prices are competitive.

Novelties Computer trinkets & Hazzard-ous mouse mats

Cybertrash
www.cybertrash.org
At last, girls! Bits of old computer recycled into jewellery, wind chimes and fridge magnets! Surprisingly attractive, too, particularly the earrings made from pre-loved inductor coils, resistors, diodes, head amps and switches, among other components. Ordering is secure and all major cards are

accepted. What happens with overseas delivery isn't too clear, but Cybertrash is set up to automatically convert foreign currency for credit cards, adding however much is necessary for the bank's fee. At an average of only $5 per item, it must be worth a try just to see what turns up.

Stardust
www.kitsch.co.uk
How much do you want a wind-up, glow-in-the-dark computer goddess (only £4)? A Dukes of Hazzard or Elvis in Vegas mousemat? How about a pineapple desk lamp? Some chilli lights to drape round that boring beige monitor? A Drinking Bird for your mug…? You're there already, aren't you?

Red Light Runner
www.redlightrunner.com
Apple collectibles, from towels and sandals with the Apple logo to mugs, pens and even a "Steve Jobs for President" sticker. Red Light Runner also sells those classy "Think different" posters, featuring Miles Davis, Callas, Lucy & Desi and Martha Graham, all at classy prices. Shipping is international.

PDAs The world in the palm of your hand

21 Store
www.21store.com
From the Handspring Visor to the wafer-thin Rex Pro DS-5, 21 Store has the compete range of PDAs and palmtops, with both Palm and Windows CE platforms. It's cheerful, fast and well organised, and you can search the complete store or head straight to one of the sections, which include global positioning systems and binoculars and night vision departments. Good images, descriptions in plain English, and overnight delivery is promised if you order before 3pm.

Widget Software
www.widget.co.uk
Selling all the latest handheld systems, EPOC devices, Palm OS, Windows CE and Nokia 9110s, this is a site that offers enough additional information to allow you to feel confident about your new purchase. Psion, Compaq and Hewlett Packard dominate each section with high-street prices throughout. There's also a bargain bin with an extensive list. Secure ordering is available and gadgets are dispatched within 7 days.

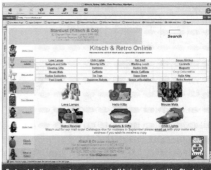

Fortunately the computer world is not all beige functionality. Stardust does a fine line in colourful kitsch, from mouse mats to, erm, Barbie

Yahoo Handhelds and Palmtops
http://fullcoverage.yahoo.com/fc/Tech/Handheld_and_Palmtop_Computers
You can't buy palmtops here but check this site out before you do, as Yahoo give you the dirt on whether the shiny toy (sorry, business tool) you want is about to be rendered obsolete by a subsequent generation. On busy days, four new palmtop-related stories are posted and there are loads of vital links.

 Before you splash the cash, read this…

IT Reviews
www.itreviews.co.uk
If you need a little more info than the single-line captions you'll find on most resellers' sites, there is a wealth of online technological support and advice to be accessed via the Net. *IT Review* is one of the best, with independent reviews by professional journalists. Hardware, software and games are all included, and the reviews are consumer-friendly rather than jargon-led. The analyses and concise final verdicts of the group tests are the most useful of these. Register your email address to receive fortnightly updates at your desktop. You might also want to take a look at…

Computer Previews http://compreviews.about.com/compute/compreview
Product Review www.productreviewnet.com
Review Finder www.reviewfinder.com
Ziff Davis www.zdnet.com

Computer games

There's no better (or cheaper) place than the Internet to get gamed up, whether you're into aliens, zombies, Ecco the Dolphin or golf

High Street — The usual suspects

Dixons

www.dixons.co.uk

Dixons is one of the best known brands in the high street, and its website looks cheap, cheerful and colourful. The homepage is packed with flashing bargain signs, as well as links to Best Buys and special deals. The games section is split into those suitable for consoles or for PCs, which can be annoying if you just want to look at all the available versions at the same time. The purchase process is logical but you do have to register before you can buy. You can find a decent range of product, in a slightly more relaxed online environment, at **www.freeserve.com/entertainment/games** – Freeserve being the free Internet service provider launched by Dixons in another century.

Electronics Boutique

www.eb.uk.com

Once the site loads you are confronted by an annoying loyalty-card pop-up. Once you've got rid of this, however, there are some featured games, a list of top sellers and a pre-ordering service for those much-hyped titles you just can't wait for. Games are listed by hardware (Nintendo, PC and so on), all of which can accessed via the funky-looking sidebar. You can post your own review and, as with Electronics Boutique's high-street shops, there is a good selection of second-hand games as well. An excellent ordering process, and no need to register tops it all off. Delivery is free within the UK, although if you're desperate you can pay £3.95 for an overnight service.

Game

www.game-retail.co.uk

You would expect a good online store from one of the best games retailers in the real world and you won't be disappointed. Once again, however, the site starts off with that ever unpopular feature known as "Loyalty pop-up time!" which confronts you even before you access the home page – it feels a bit like going to a restaurant and being asked to order before you've been given the menu. Games are grouped by machine and there are excellent descriptions of each title, complete with examples of the graphics. The charts and featured titles offer plenty of ideas; the news stories will satisfy gamers anxious to find out about upcoming releases, and there's an A-Z list for those who know what they are looking for. When you come to buy, do be careful with your clicks as you don't get any confirmation for each addition, though your titles are added to a basket which remains on the bottom of the screen. Delivery starts at £1.95 but is free if you spend more than £75.

HMV

www.hmv.co.uk

Soon after you enter this site it becomes pretty clear that HMV regards itself primarily as a music retailer and everything else is a bit of a bother. Music fills the homepage, and you have to hunt for the games section. Even once you're there, getting to a list of titles is hard. News stories are provided but scrolling and navigation are slow and registration is lengthy and complicated.

@Jakarta

www.jakarta.co.uk

@Jakarta, another branch of Dixons, has some great deals on certain games on its site. Each platform has its own button on the toolbar but the rest of the site is plagued by tiny text and the ridiculous amount of scrolling needed to find anything. One useful thing, though, is the e-zine, which has interesting articles, reviews and a bit of an insight into the games industry. Delivery costs £2.50 per order and your games should be with you within a few days.

PC World

www.pcworld.co.uk

PC World has a similar site to that of Dixons – can this be a coincidence? – with the same bargains galore image. The flashing icons can get really annoying, plus only PC and Dreamcast titles are available, and there's a rather limited choice of those. However, once you have selected a game, there is plenty of descriptive and technical information to help you choose. Pricing is clear and, as with Dixons, ordering is safe and simple.

Special Reserve Discount Club

www.ukgames.com

The online games arm of the Special Reserve Discount Club is probably the most cluttered homepage of any of the games sites. There's far too much information there to take in properly, even if you do keep scrolling all the way down. A bit of careful editing would help immensely in this respect. Getting to the checkout is equally difficult, but the hefty discounts for members might just make all the effort worthwhile.

W H Smith
www.whsmith.co.uk
Another high-street retailer whose heart, based on the evidence of this site, is not really in computer games. If you want to check out the bestseller charts, you'd better be able to recognise your Sony from your Sega as you have to click on a picture of the machine to get where you want to go. The search facility is quite speedy though, with plenty of fields to help you narrow your search. Delivery will cost you a minimum of £1.95 and a maximum of £6 in the UK (W H Smith normally charges 15 per cent of the product's value for shipping). Serious users would probably prefer to use the site for Games Paradise (see facing page), part of the W H Smith group.

Online retailers — Out there in cyberspace

Chipsworld.co.uk
www.chipsworld.co.uk
Not a site dedicated to the multifarious uses of potato but a rather good games site. It looks pretty and is easy to navigate, two characteristics that don't often go together. Along with games listed by machine, there is a featured title, a section on recent releases and a second-hand area. There

First there was Dock Green, then Freeserve, now this award-winning games site. Is there no end to Dixons' versatility?

is clear pricing information on products and email confirmation for both receipt and dispatch.

Computer Exchange

www.cex.co.uk

CEX claims to be the largest online retailer and the range is certainly good. It can be unreasonably hard to find what you want, however, if it isn't a featured item or in the charts. When you have found what you're after, clicking through gives you a brief description and then the buying process is pretty simple. The most useful feature is the five-step ordering process which shows you exactly where you are and ensures that you don't get lost. Postal delivery is free in the UK or you can pay £3.80 for a next-day service.

Gameplay

www.gameplay.com

This is an award-winning site from the Dixons stable. The homepage has some great graphics with simple, easy-to-use icons, and there's an excellent help and information section. This is about as far as it goes, though. Venturing beyond the homepage, the pages are somewhat cluttered, and the site itself is split into news, a shop and a magazine. You can search for games by machine or use the useful gift-suggestion service, but there are really too many options and inexperienced users could easily get lost. Delivery is free if you do find something to buy.

Gamesparadise.com

www.gamesparadise.com

Another homepage with too many options hides the fact that this site doesn't seem to have a full range of titles. Featured and new games dominate. You have to do quite a bit of scrolling to get anywhere, and you need to create an account before buying. There's a lot of news and info here but it's not quite the paradise the URL suggests.

Gamesstreet

www.gamesstreet.infront.co.uk

This site is organised primarily by platform, each of which you reach through a button on the home

THE EVIL EMPIRE?

Rather like a virtual baddie, the Dixons group is establishing something of a gaming empire. It has some of the strongest names under its wing.

@jakarta, PC World and Freeserve all have something to do with the high-street giant, and their purchase of a stake in Gameplay furthers this trend, making it feel as though all consoles lead inevitably to Dixons.

Some say this might not be good for the gamer but at least with online ordering you don't wait for hours to talk to a monosyllabic salesman.

The sites are all secure and easy to use but the 'bargain basement' feel (apart from Gameplay) might not suit everyone

----

www.dixons.co.uk

----

www.freeserve.com/entertainment/games

----

www.gameplay.com

----

www.@jakarta.co.uk

----

www.pcworld.co.uk

page. The well-designed graphics and clear symbols allow easy navigation but you have to scroll a way down each page for featured products and the Top 20 chart. What is good, though, is the very clear indication of games' age restrictions – useful for adults searching for suitable titles for the family. The registration process necessary before ordering is tedious, but delivery is free and takes 1-2 days.

Games Terminal
www.gamesterminal.com
Hardware logos are used to access the different game categories on this site, which makes the homepage look pretty but is not so effective if you don't recognise that a white swirl represents a Dreamcast. Otherwise, the site is quite well designed and is great for swapping and buying second-hand games. A selection of reviews and previews by customers offers shedloads of advice and is much more entertaining (and useful) than the usual marketing waffle. All prices include delivery within the UK.

Games Wire
www.gameswire.com
This is more a portal than a shopping site (although there are games to buy) and has plenty of information on the world of gaming. There is a news section and some very interesting editorial features, such as an article on violence in games, although (predictably enough) they don't regard it as any kind of problem. Finding games and specific information for your chosen machine is done by clicking on the symbols provided, which could be clearer and are no good for non-gamers and newbies. There's also an online discussion section where you can chat with other game fans. The ordering process is simple and works on a step-by-step basis, with free delivery on all orders unless you want the 24-hour service which costs £3.80.

The Game Zone
www.thegamezone.co.uk
The simple homepage on this site makes it incredibly easy to find what you want. You can search by platform or genre, so if you just want beat-'em-ups then you don't have to sift through golf and driving games. When you've chosen a game there is an excellent description with plenty of information. Getting through the order screen can be a bit confusing at times, but delivery by first class mail is free on all orders.

Simply Games
www.simplygames.co.uk
As you would expect, there's nothing but gaming products here. On loading there is yet another annoying pop-up questionnaire, but it offers you the chance to win five games, so why not fill it in anyway? After that, the site looks good with clear graphics, charts for each machine down the side and gaming news in the middle. Titles are listed in alphabetical order from

Okay, Anna Kournikova might not beat Lindsay Davenport on court but she can still take on Lara Croft

Armorines to Zelda. The prices are excellent, the site is secure and delivery is free to anywhere in the world by air mail or first class mail. If you manage to find the game you want cheaper on another site, you can email them and they promise to match the lower price.

Softwarefirst.com
www.softwarefirst.com

Although slow to load and occasionally temperamental, this is a pretty simple site which lists games by machine, including Game Boys and Apple Macs. There are some featured titles and news stories about the most popular games, and once you've placed an order through the secure server you can make use of the tracking service, although it may sometimes simply tell you that your order is being processed. They also sell DVDs and have a pre-ordering service on forthcoming titles for impatient gamers.

Software Savings
www.softwaresavings.co.uk

This is a grown-up site featuring primarily professional software but you can buy games as well. There are no funky images or graphics, but the site does offer very good prices on the limited range of titles (mostly flight simulators and other strategic games). The ordering process is mercifully short and shows clearly what you have chosen. First class recorded delivery is free on all orders, or they offer a next-day service at extra cost.

Softwarezone
www.softwarezone.com

The spartan design of this site is great for no-nonsense shoppers who like to download their software direct from the Internet, including game demos and shareware options. You can see straight away that any purchase you make is secure and the process is easy and fast, as long as you choose the correct download for your operating system. The range of titles is mind-boggling, even extending to some out-of-date (but still dearly beloved) machines such as the Sinclair spectrum. At first, the site seems difficult to browse but there's a nifty little button called "staff picks" which, if you click on it, gives you such details as how long a game took to download and what operating system is required for a selected range of titles.

 General Jungles, Amazon but no rainforest

Amazon.co.uk
www.amazon.co.uk
Amazon has recently added a new section for games to its website. It has a cross-referenced database and some abbreviated charts to give you ideas. Practical information on availability and age-restrictions is clearly marked, but what sets Amazon apart is the number and quality of its reviews. These are written by real people and unlike some sites, Amazon is not afraid to criticise (of one title the reviewer says simply "I'd rather watch paint dry" – an old joke but a refreshing change to read on an e-tailer). First class mail deliveries are £1.40, plus 42p per game.

Boxman.com
www.boxman.com
This is an international site and you need to choose the appropriate flag for your country in order to reach the correct home page. The site also sells all sorts of other products, so you have to choose games from the toolbar. Titles are listed by genre and there are some special features, but the lack of reviews or descriptions makes browsing a rather disappointing experience, although if you want to buy music or videos at the same time, you can get them all at once. Getting to the checkout stage is slow but simple, and delivery costs £1.95 with most items being shipped within three days.

E-toys.co.uk
www.e-toys.co.uk
Although this is a generic toy site you can get straight to the games section from the homepage and search it either by platform or genre. The news section is updated fairly regularly and, enticingly, each game is

"TWO FAT LADIES..."

For those of you who find computer games a bit like trying to understand the difference between garage music and grunge, Yahoo Games has kindly provided a relaxed environment where you can play electronic versions of such classics as mah jong, Chinese checkers and, erm, bingo. Yes, even on the Net there is the equivalent of an electronic voice shouting "Clickety click! Sixty-six."

Thankfully, chess and backgammon have proved more of an online mecca than Mecca's favourite. To join in the fun, just log on to http://games.yahoo.com/. You'll need to register and to have a browser which can handle Java software. After that, you're on your own.

accompanied by a selection of screenshots, much like a magazine review, allowing you to see what the game will actually be like to play. There is an express checkout for returning customers, otherwise you have to register. Standard delivery (within 3-4 days) starts at £2.50 or if you want your game within 1-2 days you can pay a whopping £6 for the express service.

Jungle.com
www.jungle.com

A decent site from one of the biggest names in Internet retailing, which also happens to be *Which?*-approved. The homepage is reasonably inviting although, again, the site's determination to convince you that there's a lorra, lorra stuff here does have an adverse effect on clarity. The revolving ads on the homepage have a hypnotic effect if you linger too long, but assuming you get past that without lapsing into a trance, you will find your visit worthwhile. The best way to steer yourself through the busy pages is to click on the "Jungle play" icon. A bar at the bottom of the page allows you to search by genre and platform or you can just click on the appropriate platform at the top of the page. There is also a list of top sellers and you can add your own reviews to games. The *Which?* Trader stamp is a guarantee of security and delivery is included in all prices. Jungle.com specialises in electronic goods so tech junkies will be able to find whatever they want here.

 **If you already know what you want**

Eidos
www1.eidosinteractive.co.uk

The people who brought you *Tomb Raider* have an e-store where you can buy 20 of their games, merchandise and play online. Delivery normally takes five days but you're asked to allow up to 28 days, which sounds like the bad old days of 1970s mail-order catalogues. Delivery charges, which by some statistical freak always seem to work out at £5.08 for the UK, are displayed early on in the checkout process.

Electronic Arts
www.ea.com

Electronic Arts have been making some of the best sports sims in the business for a while and this site is dedicated to their range. You can search by brand, genre or machine, plus there are some features and "hotspots" but the range is limited to EA and associated products and isn't what you might call impartial. Make sure you select the European store from the bottom-left menu, or you'll be lost in the US version before you know it. The ability to search specific categories on the site (such as support) is a nice touch. Delivery charges are calculated by your shopping basket.

Not every game stars scantily-clad, gun-toting überbabes. This one stars some hopeless robots and roast chicken

GameSpy Industries

www.rpgplanet.com

As the name suggests, this is a massive portal for the fans of role-playing games. It's all a bit dark and scary for the uninitiated and you almost have to be an expert to get the best out of the site. The navigation bar has all the options you need to join a game or set up your own for others to join, but the text is minute, so read carefully before you commit. As on other game-centric sites, shopping is provided by links elsewhere, and can be hard to find too.

Sega

www.dreamcast-europe.com

The official site for the Dreamcast and Dreamcast players is where you need to come to enjoy playing online with other users. They have a slim range of titles available to buy through the site, but make sure you're actually in the shop section, otherwise you'll be surfing around aimlessly wondering how to order. The advantage of this is less clutter and more up-to-the-minute information, but you won't get the discounts that dedicated retailers offer. Delivery is free on software, but if you're ordering a console as well, it's £2.50.

The Sims

www.thesims.com

Fancy a cup of tea? Well, type this URL into your address bar, go milk a cow, pasteurise the milk, put the kettle on, do the necessary and then come back to your browser page. Chances are the homepage for this genetic mutant – x chromosomes from computer games and y chromosomes from soap operas – will just about have loaded. When the screen finally fills, you'll be stunned to discover that you've only loaded the page which allows you to pick which language you want to view the site in. It's worth the wait, however, because the Sims allows you to build a virtual family – only unlike your real family, you actually have some shred of influence over what they do because you can, for example, stick an aggressively untidy character into a house full of control freaks and wait for the fireworks. Go here to understand what all the fuss is about, download videos of the characters and buy the CD-ROM.

The Station
www.everquest.com
A site dedicated to the game which mirrors its gothic-style graphics and scantily-clad female warrior characters. It isn't immediately clear where to buy but there's a "Buy EverQuest" option at the bottom of the left-hand menu. The retail service is from Electronics Boutique, which is easy enough once you're there. There is also an online forum that allows you to chat with fellow fans.

Games without guns   "Peace, man!"

Chicken Run
www.eidosinteractive.co.uk
Fast and furious game based on the film. Just pull down "Select a game".

Ecco the Dolphin
www.sega.com
Ecco falls through time and has to restore the human/dolphin paradise. Gorgeous graphics with an eco-friendly theme. Only for Dreamcast.

Hello Kitty's Cube Frenzy
www.playstation.com
Brightly coloured, *Tetris*-like puzzle game for little ones.

Myst and Riven
www.cyan.com
Extraordinary brainteaser games and fiendish logic problems to solve.

Starship Titanic
www.starshiptitanic.com
Hilarious but taxing game from the endearingly knotted mind of Douglas Adams. Rescue the stricken starship using only your wit, a few hopeless robots and some roast chicken.

Super Mario 64
www.nintendo.com/n64/super_mario64/index.html
The official homepage of the gent who started all this, and for what? A cake, that's what. This URL is attached to the official Nintendo address and has plenty of tips about strategy and secrets, but you can't actually order anything from the site unless you're in the US.

Crafts

Okay, crafts have never been what you might call groovy but the Internet is helping them finally shake off that Women's Institute stereotype. Slowly...

The Crafts Council
www.craftscouncil.org.uk
Packed with news on craft shows, events and exhibitions, plus an education section detailing workshops and seminars all over the country. There's a list of craft shops with links to those with websites, and if you're really serious about your macramé, you'll find details of how to apply for a setting up grant.

Economy of Brighton
www.economyofbrighton.co.uk
Specialising in decorative rubber stamps and hole punches, this site also sells a vast range of other art supplies including powder paint, modelling clay and Plaster of Paris at excellent prices. Accounts are available for schools, and delivery is £5 for any order up to a max of 30 kilos. You can send them a cheque if you're not keen to provide credit cards details online.

Encaustic Arts
www.encaustic.com
Large site full of tips and ideas for projects involving heating wax to make pretty pictures. It sells a rainbow of coloured wax blocks plus card, rubber stamps and even the right sort of iron for creating the best result. Postage is free on UK orders which are dispatched within two days.

Heaton Cooper
www.heatoncooper.co.uk
Site run by Cumbrian artists selling high quality paints and art supplies, including specialist items like gold leaf. Good instructions for online shoppers with clear process through the site. Postage is free on orders over £35, though there are special delivery options if you're having a watercolour crisis. A test order arrived well-packed and complete within three days. The site also has a gallery of work by the artists involved, some of which are for sale through their Lake District shop.

Hobbicraft

www.hobbicraft.co.uk

Web site for Leeds-based store selling a huge range of hobby and craft
supplies. Airfix models (remember them?), glass engraving equipment, beads,
and painting-by-number kits to mention just a few. Pictures of items are pretty
few and far between, so you need to know what you're looking for. Delivery
is promised within five working days and there's a 14 day no-quibble refund
offer on all items.

Hobby's

www.hobby.uk.com

Online version of weighty craft supplies catalogue specialising in model
making, but now featuring other creative kit like glass cutters and doll houses.
The absence of an electronic shopping basket makes ordering slightly
tedious, but the online form is clear and the company makes up for the ennui
by sending all orders over £10 by Parcel Force.

Lawrence Art Supplies

www.lawrence.co.uk

Serious art supplies for serious artists. There are few colour samples for
things like oil paints, only the names, so once again, it pays to know exactly
what you are looking for. The Special Offer section has some solid deals, but
note that prices are shown excluding VAT. If you're really desperate for your
Yellow Ochre, they offer a next-day delivery service for £12.80, otherwise, it's
£3.20 for regular postage.

Scottish Wood Craft

www.scottishwoodcraft.co.uk

Simple, but effective, site selling woodworking tools as well as delightful
handmade wooden items from chairs to bird mobiles. We particularly like the
spurtles (that's a porridge-stirring stick to you sassenachs). You can also buy
chunks of Scottish hardwoods from sustainable forests as the starting point
for your next masterpiece. Prices do not include VAT, and delivery can take up
to two weeks (longer for the larger items) but everything comes with a 30 day
money back guarantee.

Sunflower Fabrics

www.sunfabrics.demon.co.uk

Impressively forward-thinking site that's been established for over three years
with clear instructions and a comprehensive help section for people not used
to online shopping. Sunflower specialises in quilting and other needlework
supplies, and offers a lovely selection of patterns or complete quilt kits, for
reasonable prices. Small orders (under £10) incur a £1.50 handling fee, and
they also ship abroad if you want to send a kit as a gift. Because the
company reckons it could take you months to browse the 2000 images and
1000 products on the site, it has now put its catalogue on CD-ROM.

Crazes

With each new craze lasting about as long as a goldfish's memory span, the Internet is a wonderful tool to find the best, the worst and the weirdest

Modern   "The trouble with kids today..."

Beanie Babies

http://shop.store.yahoo.com/walloffame/beaniebabies.html

Because Pokémon is grabbing all the headlines, it's easy to forget that it's only a couple of years since the Beanie Babies craze was a Threat to Society As We Know It. New babies continue to pour out of the toy industry as this Wall Of Fame site proves. There's even a video called *How To Spot A Counterfeit Beanie Baby*, released in 1988, which resurfaced on the Web this summer.

Pokémon

www.pokemon.com

The official site isn't a merchandise shifting operation but a useful source of downloads if junior has a computer and an even more useful source of info about the game and the characters for parents who find they can't stomach the contemptuous look in their kid's eyes when they inadvertently confuse Clefable with Clefairy. You can find the official card game site on www.wizards.com/Pokemon and the official online store can be found on http://store.wizards.com but by the time you've figured out the ordering process (especially which goods are excluded from which countries, in Internet Explorer that crucial information always seems to be just off the screen) you could have gone down to WHSmith, bought the starter pack, read the rules booklet and be hanging outside schools trying to make trades. You can find even more Pokémon merchandise on the rather oddly named Pokéorder on www.pokéorder.com. If you're tempted by this site, buy in bulk because for a $10 order you'll pay $9.99 in shipping charges.

Tamagotchi

www.ridhughz.demon.co.uk/tamagotchi/

The world's most famous virtual pet may already have its own set of anti-sites but the epitome of "cuteness on a keychain", as it's billed, is still damned hard to get hold of. This site has links to online stores which might still have a few in stock like Toys 'R' Us. It also has tips on how to make it age quicker, which cynics may think might best be achieved with a hammer.

Teletubbies

www.living-store.com

They're still saying "Eh-Oh!" all over the world even if the halcyon days, when LaLa and co could shoot to number one faster than you could say "nunu", are long past. There's a good range of Tubby products here, from custard machines to dinner services. Ordering is secure and this site also has a variety of Winnie the Pooh and Beanie Baby accessories.

World Wrestling Federation

www.wwfshopzone.com/

Wrestling, like everything else, isn't what it used to be. The American World Wrestling Federation has reinvented what used to be a dodgy sport as slapstick for young kids and a soap opera-style running battle between good and evil for older kids. The revamp has been so successful that the WWF is one of the fastest growing brands on the Internet and its official site has a shopzone which sells T-shirts, computer games, sunglasses, sportswear and CDs. The site does ship outside the US, but shipping costs start at $30 and your items can take 28 days to arrive. You could try www.attitudezone.com which boasts it has the gear "you really want not all that sissy stuff" but you have to email for international shipping costs.

 Stuff that's no longer really happening, man

Space Invaders

http://spaceinvaders.retrogames.com

The classic arcade game of the late 1970s has its own e-shrine where you can download stuff. It has also been regenerated as a computer game you can buy from www.activision.com/games/spaceinvaders.

Table football

www.btfa.dircon.co.uk/

This is the official site for the British Table Football Association which, apart from making a welcome change from the "Buy now" ethos of much commercial cyberspace, has a small section of classified-style ads of used tables for sale, typically for around £110, and phone numbers for UK suppliers. If you buy one new from Tablesports on www.btfa.dircon.co.uk you'll have to pay at least £275 plus £35 delivery. Strangely, the company's homepage praising the versatility of this equipment describes it as "ideal for prisons". Makes you wonder how Chandler and Joey managed to afford the one they bought in *Friends*, what with the cost of that huge apartment.

Department Stores

Traditional high street names have taken to the Net the way porcupines make love: very carefully indeed

High street — Old names and new technology

Debenhams
www.debenhams.com
A sensible site for a sensible store and a safe bet for Debenhams. No flashy graphics or elaborate colour schemes, staid to look at and to search, it's useful for those who want to be in and out with no fuss. You'll find fashion, gifts, flowers and wedding items: search for a gift according to your price range and fashion by brands. Top names include Jasper Conran, Pearce II Fionda, Boxfresh and Warehouse. On the downside are the minimal descriptions and poor images that make it hard to feel confident about your order unless you've seen it in store. The pink type is hard to read. The wedding section is a complete department in itself with dresses, suits, music and hymns, and the chance to register your own wedding list.

Fortnum & Mason
www.fortnumandmason.co.uk
Despite the Piccadilly store selling everything from antiques to luggage, the online equivalent currently offers only food and drink, with the emphasis on such luxury items as antipasti, chutney, marmalade and fine wine. The need to register before you can place an order seems strange, but it simply involves an email address and a password. Best to buy in bulk as delivery is set at £5 per order, so one jar of kumquat marmalade could prove pricey.

Littlewoods
www.indexshop.com
Traditionally backward in coming forward, Littlewoods currently offer two online shopping schemes, Index, the online equivalent of the Index

catalogue, and Shop-!, an online and interactive television service. The Index site is busy, yet easy to navigate with standard categories like sound and vision, gifts and so on. These are then sub-categorised to narrow results. Cheap and cheerful, Littlewoods beats many of its competitors on price with monthly sales and three months' interest-free credit, delivery guaranteed in 48 hours, and with a large collection of their paper catalogue featured online.

Marks & Spencer
www.marks-and-spencer.co.uk
Recently revamped M & S no longer sells food online, sticking to clothes and housewares. The site has improved greatly in recent months with clear, enlarged images and descriptions of each item. But they have reverted to focusing on a limited number of individual items in the homes section which doesn't work as well as the catalogue-style grouping items together. Standard ordering system with a £3 delivery charge and guaranteed 72-hour delivery.

Only online — Cyberstores

Best of British
www.thebestofbritish.com
An online department store more of the Harrods and Selfridges ilk than Littlewoods, with clothing, gifts and household items from top British designers. Search by brand and product type or simply browse the designers' own collections. Top brands include Mulberry, Dollargrand and Lulu Guinness. You won't find discounted items but delivery is free, taking up to 21 days.

Big Save
www.bigsave.com
Big Save has gone for a busy design with as much information crammed onto one page as possible. The images and text are too small, although the site is easy to navigate with distinct categories. Not your traditional department store, it still sells everything from blenders to pashminas, designer luggage and insurance, with the added bonus of up to 50 per cent savings. Best buys include fad of the year, Micro Scooters, at the bargain price of £56, a 44 per cent saving. You need to register to buy.

AND STILL TO COME...

Despite the one-stop nature of the Internet, high street department stores have been slow to embrace the technology.

Big names such as John Lewis, House of Fraser and Dickins & Jones have as yet failed to set up a cyber equivalent. Harrods sells from a comprehensive online catalogue, but only to the US and Canada.

More are gradually joining the crowd: Bhs will be launching its own site early in 2001, possibly about the same time that Liberty, after a successful trial, will be unveiling a fuller version of its current online store

Bhs – www.bhs.co.uk
Liberty: www.liberty-of-london.com

Drugs

The legal variety. For illegal ones you'll have to buy a different kind of guide book. Prescription and over-the-counter medicines are popping up all over the Web, and despite dire warnings, there are plenty of reputable sites which don't allow customers to flout the rules

General Equipment and sports products

Academy Health

www.academyhealth.com

Stylish and calming, this site has a wide variety of products on sale: vitamins and supplements, sports nutrition, herbal remedies, skin and body care, family planning, and some over-the-counter medicines such as painkillers, indigestion and cough and cold remedies. You have to do a lot of clicking to get to the products, but there are some attractive discounts over high-street prices, and delivery is free within the UK – making this one of the most cost-effective sites. Delivery is promised within three to seven days.

Allcures.com

www.allcures.com

This is currently the UK's only full-service online pharmacy, dispensing both private and NHS prescription medicines. Allcures offers many other products: beauty, toiletries, herbal remedies and vitamins, even film. There is comprehensive health information, news, and a useful set of FAQs on medicines and other Allcures products, though you have to scroll down a very long list of questions set out in no apparent order. You also have to register to shop. The site is clear and easy, searching for products by brand or category. Postage and packing is £3.49 for standard delivery in four days, free for orders over £35. Minimal savings off high-street prices. Next day delivery is possible for £5.99. With some medicines, you may have to fill in a health questionnaire to proceed with the order. Delivers anywhere within the UK.

Boots
www.boots.co.uk
This has the same clean style and offers a similar variety of the products as Boots' high-street stores. Products come in two categories: Health/Beauty and Mother/Baby. No medicines are yet available. Shopping is easy but a price check of a few key items showed no obvious differences between online and offline prices. There is free delivery on orders over £50 and £2.95 per basket on smaller orders. Boots delivers to mainland UK in five working days.

Direct Response Marketing
www.propecia.co.uk
Another site offering Viagra, Propecia and Xenical (the latter two being for baldness and weight loss). The links to medical news about Viagra did not always work. To order, you fill in a medical questionnaire, including the name and address of your doctor, who will be informed by DRM, they claim, or you must declare that you will do this. The price of four Viagra tablets is £62, including postage and packing. Delivery within the UK is promised in seven days by recorded post. The site's medical credibility is undermined by the offer of Lure 2000 which will "increase your desirability to women, or your money back".

Getfit
www.1getfit.com
You may be in need of more drugs than you thought after browsing this site which has vitamins and supplements to halt the ageing process, give you the body of a god(dess) and the stamina of a Duracell bunny If you don't already know how Gen Dhea halts the ageing process you won't find out here either, but you can buy it online. At a high price.

MED Clinic
www.ukyes.com
You can buy Viagra, Propecia, Rogaine (also for baldness) and Xenical here. Answering a simple medical history questionnaire is all you need to do before buying. Delivery in the UK is promised the next day and is free. A typical price is £70 for two months supply of Rogaine (a little pricey – compare with £59.95 for three months supply of Rogaine from both Allcures and Pharmacy2U). This site doesn't seem as professional or as authoritative as the others offering prescription medicines.

Sidebar:

SO HOW BAD IS IT DOC.COM?
There's something very seductive about the idea of logging on for medical advice. No waiting room, no "call back in six days time when you're well", no chance of catching whatever everyone else in the waiting room has.

Trouble is, how do you know which advice you can trust? One site worth bookmarking is Netdoctor (www.netdoctor.co.uk). The site has a huge encyclopaedia of diseases and conditions, written by medical experts, a briefing about medicines written by a pharmacist and a massive directory of support groups.

NetDoctor runs an Ask the Doctor service. Be warned, it is headed by media medic Dr Hilary Jones. And the news section is a must for those interested in health. You can register to get it on your email but reading it daily might convince you that you are the undiagnosed victim of a deadly secret lurgy.

Drugs

On-Line Medical Center
www.on-linemedicalcenter.com
This US-based site sells a limited range of prescription-only 'lifestyle' medicines, including Viagra, Propecia and slimming pills. You need to have an online consultation with a doctor (claimed to be licensed in the US, a claim they can document on request) before your order is approved and an adult signature is required on delivery, via UPS Second Day Air for outside the US. Delivery is included in the prices which, as you might expect, are not exactly cheap (eg $140 for 10 Viagra tablets).

Pharmacy2U
www.pharmacy2U.co.uk
The UK's first online pharmacy sells prescription medicines, although at time o going to press this service is confined to private prescriptions. Attractive and easy to use, this site even emails advice from trained pharmacists – just as you (sometimes) get in a high-street pharmacy. Pharmacy2U also offers over-the-counter medicines, healthcare, beauty, and disability aids. Postage and packing is £2.50 (free on orders over £30 and for prescription medicines). These items cost the same as in the high street. Delivery of medicines is next day and within 2-3 days for other products; our delivery took five days but came with a free packet of vitamin C as a gesture of apology.

A good reference site if you need advice or are just curious is…

Drugs, Solvents and Intoxicants
http://area51.upsu.plym.ac.uk/~harl/index.html
Unbiased source of info which includes stuff on what symptoms you should worry about if you're taking substances like Ecstasy, benzodiazepines (a kind of tranquiliser) or simply imbibing far too much caffeine.

Arguably the least indispensable drug site on the Net. You can't buy Lockets but you can converse with a koala

Online prescribing
The debate never stops

Prescribing drugs over the Net can be easily abused. But the Royal Pharmaceutical Society of Great Britain has laid down a code of practice to ensure the public receives the same quality care from online pharmacies as from a high-street chemist. (Obviously the RPSGB assumes you get high quality care from its members. You may or may not agree.) The code's main points are:

Security and confidentiality of patient information has to be assured by encryption of data transmission

The e-pharmacist must advise when a patient's symptoms suggest a face-to-face consultation would be better. (Most of the e-pharmacy business is for repeat prescriptions where you often don't need to see a doctor)

A questionnaire must be filled in if you want a pharmacy medicine (the ones kept behind the counter in the chemist's shop)

The online pharmacy must keep proper records of medicines prescribed An online pharmacy can only operate from registered premises open to inspection by their officers.

Meanwhile, the tricky issue of online doctor consultations (where you email your symptoms to a doctor who prescribes in response) is under debate at the British Medical Association. Some say there's no substitute for a face-to-face consultation (although this could be achieved with videoconferencing technology) and there's a danger of missing a serious condition if email replaces a trip to the surgery. But for people waiting up to a week for an appointment, you can see why email is an appealing option.

Brands
The usual names: aspirin, Viagra, Lockets

Aspirin
www.aspirin.com
No online buying but you can read the history of the little white pill which Neil Armstrong took to the moon. You can also read how pain passes around the body so you can speak fluent medical-ese: "It's like this doc, I've got these sensor tissues right? I know they're only a millionth of a millimetre in diameter on average, but they're hurting like hell... can you give me something?"

Lockets
www.doubleaction.co.uk
Presumably if you have a cold you should log-on to the Locket site for some light relief or helpful advice to get rid of the nasty bug. Pick up a 'fun" sick

certificate to send to your boss or join the chat room. As for cures, the best they can do is give advice like "keep warm and drink lots of fluids". No double-action cures to buy. here but there is a talking koala bear.

Savlon
www.familyfirstaid.co.uk
None of your favourite-smelling first aid treatment but a family-friendly guide to all those minor problems we all endure and that only Savlon can help remedy: cuts, bruises, grazes, burns and allergies to... close relatives. The online guide to recognising the difference between a child's graze and a life-threatening stitch job doesn't tell you anything your mother doesn't know.

Viagra
www.viagra.com
Don't be put off by the cheesy image of a couple with a new! improved! sex life (the wife looks so happy you expect her to break into a *Volare*-style chorus of "Vi-agra! Wo-oh-oh-oh!"). The site itself is full of self-evaluation questions, success stories and info but you have to buy elsewhere.

 **And finally** **For hypochondriacs only**

Patient UK
www.patient.co.uk
The aim is to help you get the best out of the NHS. You may think this is a job big enough to occupy the chap who took just six days to make the world but no, this task has fallen to a humble website. The medicines section links to the British National Formulary, will help you find out what you're feeding into your body. You should be warned however of two things. The new guidelines on everything from hepatitis to osteoporosis involve words only your doc will understand. You may also feel slightly paranoid after your visit.

Eco Living

You don't have to be Swampy to live an environmentally sound life. Online you can find anything from "clothes with a conscience" from Canada to magnetic water softeners and solar-powered energy systems

The Centre for Alternative Technology
www.cat.org.uk - secure
Primarily an education and research organisation, CAT's online shop is a virtual treasure trove of everything a person could need in order to live an environmentally friendly life. Many of the products will save you money in the long run, too. Lots of gift ideas for children to get them interested in eco-concerns, like a paper making press and a kit to help them construct their own solar powered models. Shipping and handling charges vary depending on the item and are calculated on site.

Eco-Fibre
http://freespace.virgin.net/eco.cellulose/
A company in Nottingham called Save It has developed a fibre made from recycled paper that has several industrial uses like sound proofing panels. The site is full of technical data, but the loft insulation section is easier to use, outlining the fibre's non-toxic, non-irritant properties and that it complies with the British Standard for thermal insulation. Email for further details.

Eco Shop
www.solar.org.uk/ecoshop
All kinds of solar-powered devices, from bike lamps to garden power stations that run your pond pumps and outdoor lights. There's even a sun-powered baseball cap with integral fan to keep you cool when the globe really warms up. Every item comes with a warranty and delivery is free in mainland UK.

Ethical Junction
www.ethical-junction.org
Limited choice at the moment, but this online mall is set to house an entire high street of fair-trading, earth-conscious retailers. Divided into categories like Ethical Trading and Conservation and Energy, current shop links include

Oxfam, The Pure Wine Company and Wind and Sun for those who would like nothing better than to install a solar or wind energy system.

Friends of The Earth
www.foe.co.uk
A great starting place for those looking to green up their lives. There's nothing to buy, except membership and a subscription to their magazine, but there's plenty of information on recycling, food issues and green energy, plus shedloads of links to other environmental sites where you can get all the kit you need to feel good about your impact on the planet.

Greencare
www.greencare.co.uk
A wide selection of recycling options for offices is offered on this laudable but sometimes temperamental web site. The company offers a collection service for items like fluorescent tubes, toner cartridges and drinks cans which they clean and sell on rather than letting them end up as land fill. There are also franchise opportunities for those looking to make money from being green.

Mad River Clothing Company
www.madriverclothing.com
Canadian firm selling "clothing with a conscience" for kids from 6 months to 14 years old, made mostly from locally produced organic cotton, hemp and eco-spun fleece. The clothes are stylish and look hardwearing, with the bonus that no one will have anything similar. Mad River will ship internationally (charges start at CA$9.50) and donate part of their profits to Unicef.

The Natural Collection
www.greenstore.co.uk
Glamorous catalogue of products for home and personal use that promise to have minimal impact on the environment. This is a brilliant place to come for unbleached cotton bed linen, or magnetic water softeners for your washing machine. The hemp section is packed with items made from the new-age crop, from socks to soap. Delivery starts at £1.75 but is free for orders over £100, and if you want next day delivery it will cost an extra £5. Customer service is excellent and orders almost always arrive within five days.

The Recycled Bottle Glass Centre Ltd
www.rbgc.co.uk
Just a quick look at some of the glorious stained glass panels that this community venture in Plymouth has produced from locally collected bottles, will convince even the most cynical of the advantages of recycling. Using a patented process, old bottles are turned into recycled glass in a variety of colours which you can then purchase in sheets for your own project, or commission a unique stained glass piece for yourself. There's an online enquiry form, or you can phone for price details and further information.

Educational

The Internet really started life as an educational tool for academics. Of course these days, the definition of learning has broadened somewhat to include detective stories starring Barbie and simulating an epidemic

Art Education
www.art-education.co.uk
This is a shockingly inartistic web site for a business that specialises in art tuition videos. But if you're dying to master, airbrushing, oils, drawing, pastels, watercolours, etc, you will find a pretty large range of three hour VHS videos on offer. Each video costs £15.99, including postage and packing.

BBC Shop
www.bbcshop.com
The Education section sells books, videos and CD-ROMs, poorly organised in an A-Z listing of titles. The range is heavily influenced by what's on the national curriculum and though you'll find decent, well-produced stuff, with the likes of a *Hamlet* CD-ROM costing £88, you won't find too many bargains.

Berlitz
www.berlitz.com
Berlitz asks you to select a website language (which might be one way to practice that rusty Finnish) before you go on to browse or search its impressive selection of language books, tapes and CDs. Decent product descriptions help prevent you being overwhelmed by choice, and the site is admirably clear. So far so good – until you reach the checkout. Should a US$8.95 phrasebook really cost $17.28 to ship to the UK?

Brilliant Publications
www.brilliantpublications.co.uk
Brilliant's designer hasn't quite grasped the idea that while kid stuff is on sale here, the site is really aimed at adults. Huge pictures and primary colours galore obscure the fact that Brilliant does actually have an attractive selection of posters and books on this site. If your order comes to less than £5, you should add 10% for postage and packing.

Discovery School
http://school.discovery.com
The Discovery Channel has teamed up with the US's largest school supplier, JL Hammett, to sell a huge range of educational videos, books and software aimed at adults as well as children. If you can stomach entering the Family Learning Store, you'll quickly find yourself browsing through hundreds of products including craft activity kits and the rather more exciting-sounding Epidemic Simulation Kit. This is a plush, well designed site. Postage and packing to the UK will add from 15% of the checkout price to the total.

Dorling Kindersley
www.dk.com/uk
DK's top quality range of books and software are on sale here. Categories include arts and crafts, languages, DIY and science, and you can select your age range (child to adult) before you start searching. Plenty of small but clear pictures help make the site a rare pleasure to use.

Europress
www.europress.co.uk
This simple but well designed site offers the usual educational categories (science, maths, English, etc), mainly for primary, GCSE and A-level pupils and products allied to the national curriculum. Free delivery in the UK.

Green Board Game Company
www.greenboardgames.com
This range of educational board games is aimed at primary school ages and up. Categories include nature, maths and history, which features *Sophie's World*, a game based on the best-selling novel. For bonus points, precocious kids can talk for a minute on a 'big question debated by philosophers for centuries'. If that doesn't put you off, you'll love the small but high quality selection of games on offer. Pity prices aren't posted until the checkout.

Learning Store
www.learningstore.co.uk
Search over 1,000 educational PC software titles at this very easy to navigate site. The CD-ROMs are arranged into subject and age categories and there are plenty to choose from. The educational value of the products isn't always clear, but who could resist *Detective Barbie's Mystery of the Carnival Caper*? Savings of at least £5 are on offer and shipping takes from 24-48 hours.

Linguaphone
www.linguaphone.co.uk
Simply fill in the boxes: "I speak_____. I want to learn_____". It's that simple. Or is it? You'll have to decide which of the staggering selection will suit your needs. If you want to learn French, you could pay anything from £12.99 for a travel pack to £349.99 for the combination course. Product

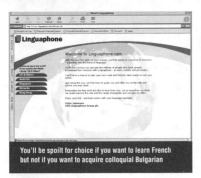

You'll be spoilt for choice if you want to learn French but not if you want to acquire colloquial Bulgarian

descriptions could be better. Ordering is simple and delivery takes up to five working days costing £7.90 or £4.95 for a travel pack.

Nishat Books
www.nishat.com
Nishat has 15 years' experience in exporting educational titles from "all major UK publishers" around the world, and a large selection of books on every subject area from primary to university level are featured on this clear, simply designed site. But you have to register to search and even then you have to enter a title, author or ISBN number – you can't search by subject.

Osborne Books
www.osbornebooks.co.uk
Based in Worcester, this small bookseller specialises in business, accounting and finance education. The site's neatly designed and simple to use, but the range is not great. Browse through what's on offer and you'll find titles ranging from Costing Reports to the more mysterious *A Fiery Glow in the Darkness*.

Proops Educational Packages
www.proops.com
Proops sells an eccentric selection of educational science, technology and construction kits. Want to build a water-powered rocket? You'll find the parts here (though you might also want to buy the instruction brochure). Also on offer are kits teaching basic laws of physics, solar power parts, flight motors, etc. VAT is added along with shipping (Royal Mail rates) at the checkout.

Show How To
www.showhowto.com
Log on here for "Fun Modern Learning!!!". Search through a vast selection of videos in categories from martial arts to theology. The videos aren't cheap (averaging around $40 with shipping from $7.75) and you can save money on the right title. The gambling title *Beat a Cheat* has to be a bargain at $29.98.

SMARRT
www.zebra.co.uk/smarrt
For less than £9, all-in, you too can get "the biggest advance in accounting education in over 500 years". Hmm, accountants underselling themselves...

Films, video & DVD

Let the Web help you buy cult horror classics (*Bananas In Pyjamas*), documentaries (*Dr Goldfoot And The Girl Bombs*) or blockbusters (*Howard The Duck*)

 Mainstream movies and a cast of thousands

Black Star

www.blackstar.co.uk

Exemplary home video and DVD site with a huge catalogue to help you find that movie you sort of remember where Dustin Hoffman is a seedy pimp (*Midnight Cowboy*, if you're interested). You can search by title, star, or director and each film has mini-synopsis to help in your selection. The Instant Video Library section where popular and classic films are on sale for only £5.99 each is particularly good. Other prices vary but shipping is fast and free on UK orders, although you have to register with the site before you can buy.

DVD Street

www.dvdstreet.infront.co.uk

For those lucky people who have a DVD player, this site claims to sell the biggest online selection of DVDs. They also have an outstanding technical guide to the issues of aspect ratio and DVD territory codes which can confuse many users. The site features video-streamed trailers playable through Real Player 8 Basic, which you can download for free, and there are loads of good special offers which change every week. Prices include delivery within the UK.

DVD World

www.dvdworld.co.uk

This site claims to stock every DVD available in the UK, and some prices are heavily discounted, so it's worth checking back regularly for new deals. Their interesting ideas include a bargain bundles section where you can buy *Pretty*

Woman together with *Runaway Bride* for only £25.99. You can also buy DVD players through the site or drool over other expensive items of home cinema. Delivery is free within the UK and if you order more than five discs, they will send your choices by registered post at no extra charge.

Film World
www.filmworld.co.uk
The online shop of this excellent news and review site sells videos and DVDs at around 20 – 25 per cent less than on the high street. The emphasis is on smaller independent and foreign films, with honest reviews of every title. Shipping costs £1.25 per video or DVD and since some titles are not always in stock, they email you with an order confirmation and expected delivery date.

Mr Benson's World of Home Entertainment
www.bensonsworld.co.uk
You can search through the 25,000 or so titles on this entertaining site, or just browse the categories to see what takes your fancy. There are some interesting film choices highlighted on the home page – when we looked it featured the 1922 Inuit documentary *Nanook Of The North*, while the World Cinema category had films in Mandarin, Farsi, Bengali and Welsh. But blockbuster fans needn't worry: there's plenty for them, too. Prices compare well with other online stores and postage is free on all UK video and DVD orders.

Odeon Filmstore
www.filmstore.com
All the usual titles are available from Odeon Cinema's online store, as well as posters and other film merchandise. The site hosts regular competitions with some excellent prizes, and there is also a selection of television programmes on video, such as *Bananas In Pyjamas* and *Brideshead Revisited*. Shipping starts at £1.85 and goes up to a maximum of £6.25, and you can track the progress of your order through the site, although it may only tell you that it's being processed.

Red Hot Monkey
www.redhotmonkey.com
This site is a DVD specialist which offers excellent prices, with the Hot Deals section offering particular savings. There's a pre-ordering service with a 20 per cent discount on upcoming releases, and a Director's Chair section (where

Black Star is a great movie site – good search facility, huge catalogue, cheap classic movies and free delivery

a selection of movies will be reviewed every week to help you build your film collection) has been promised for the future. Delivery anywhere in the world is free, and UK orders are sent by first class mail.

Video Empire

www.videoempire.co.uk

Efficient and user-friendly site, selling new and used videos at good prices. They have an extensive catalogue, including a section of Japanese Manga videos, and a good help section if you're confused about video formats. There's also an online form to complete if you want the site to track down any title you can't find listed. Delivery costs £1.75 for the first video and 50p for each extra item, and order should arrive within five days.

The Video Shop

www.videoshop.co.uk

This site is a joy for film fans as it's clearly run by enthusiasts. There's an excellent selection of unusual films, as well as the more obvious ones, and the catalogue is divided into genres for easy browsing, or you can simply use the search facility. They also offer to track down old and out-of-print tapes for a fee of £13, and claim a 90-per cent success rate for the service. A forward-looking site, it accepts payment in euros and can deliver items all over the world. Shipping in the UK is £2 for up to four tapes with every subsequent tape costing 50p, but DVD postage is free.

VideoZone

www.videozone.co.uk

This very basic site relies on its search engine to take you where you want to go, rather than having pages you can browse and enjoy along the way. Still, if you're in a hurry, you might appreciate the direct approach. Be careful, though: if you click on the title that interests you after you get your search results (expecting to see further details), the site puts it straight into your shopping basket. Delivery is calculated online and depends on the size of your order.

Looking for a Worldwide Prayer Guide? You can find it at Chapter And Verse, a Christian resource centre site

The following sell a range of films on video and DVD, as well as other items like books and CDs. Their catalogues may not be extensive, but as long as you stick to the mainstream, they're certainly worth checking for price comparisons:

www.amazon.co.uk	Amazon
www.dvdplus.co.uk	DVD Plus
www.gameplay.com	Game Play
www.jungle.com	Jungle
www.towereurope.co.uk	Tower Records
www.whsmith.co.uk	WH Smith
www.yalplay.co.uk	Yalplay

Specialist For the "cognoscenti"

The American Film Foundation
www.americanfilmfoundation.com
The AFF makes and sells videos of independent features and short documentaries on a wide range of subjects which often pop up in the documentary categories at the Oscars. They're based in California but will ship abroad if you email them through the site. But make sure you're getting a UK-compatible format, which means PAL, not the US NTSC version.

The BBC Shop
www.bbcshop.com
Find your favourite Beeb programmes on video here, whether it's *EastEnders* or *I Claudius* (sometimes it's hard to tell the difference). Some productions are also available on DVD. The site is easy to use, and has a good database search. Postage charges start at £1.95 for a three-day service or £2.95 for next day, but if you buy more than five items delivery is free.

Carlton Video
www.carltonvideo.co.uk
This is the online store for videos of Carlton Television's TV programmes, ranging from new programmes such as *Monsignor Renard* (starring John Thaw) and the recent remake of *The Railway Children*, to cult classic series like *The Prisoner* and *Thunderbirds*. Delivery costs £1.90 for the first item and £1.30 for each subsequent one up to a maximum charge of £6.25, and goods are dispatched within 24 hours if they are in stock.

Chapter And Verse
www.chapterandverse.co.uk
Religion enters the 21st century with this straightforward Christian resource centre selling videos with a Christian theme, including gospel concerts and

BLANKETY BLANK TAPE

If you're like most people, you will have re-used your home video tapes until the opening frames are a hectic mishmash of last week's *Friends*, an ancient musical your mum wanted to tape, and that unwatched second half of last year's FA Cup semi-final.

So why not get some new tapes and throw out the old ones before they tangle in your VCR and cost you a packet to remove? Blankshop sells blank tapes of every make and length in packs of ten.

The prices knock spots off buying in the high street, and while you're there you can stock up on blank audio tapes and recordable CDs.

www.blankshop.com

children's morality tales. Books, CDs and software are also available. You can order online or by phone or fax and items in stock will be sent within two days (God willing). Delivery charges start at £1 and are free on orders over £30.

FRIENDLY GUIDANCE

Building a film collection is a serious business that can take over your life, not to mention your living room. What you need is some friendly guidance on which movies are worth buying to keep and which are only good for occasional viewing when they crop up on television. So before you rush out to splash out on an expensive DVD of the latest teen sensation flick, check out the web sites below for some informed film fan advice and juicy insider gossip.

Ain't It Cool News
www.aintitcoolnews.com

Film.com
www.film.com

The Internet Movie Database
www.imdb.com

Movies.com
www.movies.go.com

My Movies
www.mymovies.net

Creepy Classics Video
www.abulsme.com/creepy
Tucked in among the gruesome movie trivia and US horror convention information is a charming little store selling copies of cult classics like 1956's *Gamma People* and 1968's *Macabre Serenade*, along with books, CDs and t-shirts. There is an online order form, but you will have to email the site to arrange international shipping.

Science Fiction Continuum
www.sfcontinuum.com
"Where reality hits the road" is the tag line of this site, and it's not wrong. Where else could you find a copy of *Dr Goldfoot And The Girl Bombs*? This title is just one of the joys to be found in the spectacular B-movies section which accompanies the site's more conventional sci-fi fare and UFO documentaries. It's a US operation, but overseas orders will be sent via registered airmail and they will only charge for the service at cost.

Viaduc Video
www.viaducvideo.com
This European documentary video site sells films in English, German or French. You can search the index by key word, but check very carefully that the format you are buying is compatible with your video player or there could be tears. Prices are shown in French francs and euros, but the site is secure so you can let your credit card do the maths for you if you have a rough idea of the cost.

Westerns
www.westerns.com
Roy Rogers and Tex Ritter feature heavily in the Trading Post section of this tribute site to classic Westerns. Many of the titles are pretty obscure, and frustratingly they don't sell such classics as *The Searchers* or *Red River*, but if you've been hunting for a copy of *The Gay Amigo*, you are going to be very happy here.

Fishing

Angling may be a
low-tech sport but the
Net offers a surprising
variety of items, from a
bonefishing holiday in the Bahamas
to a "liquid smell attractant" for carp-chasers

Beekay International
www.beekay.force9.co.uk
The carp is king at Beekay International. You can buy carp books, carp
videos, carp t-shirts and bait from the Kevin Maddocks Carp Bait Range
(how about a "liquid smell" attractant? Choose from a big selection including
tangerine and double cream). Trout and pike do occasionally get a look-in,
but there's no mistaking the star fish here. Delivery costs £2 per item, up to
a maximum of £6, and delivery is promised within seven working days.

Bonefish Adventure
www.bonefishadventure.com
If you want to fly fish for bonefish, you can buy the equipment and even a
bonefishing holiday in the Bahamas here. Folding rods, reels, luggage and
tropical accessories are all available for dispatch within 24 hours. Delivery is
free for orders over £100, and there's a seven-day refund offer. Dorset-based
Carol and Graham Pepler are bonefishing enthusiasts, and there are plenty of
photos of them in action to browse through while you make your selection.

Flymail
www.flymail.com
If Mini Nobblers and Boobys are your thing, this is the place to head for.
Unadventurous but easy to navigate, this Aberystwyth-based site offers a
huge selection of fishing flies from 30p a pack, with UK delivery from just 60p.
There are just two minor downsides: the dodgy vari-blue colour scheme (no
doubt intended to remind customers of their favourite fish havens), and the
registration that's required if you want to receive information on special offers.

Harris Angling Company
www.harrisangling.co.uk
Hundreds of types of lures are on sale here, along with books, videos, hooks,

lines and collectibles (including pewter common carp lapel pins – though the pike is the favoured fish here). You'll also find fishing tips and techniques, a readers' photos page and a selection of half-price bargains of the day, from cut-price lures to a tackle organiser's cabinet. Ordering is straightforward, delivery is free in the UK, and your kit should be with you within 48 hours.

Sharpes of Aberdeen
www.sharpes.net/sharpes/home.html

Founded in 1920, Sharpes sells high-class rods, reels, nets and accessories. This old-fashioned site features in-depth, if overblown, product descriptions and background info on everything from Stealth Rods to the Millennium Bug (a high-tech fly that emits subtle light and the "correct frequency of sound"). This is a site to browse at leisure, and you'll no doubt find the answer to your fishing prayers – provided you're armed with plenty of cash. Perhaps the prices are given in US dollars rather than sterling to soften the blow.

Summerlands Tackle
www.summerlands.co.uk

This large, crowded site is packed with fishing news and articles, pictures and products. On the downside, the thousands of items available are not arranged in any obvious order, so if you know what you want, you'll have to search hard to find it. On the plus side, this is an endearingly non-corporate site, driven by obvious enthusiasm as well as a desire to spread the catch of this Devon-based store. Postage is from £3.95 for a rod.

Thos Turner & Sons
www.turners1838fly.demon.co.uk

Antique and second-hand fly-fishing tackle are what's on offer at this site. Flies, rods, centre pinwheels and more are graded from A ("pristine") to D ("well-used. Flaws as stated").
There are plenty of pictures and a lot to choose from, but the organisation is poor. You'll have to scroll through the goods to find what you want – product categories are evidently an alien concept at this site. Postage costs vary according to the weight and your insurance requirements, but worryingly, there's no evidence of a secure ordering system. If you really want to buy an antique gut-eyed salmon fly for a fiver online, you'll have to e-mail your credit card details to the store.

Turner & Sons specialise in antique and second-hand gear but products are not properly categorised

Flowers & Gifts

You can say it with flowers,
jet skis, or a pair of skull-shaped
maracas. Call us fuddy-duddies,
but we'd advise you to think hard
before saying it with maracas

 Digital sentiments for that special occasion

Cyber Card
www.cybercard.co.uk
Search Cyber Cards' extensive range of images to create your own card for
whatever occasion and have it posted to the recipient, all for £2.50. If it's a
little too late even for that, you can always use their electronic card service.

Hallmark
www.hallmark.com
Delivers cards and gifts to the United States only, but Hallmark does deliver
e-cards globally. Some can only be viewed with a Flash plug-in.

Moonpig
www.moonpig.com
For £1.99 plus postage your chosen card with message can be delivered
anywhere in the UK by the following day. Search by occasion and popular
brands including Dot, Bestie and Fred and the Naughty Filter will help whittle
your selection down to the cleanest or dirtiest cards according to your whim.

Occasions Observed
www.ocob.co.uk
Simple and elegant, Occasions offers a limited selection of hand-made cards
using paper collages, painting on silk and ceramic craft skills. Average price of
£4 with 60p added for postage no matter how many cards you buy, and you
can even have the message written in the hand-writing most like your own.

Flowers | Roses, posies, sprays and bouquets

Floritel
www.floritel.co.uk

Floritel's worldwide service allows you to specify how much you would like to spend and then it makes the bouquet up accordingly. Images and descriptions of existing arrangements are available so you have more of an idea of what your money will get you and you can specify the type of arrangement and the colours used. A bouquet of long-stem roses will set you back a reasonable £18, but delivery is charged on top of that at £10. Despite this being a complicated idea, ordering is simple and there's a minimum delivery time of four hours.

Flower Card
www.flowercard.com

Flower cards are an unusual alternative to your typical bouquet; it's only a pity that the range is limited to six cards. Prices range from around £7 to £15, including delivery, and you basically get a card sprouting fresh flowers. With the ordinary secure delivery system you can specify the date that you would like the card to be delivered, but express delivery is not connected to a secure server, so emailing or faxing your order is advisable.

Flowers Direct UK
www.flowersdirectuk.co.uk

Next-day delivery flower service, with prices ranging from £15 to £50. Large selection includes roses, English and Continental bouquets with full description and images. The delivery charge is a standard £3.95.

Flowers Say
www.flowerssay.co.uk

If you're looking for the longer-lasting bouquet, Flowers Say sells artificial arrangements alongside their natural bouquets, cut flowers and Spring flowering bulb collections. It's sparse on details, so buyers need to put their faith in the arrangement shown and hope it turns up looking like the picture. Whether artificial or the real thing, bouquet prices range from £10 to £20 with postage and packing an additional £3.50. Good value for money if the bouquets live up to their portraits.

Interflora
www.interflora.co.uk
Comprehensive site where you can search according to occasion, price, type and colour of flower. Prices range from £12.50 for a single red rose in a bottle, to £45 for the most expensive bouquet. As you would expect from Interflora, it offers a concise description of each arrangement along with an enlarged image so you know what you're getting for your cash. Reliable, if not unusual.

 From the trendy to the tasteless, presents to go

Alternative Gift Company
www.alt-gifts.co.uk
Alternative Gifts lives up to its name, selling trendy loot you're unlikely to find in your local John Lewis. These are presents for the more flexible bank balance, two of the ritzier items being a Giavarra silver, ruby-encrusted business card holder for £395 and a revolving CD and magazine rack for under £100. There are more modest gift-shop-style presents including chrome Coke Can Dispensers, £7.99, and Fish Alarm clocks for £15. Easy to navigate, the site could be improved with more detailed descriptions, as you'll be left none the wiser as to what the Starship Earth 2 is, and why it costs £575.

Boxed Up
www.boxedup.co.uk
The gifts from this stylishly designed site fall under the categories of Creative, Indulgence, Comfort and Pleasure. If you know a keen gardener trapped in a gardenless flat, the indoor garden box, complete with terracotta pots, seeds and soil scoop, should be of interest at £20. If you're looking for a gourmet gift, the curry boxes or Chinese feast boxes for under £30 should be right up your street. Only problem came with trying to discover the cost of delivery – you have to process your order first. Great gifts – poor connection.

Cody's
www.codys.co.uk
The ultimate gift solution, Cody's offers gift advisors, vouchers, reminders and emergency remedies. It offers the usual chocolates and homewares along with so-called "Wow" gifts; a jet ski for just under £7,000 for example, or a home waterfall, £60 – ideal for any friend who yearns to return to nature. Unique experiences include the Formula 1 scholarship for £304 and the luxury health break that will help rejuvenate any tired soul. The images are clear and with the choice of searching according to gender, occasion, personality or price, it's worth searching despite the complicated ordering form.

Found

www.foundat.co.uk

Despite living up to its claim of offering beautiful things via the Net, Found makes online shopping too frustrating to warrant moving far beyond the first page.You click on each room category, and an image of that room will appear, along with the opportunity to buy all of what you see. Unfortunately the pictures, though pretty, are too overcrowded to offer a good look at what you're buying, there are no descriptions of the products on offer, and some of these seem priced for the pockets of trendhounds only. Most annoyingly, there is no direct link to the order form if you do see something you like. For your living room, the cheapest cushion costs £45 and the linen duvet covers will set you back a couple of hundred pounds. Nice toasting forks, though.

Gift Delivery Company

www.giftdeliveryco.com

Despite the ordinary homepage, this site boasts exciting, if extravagant, activity gifts. Two flights to Brussels wrapped in a box of Belgian chocolates is a bargain at £65, although the balloon ride for £149 seems a little stratospheric. They do offer the typical chocolates and flowers, but they should stick to dealing in their more unusual items. May look ordinary in terms of design but well worth a look for a special gift.

Gift Inspiration

www.giftinspiration.com

Selling both luxurious (see the Sari Photo Albums), and fun items (check out the Cat Napping Cushion & Pyjama Case), here's a shop that offers something a little more interesting than his 'n' her chrome pens. Prices generally range from £10 for a Hangover Cure, to £25 for the Oriental Lotus Ceramic Bowl, with free delivery. Gift Inspiration also sells stuff you may have seen in style magazines and coveted, such as those transparent PVC wall planners, £10.95, or a fine rose glass ball to fill with fragrant oil and hang in a window, £19.99. Search through his, her, kid and friends categories or head straight for the Inspiration section for the best buys. Original and easy to use.

The Gift Store

www.giftstore.co.uk

If you can bear to ignore its pedestrian, Union Jack -bedecked design, you will find this site quite useful. Categories include run-of-the-mill chocolates, flowers and balloons, alongside magic sets, juggling equipment and Majorcan Pearls. A Cornish clotted cream tea for £5.50 or a saffron cake for £7.50 have to be among the best gift items, although the personalised front page of a tabloid newspaper comes a pretty close second at £24.99. No registration is needed and all the information is contained on one page so you don't need to spend time searching. Marks are for content, not design, and delivery charges can be steep – at £6.55 for a £7.50 cake, you might be better brushing up on your home baking skills.

Hugs & Cuddles

www.hugsandcuddles.co.uk

Hugs & Cuddles offer furry friends old-style, and has teddies galore to suit every pocket. None of your Forever Friends bears here. Each comes with brief description and character reference, with prices ranging from Bearalia at £179.99 to Tennyson at £18.69. Ordering is easy and bears are dispatched free by first class post, though you can opt for next-day delivery for £3.00.

I Love Lucy

http://shop.store.yahoo.com/nylascollectibles/info.html

Yahoo.com's memorabilia and collectibles shopping areas should be the centre of any true kitsch fan's shopping world. Nyla's pages include classic tat and trivia ranging from cute tractors to delight the most difficult-to-please John Deere driver to a $19 ceramic I Love Lucy TV. In pink, naturally. Most of the companies here ship to the UK: Nyla recommends you estimate postage using the calc at http://ircalc.usps.gov/. Thanks, honey.

Oxfam

http://oxfam.org.uk/buy.htm

You're unlikely to find Ghanaian clay pots or Mankind Vases from El Salvador just anywhere. Divided into average food, home and gift categories, the range is limited but not pricey. Peruvian Pan Pipes and Maracas for under a tenner each are just two of the more unusual presents on offer. Delivery is slow at £3.50 for 14-28 days or £8.50 for 7 days, but worth the wait.

Propagangsta

www.propagangsta.com

This bright and stylish site offers equally appealing and competitively priced gifts. Help to deck your friend's new home out with a lava lamp for £20 or an inflatable chair for £10. Descriptions are available so you can read what exactly a mystic 8 ball is before you buy one. Postage and packing is only £2.95, and the only down-fall is that you need to log on before you can buy.

Propagangsta is a bright, stylish gift site which tries to turn a profit by saving you money. It'll never catch on

Rennie Mackintosh

www.rennie-mackintosh.co.uk

This site offers a large range of jewellery and homewares inspired by the artist. For those who want to recreate that Willow Tea Rooms ambience at home, an Argyle chair will set you back £405, and a table lamp £89. If you'd just like a little piece of Mackintosh, the jewellery range includes rings for under £10 and bracelets for £50. Ordering is simple and the site includes information about each product and design, with clear images.

Urban Man

http://194.154.190.82/

This lifestyle site for the man's man includes its own shopping warehouse filled with presents for the more sophisticated male in your life. Order a chrome Oil & Vinegar set for £29.44 and the matching Toast Rack for £10.91. Unimaginative presents let this otherwise well thought out e-zine down, but it's useful if you're shopping for the strait-laced business man who will appreciate chrome calculators and pen sets. Not sure how such gifts will go down with white-water rafting and sky diving man.

Wheesh

www.wheesh.com

Advertised as Online Gifts in a Hurry, with Wheesh you don't need to register, navigate through any flashy graphics or pay any delivery charge. Standard categories include For Him, Her and Home, but it's hard to determine the market Wheesh is aiming at. Gifts range from a bright, rose-painted Pedestal Bowl for £15 that resembles something your granny has stashed away in her pantry, to a trendy Mauve Bubble Clock, also for £15. Novel items include a Mouse Mat Calculator, £10, and a Pocket Spy Monocular, £35. One that requires time to search, so not that fast after all.

 **Not to be given lightly**

City Morgue

www.citymorguegiftshop.com/

"Welcome to the best place for gothic, mortuary, forensic and death related gifts" this site greets you cheerily. Guide your cursor past the flying skulls and about halfway down the home page you find a button for the gift shop. Click here and you enter a strange world of skull maracas, model guillotines and celebrity death certificates. You can order online, if you're that way inclined.

Who gives a fish?

www.whogivesafish.com/

Who indeed! Well, the creator of this site cares very deeply about fish car stickers. In America (where else?) the old Christian fish sticker was challenged by a Darwin fish sticker, which had evolved legs. So the Christians hit back with a sticker which shows the Jesus fish eating the Darwin fish. So, the creator of this site has hit back at both sides with a "Whatever" fish sticker. Well, how else was he supposed to react? Yours for only $5.

Food

Jamie, Delia et al have made us expect more from our meals these days. The Net can help you track down stunning eats for impressive dining, or just get a stack of baked beans delivered to your door

General So what do you want to cook?

Fabulous Foods

www.fabulousfoods.com

American gourmet site devoted to good food in all its forms. There are lots of different transatlantic recipes to try (it's not all hamburgers and hotdogs over there), especially in the healthy eating and seasonal favourites sections. You can sign up for a newsletter tailored to your eating habits, like vegetarian or low fat, or just surf around with your mouth watering.

Simply Food

www.simplyfood.com

Huge portal site set up by the Carlton Food Network, packed with recipes, foodie competitions, restaurant reviews, cookery advice and links to food shopping or cooking sites. A great place to start when you're looking for culinary inspiration.

Supermarkets Fresh pasta or Spam, it's all here

Asda

www.asda.co.uk

Unsurprisingly, the Asda site is fairly basic with very few bells and whistles to distract you. If you're looking to have food or items of George clothing delivered, you will need to register with them for a CD-ROM or catalogue from which to choose your shopping. Ours took a while to arrive, but its instructions were straightforward and the shopping process easy and fast.

Budgens
www.budgens.co.uk
Check this site to find out if Budgens delivers in your area. If it does, it will send you a free CD-ROM which you have to load before you can shop. Service was slightly restricted in coverage at the time of going to press, but if you do qualify, your groceries arrive quickly and service is very helpful. Delivery is free on orders over £50 (it's £3 under that amount) on Mondays to Saturdays between 8am and 10pm, plus you can chose to pay the van driver by cheque if you're not keen to hand over your credit card details.

The Food Ferry
www.foodferry.co.uk
Bespoke grocery delivery service only operating in central London when we visited, but offering a wide selection of brand name foods, fresh fruit and vegetables, plus specialist items like coffee from Whittards or ready meals from The Pie Man. The site is user-friendly and promises next-day delivery or same-day delivery for the truly panic-stricken. Delivery charges vary between £2 and £6.50 depending on the time of day you select, and the length of slot you will accept (a one-hour slot being more expensive than a four-hour one).

Iceland
www.iceland.co.uk
The freezer giant has spent wads of money convincing people that it sells more than frozen death-burgers and cheap ice cream, and this site will come as a pleasant surprise to those who still haven't got the message. There's an online shopping demo for newbies, highlighted special offers, and all items are marked if they can be microwaved. Iceland guarantees its own-brand products are GM-free, and it has also banned artificial colours, flavours and, where possible, preservatives from its range. The minimum spend is £40 for home delivery, but it does claim to cover 97 per cent of the population.

Sainsburys
www.sainsburys.co.uk
Fast and efficient with plenty of information on how to shop online, plus current special offers in the store. Unlike some sites, you can look around before you register, which is a help if you're unsure about how the system actually works. Delivery costs £5, is available seven days a week, and our order arrived well within its two-hour time-slot, with only a couple of items substituted. If you lose your Internet connection halfway through shopping, Sainsburys promises that what you have in your basket will be saved until you are able to log on again, avoiding any tedious refilling. One black mark, though – when we tested the site, it was unable to fully support Macs, but Sainsburys assured us they were working on the problem.

Hampers If it comes in wicker, it's here

The Internet is groaning under the cyberweight of sites that will send a basket of goodies wherever it's needed. Hampers are always a welcome gift as long as the food and booze inside them are top notch. The following sites have a wide selection in a range of prices, and delivery costs are reasonable.

Clearwater Hampers
www.hamper.com
Innovative and reasonably priced, with some good choices in the themed hampers section.

Gourmet Ireland
www.gourmetireland.com
Celtic food and drink gifts, with the emphasis on natural products and gorgeous presentation.

All Occasions
www.alloccasions.co.uk
Everything from wine and chocolates to a full Christmas blowout. The hampers themselves are top quality too.

Worldwide Hampers
www.worldwide-hampers.com
An annoying and cheap-looking site that first takes you through an online mall, but once you are there, the hampers contain high quality food, many with a Scottish flavour.

800 Hampers
www.800hampers.com
Scottish hampers starting at £17.99 and stuffed with Highland goodies. They also ship all over the world.

French Hampers
www.frenchhampers.co.uk
As you might expect, gourmet food packages from across the Channel. Le Napoleon will set you back a whopping £3500, but it will feed 20 people.

Festive Feasts
www.festivefeasts.co.uk
Christmas hampers and grocery packages featuring familiar brands as well as special treats. Just in case you didn't eat enough then anyway. You can also set up a Christmas savings account through the site.

Tesco

www.tesco.com

The homepage can link you to deals on books, housewares, phones, financial products and computers as well as get baked beans delivered to your door. The registration process can be temperamental (particularly if you're using Internet Explorer 5.0), and you have to register as a Clubcard holder before it will accept you as a customer. Once you've registered though, the service is excellent, with options to specify if you will accept substitutions if an item is not in stock, and all special offers are brought to your attention so you don't miss out on in-store deals. Delivery costs £5, but make sure the service covers your postcode before you get going.

Waitrose

www.waitrose.com

At present, Waitrose will only deliver wine, organic groceries, flowers, gifts and chocolates to your door. The organic boxes contain a good selection of either vegetables, salad or fruit or a mixture of each, and are delivered between Tuesday and Friday to ensure freshness. Waitrose strives to buy as much produce as possible from British farmers, and all organic boxes have to be ordered at least two days in advance. For wine delivery you must register with the site, after which you can keep notes on the wines you like, or set up a wish list for future purchases or gifts.

Let's hear it for happy, chemical-free eating. iorganic can sell you the food, deliver it overnight, *and* tell you how to cook it. The prices are good, too

 **GM and pesticides not welcome**

Cooks Delight
www.cooksdelight.co.uk
Certified organic and biodynamic food will soon be available online from this
company in the Chilterns. The online shop was just about to launch when we
looked, but in the meantime you can browse organic recipes and even poems
about green issues such as smoking and cloning (although the poet hasn't yet
found a good rhyme for genetic modification).

The Fresh Food Company
www.freshfood.co.uk
This online organic supermarket has a good specific product or recipe search
facility, or you can just browse the site to see the full range. Some of the box
descriptions, such as The Sunshine Box – which just says it contains eight
Mediterranean fruits – are somewhat vague about what's on offer, and the
prices can be steep compared with similar sites. However, there are many
organic items you may not easily find elsewhere. Delivery is on Thursdays
only and you have to give a week's notice for your order.

Greenwich Organic Foods
www.greenwichorganic.co.uk
This is the site of an organic supermarket in SouthEast London which will
deliver locally. There's plenty of choice and the prices for the vegetable and
fruit boxes are reasonable. If you're in need of organic meat and poultry, you
can add a variety to your order by contacting Sparks Organic Butchers
through the site. Different postcodes get deliveries on different days, so this
site won't be able to help you in a last-minute organic emergency.

Iorganic
www.iorganic.com
Full-service organic supermarket site with all the usual food stuffs as well as
news and recipes for organic food fans. It strives to keep the cost of quality
food within reach of everyone, and certainly the prices compare very well with
supermarket organics. Delivery is free if your total is more than £30 and any
orders received before 10am on Mondays to Thursdays will be delivered
before 4.30pm the following day, apart from the organic wines which may
take two to three days to arrive.

Meat Direct
www.meatdirect.co.uk
If you're worried about how many heads the pig had before it was turned into
sausages, ease your concerns by ordering from the organic section of this
meat delivery company. There are hampers and bulk buys for those with

hearty appetites or capacious freezers, but even the smaller packs are reasonably priced in comparison to supermarket organics. Delivery costs £4 for orders under 10kg and is guaranteed for next day if you order before 11am. There's a small extra charge for a Saturday drop.

Organic Delivery
www.organicdelivery.co.uk
Another London-only vegetable box scheme that has expanded to include more general organic groceries such as milk and bread. If you live in the area covered, there's a free bag of potatoes on offer with your first order. Different postcodes get their delivery on specific days of the week, and you can order up until 5pm on the day before your delivery is due.

Organics Direct
www.organicsdirect.com
Register your delivery address and instructions once and after that you only have to give your name, postcode and phone number and the site remembers the rest. Weekly or fortnightly deliveries of super-fresh organic vegetables can be set up, saving you money in the long term, or choose from the excellent selection for a one-off delivery of organic groceries, from breakfast cereals to baby food. It may take a while to complete your order, especially if you're looking for something specific, as you have to scroll down through every item rather than jumping quickly from category to category, but it's a good way to see the whole range. If you are ordering a vegetable box, delivery is free on orders under 20kg; otherwise it's £5.95.

Simply Organic Food Company
www.simplyorganic.net
Brilliantly easy-to-use site where the food is divided into aisles. It's a doddle to skip through and see what's there, and to find exactly what you need. There's everything you'd expect from a supermarket, including chilled meals, dairy products, baby food and even organic toiletries. You can choose which fruit and veg you want, or save money with one of the box offers. Orders placed before 8pm on a weekday will usually be delivered by 12pm two days later (except Sundays and Mondays). Delivery costs £5 per order, but if you're a regular customer spending more than £60, it's free anywhere in the UK.

Somerset Organics
www.somersetorganics.co.uk
A group of West Country farms have got together to provide an organic site where you can get a variety of quality meats, including duck, delivered anywhere in the country. You can order either individual cuts or boxes for you to freeze or share with a friend. Since you're buying direct, prices are lower than buying organic in a supermarket, and delivery is only £4.99, so on bulk orders the savings can be huge. The farms deliver on Tuesdays to Fridays and only need two days' notice to put your order together.

Swaddles Green Farm

www.swaddles.co.uk

Selling their own naturally raised meat as well as other organic groceries, Swaddles farm is devoted to promoting the cause of good food for all. There's a fabulous ready-prepared meal selection for dinner party cheats (pretend you've always known how to bone a chicken), as well as children's meals to satisfy both parent and offspring. Orders have to be over £25 and delivery is free in the SouthEast on Wednesdays to Fridays, with charges depending on the order value for the rest of the country.

 Speciality Don't surf on an empty stomach

Butler's Cheese Shop

www.butlerscheeses.co.uk

This site may be lacking in visual inspiration but it's easy to use, focusing on a small range of quality cheeses. You can read descriptions and strength levels for favourites like crumbly Lancashire, down to more exotic vintage varieties. Each cheese is sold in 200g, 400g and 2,250g weights, and the smallest wedge is around £2. Better to by in bulk, however, as shipping is charged at a hefty £6.

Carmichael Meats

www.carmichael.co.uk

This Scottish site sells traditionally farmed meats, with beef and lamb products and also top quality venison on offer. Although not fully organic, Carmichael prides itself on humane farming methods. The site is quite basic, but the order form is secure and deliveries cost £11.50 per 10kg, although if you spend more than £100 it's free.

Chandos Deli

www.chandosdeli.com

This Bristol deli offers delivery of its range of treat foods and store-cupboard essentials for keen cooks. The recipe section has links to suitable wines to enjoy with your meal, and some really quite obscure ingredients can be tracked down here. Delivery within two days costs £4.99 for orders under £100 (it's free above that) although for Northern Ireland or the Highlands of Scotland, you have to wait around seven days for it to arrive.

GET OILY

The sunflower yellow pages serve this olive oil site well. You probably thought oil was oil, but Get Oily believes every oil has a story.

You can read up on the differences between Italian, Spanish and Greek oils, or head straight for the shop to buy your sunflower, extra virgin, blended and Artemis' own olive oil.

To encourage you to go the whole hog and buy their five-litre tins, there are details of oil-only recipes and how you too can look like Sophia Loren, as long as you cook with the right oil.

---

www.getoily.com

If you're after real Scottish smoked foods (instead of imported foods that are merely smoked there), the Galloway Smokehouse is for you

Fifth Sense Trading Company Ltd.

www.fifthsense.com

Delicious marinades, chutneys and sauces are among the large range of yummy foodstuffs that this site imports from the US. The emphasis is on natural ingredients and on being able to produce gourmet food at very short notice. There are good sections on Southwestern food (some items have an almighty kick to them) and Asian specialities. Shipping is free on orders over £65, otherwise it's £4.50, and takes four to 10 days, although our test order arrived in only three days (and was all gone two days later). Yummy.

Gourmet World

www.gourmet-world.com

If you're trying to avoid artificial flavours and colourings as well as genetically modified ingredients, but you still want outstanding quality and taste in your food, this site could be the answer to your prayers. With lots of tip top foods from around the world, all made with natural ingredients, you can stock up your larder or put together a gift box for a hungry friend. Delivery is free on orders over £50; otherwise it's £5.95.

Le Gourmet Français

www.jayfruit.co.uk

You may not be impressed when the homepage reveals that this company is based in Rickmansworth, but they do import classic food goodies direct from French producers. The site is one for those with an adventurous palate, with categories including foie gras, terrine and truffles. It offers reasonable prices for such delicacies, with five dozen Burgundy snails selling for £12, and four stuffed quails marinated in cider for the same. Ironically, the Speciality section is far tamer, with a selection of roasted peppers and oils. Delivery is charged at £4.99 and the minimum order is £20.

Galloway Smokehouse
www.gallowaysmokehouse.co.uk
Smoked Scottish Salmon (as opposed to Scottish Smoked Salmon, the difference being that Smoked Scottish is fish caught in Scotland, rather than imported and just smoked there) is the main draw on this independent smokehouse site. Since you're buying direct, the prices – especially if you're in the market for a whole side of salmon – are excellent at around £20 per kilo for the really good stuff. It also sells smoked trout, venison and duck. Standard delivery is steep at £6, so a bulk order might be more cost effective.

Martins Sea Fresh Local Fish
www.martins-seafresh.co.uk
Live lobster and crabs, along with other fish and shellfish from a Cornish fishmonger, delivered direct from the boats to your door. If it's freshness you're after, this is the service you're looking for, and it supports responsible practice to help the UK's beleaguered fish stocks. Availability on most items depends on the day's catch, so check back regularly if you're after something specific. If you order by noon, your fish will be with you the next day.

Shop Italy
www.shopitaly.co.uk
There are a few foodie items to buy on this large Italian shopping site, but for a full range of deli produce, you'll have to click on the homepage for:

Delicious
www.delicious.uk.com
From the tasteful green-and-red backdrop of Shop Italy, the Delicatessen link leads you to Delicious. Moving into consumer Italy rather than traditional Italian produce, the catalogue is comprehensive if lacking innovation. You can pick up all the Italian delicacies you find on the high street, like Panettone cake, salami piccante, pancetta and fresh pasta, but the prices are what you would pay on the high street too.

Take It From Here
www.tifh.co.uk
This online deli stocks all the essentials you need to produce a traditional Italian meal – fresh pasta, pesto sauces and Amaretti biscuits for dessert. The range is a little limited, however, and it seems expensive (£3.20 for 500g of salmon-filled tortellini), although the quality should make up for that. There are some good special deals, but buy in bulk as delivery is £4.50 for a next-day service if you order by 2.30pm.

Norburys Fine Foods
www.norburys.co.uk
This global delicatessen sells cheeses from around the world, coffees from South America and marmalades from exotic Suffolk. Some of the prices are high, even compared with premium supermarket and fine food brands. Chutney costing £3.85, and coffee costing £7.50 seems excessive, so you're probably paying for the overheads and the novelty factor rather than the actual food. The dull design doesn't particularly inspire either, so our advice would be to be careful which items you actually buy, or shop around for cheaper and more original tasty treats.

Britgrub It's not all fish and chips

Waving the flag for much-maligned traditional British cooking, the following sites offer some tasty stuff for the patriotic foodie:

Jack Scaife Butchers
www.jackscaife.co.uk
People who have been wondering what bacon used to taste like before they started injecting it with saline and painting it pink, can find out by ordering from this Yorkshire butcher who offers traditional British cured meats, as well as sausages and black pudding.

Grayson & Starts Sausages By Post
www.sausagesbypost.co.uk
Pork, beef, even venison sausages made by a family butcher and delivered to your door. Prices are reasonable given some products' prize-winning status.

Harpers Food
www.harpersfood.co.uk
Tasty, solid British food without a hint of lemon grass or balsamic vinegar. Meat pies, game, fruit puddings and a variety of Christmas staples will keep any gastro-Brit happy.

Mrs Elizabeth King's Pork Pies
www.emnet.co.uk/kingporkpies
Top quality traditional pork pies supplied ready to bake at home, including a whopping five-pounder if you've invited the whole pub back to your place.

Proper Cornish
www.propercornish.co.uk
Cornish pasties, both veggie and meaty, made to an authentic recipe supplied cooked or ready to bake.

The Oxey Herd
www.oxeybeef.co.uk
Desperate Dan wannabes can buy a whole cow (but not the pies) from this farm site based near Leicester. Reared naturally and butchered locally, the beef arrives at your door frozen in packs made up of prime cuts, mince, stewing beef, sausages and burgers. It's not a delivery for the faint-hearted, but the savings are immense when compared with buying the same amount of quality beef from a supermarket. Depending on the size of the cow, the cost is between £130 and £185 (£2.65 per pound), with delivery extra unless you live within 50 miles of the farm.

Pepperama
www.pepperama.co.uk
You could be mistaken for thinking this is the site for disgusting Pepperami, especially when you see the comical cartoons, but this is actually the place to buy the hottest pepper sauces from around the globe. Macho eaters can choose from Mexican Iguana Mean Green Jalapeno, the "XXXHot" Mad Dog Inferno or the Caribbean Brutal Bajun. Each is priced around the £4 mark and delivery costs £2.50. The Chile Facts page will entertain any spice bores.

Porcini
www.porcini.co.uk
This vast selection of fine foods and drinks – from rare Australian coffee to chocolate-pecan brownies and smoked eel – compares well with high-street deli prices. Arranged in clear sections, the site is well laid out and easy to use. Beautifully presented hampers and food gifts are also on offer and the magazine and recipe sections have plenty of inspirational food ideas for everyday or special occasions. Delivery costs £4.95.

Qing Lung Shopping Centre
www.qinglung.co.uk
The Chung King Supermarket has pages on this Chinese goods shopping site offering a range of Oriental foods and delicacies for home delivery. Whether your recipe calls for bamboo shoots or Szechuan peppercorns, you should be able to find those specialist items here. Delivery is calculated at the checkout and depends on the weight of your order.

Snackmix
www.snackmix.co.uk
If you're a bit of a snack monster, this site could save you a fortune. Bulk boxes of favourite nibbles and drinks – such as Kettle Chips, flapjacks and Purdeys – are available here at cash-and-carry prices. You have to order at least £35 worth of goodies, but it's a fantastic site if you're having a party and need a tortilla chip mountain and a Red Bull lake. Or you can just munch your way through them on your own. Delivery costs £3.99 within the UK.

The Teddington Cheese
www.teddingtoncheese.co.uk
You can almost smell the goods on this beautiful site brimming with British
and European farmhouse cheeses that make supermarket offerings look
pathetic by comparison. You can buy a chunk of your favourite, or order an
entire cheese board for a special event. It also runs a Cheese Club where you
can sign up to receive a selection of their finest goods throughout the year.
Get your order in before 12noon for next-day delivery which costs £5.95.

 **A moment on the lips...**

Cakes Direct
www.thin-end.co.uk
A little old lady in Cornwall is probably responsible for setting up this site
which sells all the harvest-festival favourites, fruit, carrot, saffron and
chocolate cakes. You can also get clotted cream teas by post, if you're really
not bothered about your weight. You have to memorise your choices as there
are no direct links to the online order form. They are modern enough to cater
for those of the vegan and healthy persuasion, and prices are around £10 for
small cakes or £15 for medium. Delivery is via courier and takes two to three
days, although rush orders can be taken by phone.

How Rude Can You Get Cakes
www.rudecakes.co.uk
Favourite body parts, pages from the Kama Sutra, or, ahem, marital aids can
all be sculpted in cake, icing and whipped cream (naturally) for a particularly
individual celebration. Email the company through the site with your cake idea
and they will contact you to discuss details and delivery.

Photo Toppings
www.intercake.co.uk
Make sure the birthday girl or boy knows whose cake it is by plastering their
ugly mug all over the top. There is a choice of designs, although pictures of
the cakes are not as plentiful as you might hope, so all you have to do is fill in
the order form, attach a picture file, and send it through. You can also request
a personalised chocolate bar as a special gift.

The Village Bakery
www.village-bakery.com
Cakes and buns, shortbread and fruit slices – all organic to boot – can be
delivered to your door from this Cumbrian bakery. There are codes to indicate
which items are sugar or gluten-free, and although there are no pictures of the
goodies on the site, the descriptions will make your mouth water anyway.
Many products, especially the breads, freeze well so why not buy in bulk?

Special diets — For the sick and the religious

Allergy Free
www.allergyfreedirect.co.uk

Not only do they refuse to stock GM food products, this site is helpfully aimed at the growing number of people who suffer from food intolerances. Common allergies like nuts, eggs, wheat and dairy products are all catered for, and the site also has a collection of articles and information pages to help people shopping and cooking for allergic eaters. When we visited it was still only an online list of products that to be ordered via email or phone, but it is working towards a shopping basket system for the near future.

Clearspring
www.clearspring.co.uk

Lots of food here for folk following vegetarian, vegan or macrobiotic diets. It specialises in Japanese products, but there's far more than the brown rice and soya milk usually associated with strict health foods, with exotic oils and seasonings also on offer. There's a secure server for your card details and if you get your order in before 2pm it will be delivered the next working day.

Diabetic Emporium & Confectioner
www.diabeticemporium.com

US-based online catalogue with more than 1000 specialty foods for diabetics, including normally forbidden items like cakes and sweets. There are nutritional

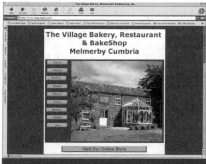

This country bakery delivers organic cakes, buns and frui slices to your door, and has codes to indicate sugar or gluten-free products

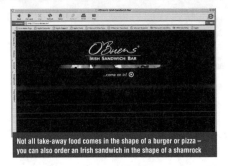

Not all take-away food comes in the shape of a burger or pizza – you can also order an Irish sandwich in the shape of a shamrock

facts for each product and although the site may not be very inspiring in its presentation, it's a boon for those struggling with a sugar-free diet. There is an online order form, but you have to email your request for international shipping and the site will calculate the cost for you.

Food 4 Thought
www.food4tht.com
This US site offers a wide variety of 100-per-cent kosher food for you to select, or you can choose one of their ready-made baskets of gourmet goodies. They do ship internationally but you will have to email them for shipping costs and delivery advice.

Lifestyle Healthcare
www.glutenfree.co.uk
An impressive range of gluten-free baked goods for people with coeliac disease, including everyday items such as bread and cake along with welcome extras such as fruit-and-custard turnovers and ready-to-roll pastry. Prices are reasonable, but you have to buy all items in multiples of six, so make sure there's room in your freezer. Delivery is calculated at the checkout, but as all goods are baked to order, you need to specify when you want them and the site will endeavour to deliver them when you require.

Lumen Foods
www.lumenfds.com
Selling "animal replacement products" may make this site sound a bit scary, but in reality this is a good place to buy bulk soya-protein products for those following any kind of meat-free diet. Since Lumen is also the manufacturer, prices are very competitive, although you will have to pay for shipping from the US. Email them through the site for an international UPS delivery quote which will depend on the weight of your order.

Sugarless Shop

www.sugarlessshop.com

Suppliers of a wide range of sugar-free foods including candy, baking products, desserts, snacks and spreads for diabetics and anyone on a restricted sugar diet. Overseas shipping is planned for the future, so email your interest for them to notify you when it's available.

Vegan Store

www.veganstore.co.uk

Online store for all products furthering a vegan lifestyle for delivery all over the UK and Europe. Leather-free boots, shoes, belts and wallets are for sale, as well as a wide range of vegan store cupboard, sausage and burger mix, vegan stock powder, chocolate-nut spread and others. Orders over £15 are sent via Parcelforce's two-day service and the site will email you with the cost of postage once you have ordered.

Take-Away No cooking, no washing up – perfect

Domino's

www.dominos.co.uk

First check to see whether this reputable pizza shop delivers in your area. If it does, register your contact details and away you go. The standard menu of starters, pizzas and desserts is available with prices and pictures which, obviously, resemble nothing that will turn up on your doorstep. You can opt to collect or have them deliver (delivery payments are required in cash). A useful system if you're stuck at work and fancy a Mighty Meaty.

O'Briens Sandwich Bar

www.obriens.ie

If you're lucky enough to live in the right areas of Ireland, you can get lunch delivered from this chain of yummy sandwich shops across the country. Choose your bread and fillings, with special items like Irish Whiskey Salami making it a delicious prospect, then click to buy, and your food is on its way. You have to register before you can order, but it's definitely worth it.

You can book a table online through Book2Eat if you're in London. Can't be long till you get to email the chef

The Virtual Sandwich Company
www.virtualsandwich.com

Fill in your postcode to see if it delivers to your area. If it does, this site will email you a menu from which to choose your lunch. We had a little trouble with the ordering, but we are assured by a regular user that the site works well. You'll just have to try it and see.

 "Your usual table?"

Book2Eat
www.book2eat.com

Get a free glass of champagne at one wharf restaurant, or 10 per cent off your drinks at a Vietnamese restaurant – everything is possible with Book2Eat, London's online restaurant-booking service. You can search restaurants by category (overpriced, overhyped – okay, the real categories include romantic, late, trendy), or scan alphabetically. Judging from the list of benefits designed to induce corporate membership, this site is aimed at those who organise regular business lunches but it's still a rather nifty idea. Someday every town in Britain will have one of these.

soviet canteen
www.sovietcanteen.com

"Authentic Russian food is about fatty meat, greasy soup and overcooked cabbage. That's why you won't find any at the Soviet Canteen." It's hard to resist a website that tells it like it is. This restaurant deserves to last rather longer than the Russian revolution. You sense a celebrity chef in the offing.

Football

A Dukla Prague away kit, rare Norwich Hospital Cup semi-final programmes from 1989, even trophies, can all be found online if you give 110 per cent and cover every virtual blade of grass on the pitch

General For kit, shinguards, goalposts etc

Go4soccer
www.go4soccer.com
Not the first site to describe itself as a one-stop shop and certainly not the last, this pretty much lives up to its billing with kit, equipment, software, coaching CDs. The kit selection isn't quite one-stop though if you support Walsall or anybody who doesn't play in a Nike kit you'll be disappointed.

JJB Sports
www.jjb.co.uk
General sports retailer with a small range of replica kits for international sides and Wigan Athletic, a selection which may be related to the fact that JJB owns the club. Latics fans are spoilt for choice. Otherwise, peruse the trainers.

Kitbag
www.kitbag.com
The usual selection of replica kits plus Bolton Wanderers and Derry City. Too much stuff with the wrong shaped ball but the range of extras is impressive especially if you're willing and able to splash out £19.95 on a paint-it-yourself model of White Hart Lane. (Bizarrely, it's only £16.98 if you're outside the EC).

Kitman
www.kitman.co.uk/aboutus.stm
Worth visiting if you like nauseating shades of green and seeing self-raising footballs. The online catalogue is rather clumsily presented and actually

consists entirely of Jako kit which doesn't do the site any favours because if you're persistent you can find other products elsewhere. This is actually aimed at football club secretaries who have too little to do and enough patience to muddle through in search of the right deal on their next consignment of embroidered badges.

You may also find these general sports retail sites of use:
http://sportselite.com
www.sportshackuk.com/simple
www.firstsport.co.uk although it has a seriously irritating interface
www.sweatband.com/sweatband/default.asp
www.sportswearhouse.co.uk

 **Buy now, sell at a vast profit later**

Christies
www.christies.com
The auction house doesn't just sell Fabergé eggs, the international gavel banger also puts a hell of a lot of football memorabilia under the hammer, including the shirt in which Sir Geoff Hurst scored *that* hat-trick in 1966. Company policy is not to sell stuff online so if you're serious about buying. you'd better turn up in person or get on the blower.

Corinthians
www.corinthianplc.com/J/index.htm
Probably the only place in the world where you can buy a team including Johan Cruyff, Pelé, Ferenc Puskas, Franz Beckenbauer, Diego and Maradona and Gordon Banks for less than £200 including postage and packing. Older readers will still no doubt prefer Subbuteo.

Euroshirts
www.euroshirts.com
The ideal place to part with £39.99 in electronic funds in return for an extra large replica home strip for Paraguay's Sportivo Luqeno. The good news is that you can order online, the not so good news is that the site says you will have to wait 28 days for delivery, slightly longer than it used to take for the postie to deliver Charles Atlas' Bullworker.

Football Directory
www.footballdirectory.co.uk
You cannot bypass this site if you want to know where on the web you can find someone to sell you (in no particular order) floodlights, club ties,

Euroshirt is even more ambitious than its title might suggest, it's almost certainly the only place on the Internet to buy authentic replica Paraguayan First Division football shirts.

footballing figurines... This site even tells you where to buy a trophy (calm down, Plymouth Argyle fans) as well as pointing you to the usual stuff like replica kits.

Jon Learmouth

www.learmouth.com/football_mem/index.htm

You can't actually buy anything from this site at all but Jon Learmouth's private cyber-realm is full of is advice on how to collect everything from football programmes to the cards you used to swap as kids. Or not. A good place to start your online quest for that elusive item of memorabilia.

Philosophy Football

www.netline.co.uk/philosophy

The thinking person's replica shirt store or, if you're not a fan, the place where football first became deeply pretentious. Philosophy Football's eclectic range of shirts enables the buyer to pretend they are anybody from Albert Camus to Lev Yashin to Cain (to name just three keepers). And secure ordering online to boot! Postage and packing for the first shirt is £1.65 in the UK.

Roy of the Rovers

www.royoftherovers.com

You can get £2 off *Roy of the Rovers: The Playing Years* and buy last Christmas's *Roy* annual for £3.50. That's as long as you're not blinded by the luminous yellow in which this site is so inconsiderately bathed.

Signs of the times
members.aol.com/ianphipps
This virtual extravaganza of celebritous autographs has a very good football section marred only by the inclusion of Jim Rosenthal and by the decision to define Gaby Yorath as a footballing celeb. Probably worth perusing along with the confusing, but packed, www.autograph-hunter.com.

Soccer Books
www.soccer-books.co.uk
Books, great collection of videos, that immortal CD of famous Scottish World Cup anthems and the little red book of Chinese football. No, that wasn't a joke. Well, not by us anyway. All this and more can be ordered securely online from a site which also has a deep catalogue of books about smaller clubs.

CLUB SHOPS

These club sites are among those which sell the usual panoply of kits, books, videos, toilet seat covers, underwear etc

http://shop.manutd.com

www.arsenal.co.uk

www.astonvilla-fc.co.uk

www.barnsleyfc.co.uk

www.celticfc.co.uk

www.evertonfc.com

www.hartlepoolunited.co.uk

www.montrosefc.co.uk

www.rangers.co.uk/home.htm

www.seagulls.co.uk

www.whufc.co.uk

Steve Earl football programmes
http://www.footballprogs.freeserve.co.uk
You'll never find another football programme site quite like this. This is probably the nearest equivalent on the Internet to a garage stuffed full of the kind of stuff mum was always trying to throw away. Among the "big match" programmes listed here is the 1989 Norwich Hospital Cup semi-final between Norwich and Ipswich. Yours for just £1 but you'll have to print the list out and send it to him in the post.

Toffs
www.toffs.com
Toffs doesn't stand for snobs but for The Old Fashioned Football Shirts company. This is a treat for those who remember the game before clubs changed strips more often than some fans changed socks. You can order online on a secure server but you have to know which Dukla Prague away kit you want because the full catalogue of 600 kits isn't online yet.

Yahoo auctions soccer
http://list.auctions.yahoo.com/21864-category-leaf.html?alocale=1us
Some of the items on display in this auction category are so cheap you feel like making a ludicrously high bid to make sure you get that *FA Book For Boys*. Amid all the gems you do get some real drivel like, er, the kitsch classic *Legs Eleven: Zoe Ball's Football Dream Team*. If you're trying to build up your collection you will also find football memorabilia regularly auctioned off on www.amazon.co.uk.

Free stuff

Yes, there really is free stuff on the Net (even if it doesn't yet extend to lunch). Whether it's worth having is another matter, and like the real world, there's always a catch...

General — Your gateways to the giveaways

British free stuff

www.britishfreestuff.co.uk/default.asp

Americans, forming at least 50 per cent of the world's online population as they do, are constantly bombarded with invitations to get something for nothing. Bargain-hunting Brits generally find cyberspace a less generous place although, in the last year, companies like this have sprung up. This site, which directs visitors to myriad offers, also illustrates some of the drawbacks of this sector of the Net. Some of the products allegedly available here for the princely sum of nothing are only free when you sign up, say, to a phone service or enter a competition. Some, like the legendary South Park brooch pointed to here, is no longer free at all. Overall, though, a good launch pad.

Freebies

www.jfreebies.com/main.php3

Among the free categories listed here is, slightly confusingly, "toys and babies". On closer inspection this turns not to be to part of a government drive to speed up adoption, but a link to a site which will announce junior's arrival online for free. A lot of the freebies pointed to here are hi-tech and there's the usual competitions for the lucky and gullible to enter.

Free cash for you!

http://freecashforyou.co.uk/

When people start offering you money for nothing there's always a snag. In this case the catch involves being paid to do things like read emails (imagine how boring they must be if people have to be paid to read them) or to surf the Internet. Anybody who follows some of the advice on this site will probably find themselves shunned by their virtual friends, colleagues and pets.

Free online
www.nothingisfor.free-online.co.uk/
The web address is an exercise in post-modern Internet irony, as this site goes on to prove that you can indeed get quite a lot of IT-related stuff for free. There still, however, seems to be no such thing as a free lunch.

Free stuff UK
www.freeukstuff.co.uk/
An essential gateway for the aspiring British freeloader. Of course the reality of what you can get free over the Net isn't always as glamorous as the idea, as the invitations to get a free Kiss FM car sticker or University of Glasgow engineering department poster clearly show. The pick of this crop is probably the free software and free webspace.

X-ray specs!
www.bio-imaging.com/pages/freebee.htm
Free X-ray specs! You've always wanted to look down at your hand and see through the skin to the skeletal bones, haven't you? No, thought not. But you'll need free specs of some kind if you stare at this site for too long.

If you're interested in one of the following products, you might want to consider visiting these sites:

Casino CD-ROM
www.gamble.co.uk/free_casino_cd.htm
The "hottest gambling casino software on the Internet". That's hot as in always in demand, rather than anything which is particularly effective for gambling. (If it was, do you think they'd be giving it away?) Just fill in the form on the slightly sinister, anonymous, black and yellow Web page.

Cadbury's Chocolate
www.in2cadbury.com/indexex.html
Yes, you do indeed get 'free' chocolate – but only if you've already got five Cadbury wrappers.

Charity
www.thehungersite.com/cgi-bin/WebObjects/HungerSite
Free food for the hungry! Sounds too good to be true but for once it isn't. Just visit the site, make a couple of clicks and someone in need gets a 1/4 cup of rice from one of the site's sponsors.

POETRY FOR NOTHING!

As always, there's a catch and the catch in this instance is that the poet in question happens to be William McGonagall.

Infamous, inimitable and, so critics have said, poetically illiterate, the Dundee-born, Victorian clerk-cum-poet wrote these immortal words: "A chicken is a noble beast/The cow is much for-lorner/Standing in the pouring rain/With a leg at every corner."

For more in the same vein (but a different arm) log on to *www.dundee22.freeserve.co.uk/* where you'll also find a great portrait of the man himself looking uncannily like Quentin Crisp.

Gadgets

www.zdnet.co.uk/athome/free_stuff/

Free consumer electronics and computer-type products appear here. You also get the chance to win stuff, which is stretching the meaning of 'free' a bit far.

Mouse mats

www.hotmat.com/index.htm

Still not quite as good as a free lunch, this site offers you a free mouse mat in exchange for your address. In fact, if you're really keen they'll give you a mouse mat every year for free wherever you're living in the world or solar system. Desperate or charitable? It's your call.

Sausages

www.bangers.co.uk/home_frset.htm

Billed as free sausages from Wall's (by a linking site), this site actually offers a 30p voucher off your next purchase – only by the time you've sat through the blank screen filled with animated words like "succulent" you're probably thinking it would be less painful to pay full price.

Shaving gel

www.shave.com/store/store_html_docs/free_stuff.epl

The people from King of Shaves are so convinced that you'll like their gel, they'll send you a free sample. The only trouble is, you can't ask for your money back if you don't like it.

Videos

www.nissan.co.uk

The fact that Nissan are keen to give away videos about their new Primera is perfectly understandable. Why anybody who isn't an employee or family member should want one is another question, but heck, here's the address.

After perusing www.bio-imaging.com/pages/freebee.htm you'll probably need free X-ray specs

Gadgets

Online shopping is never more fun than when you're looking for something utterly ephemeral – like a talking backseat-driver toy, a crossbow and a pair of aspirin cufflinks

General   Ain't you got fun...

21store

www.21store.com

It's not often you see a link from an electronic product to the White House, even if the story concerned – that people using global-positioning systems will be able to position themselves more accurately – doesn't seem exactly Earth-shattering. There are a few gadgets here but most of the site is dedicated to a dazzling array of electronic gizmos. The home page is a bit unappetising with product categories listed in small type on a side bar. Clicking through brings all the technical specs you could need. The buying process is well organised and you can register your details or use the express checkout.

Adventure Kit

www.adventurekit.co.uk

The home page, loosely disguised as a sheet of paper with torn edges, offers you an amazing photo-led menu of products in categories from kayaks to hot dogs. (Actually, the hot dog symbolises tuck and you can buy Mum's apple and custard pudding – funny, Mum didn't mention she was baking one of those). The buying process is secure and as easy as falling out of a kayak – so easy that it's easy to miss the products at the bottom of the scroll bar which are great for gift ideas. Credit-card ordering is secure, there are five levels of shipping costs and delivery is within 10 working days in the UK.

Big Boys Toys

www.big-boys-toys.co.uk

Once you've got over the stigma of accessing a site with such as risqué name, you'll find a logical set up with simple categories like 'outdoor' and 'high-tech'. You will need to download Flash if you haven't got it, though. Products have detailed descriptions and customers' opinions. Discounts over high-street retailers are clearly indicated and buying is simple. There is also the added advantage of free delivery on many items.

Boys Stuff
www.boysstuff.co.uk
An attractive homepage disfigured by yet another Carry On-style pun about "toys for big boys" leads to a list of categories which is pretty easy to follow. The nine hottest products are shown with excellent photos, but you do wonder if the site has been designed and edited by a feminist collective who regard men as several links down the evolutionary chain, and who can only be sold to by appealing to simple drives like lust and violence. There's a jokey invitation to win your office wars by buying a William Tell crossbow (yours for £26 but the price does not include delivery, an apple or a small boy on which to stand the apple). Then, if you click to confirm your order of the crossbow, the phrase "Don't listen to her" appears. The rest of the site is just as slick with secure ordering and an easy-peasy checkout process.

Gadget Shop
www.gadgetshop.com
Having a strong brand on the high street doesn't always translate into a good online service. Fortunately the Gadget Shop site is well laid out and easy to use. You can search for products by category (even if some of the category names are a bit cryptic – "Blue", for instance). There's a gift selector to point you at gadgets which cost above and below £20. You have to register to buy and the process is lengthy but logical.

Initial Ideas
www.initialideas.co.uk
For a site which likes to call itself "the inspiring gifts catalogue", the home page lacks, well, inspiration. Even the fact that some items have 40 per cent off is mentioned, casually, in rather tasteful type. Among the products to have prices slashed are a combined heart-rate monitor/wristwatch, and a metal model of a London taxicab, down from £1.99 to £1.19. You can order online behind the defensive shield of 128-bit encryption – the nearest thing online shopping has to America's Star Wars defensive shield.

Innovations
www.innovations.co.uk
This is the web site from the people who make the catalogue that you love to receive. As soon as the home page downloads it reminds you that you don't have any items in your shopping basket which seems a bit premature. There is a dedicated Sony shop and an optional registration service for repeat shoppers. The products aren't as wacky as you might expect, or maybe it just seems that way because even the *feng shui* rock garden sounds mainstream

by now. If you key in the URL for this entry, you will be redirected to the new Innovations page which, on this reviewer's last visit, had a temporary URL so complicated it could have been one Einstein's longer mathematical formulas.

I Want One Of Those

www.iwantoneofthose.com

A great name for a site, and it doesn't disappoint with loads of desirable gadgets. There's a category sidebar which is good, as the links are not clearly marked. The site is targeted at men, with a busty e-host (Brigitte Nielsen with Heinz tomato soup hair) to talk you through. You have to register to buy and there is a raft of technical information which you may or may not find useful. The gadgets on display vary from a pair of aspirin cufflinks to a catamaran which, to be pedantic, is a bit too clunky and too dear (at a recommended retail price of £1 million) to be defined by a word as trivial as gadget.

Obsessions

www.obsessions.co.uk

Finding what you want is easy on this pleasantly low-key site and there are plenty of suggestions if you're stuck for a gift, although buying your significant other a TLC Pulse Point called PMT might not be a wise move. You can have your gift wrapped but even Austin Powers would reject the paper on offer as too flamboyant. The buying process is incredibly simple, with email confirmation for every product.

SLAP THAT BASS...

With 57,100 web pages (and counting) devoted to the Billy Bass singing fish, it is the biggest online craze since Mahir the Turk. And here, as on so many other goods, the Net can save you money as this price check shows.

www.propagangsta.co.uk £14.99

------

www.gadgetshop.co.uk £29.95

------

www.kitsch.co.uk £30.00

Blackbushe market £27.00

Premier Direct

www.premierdirect.co.uk

You'll find gadgets with a purpose here. Even the remote-controlled flying saucer (every home should have one!) is claimed to relieve stress, although the price (a mere £59.95) might give the fiscally prudent a panic attack. Then there's the breath-analyser (or breathalyser to most of us) and the inevitable pheromones, for single men for whom the stress of not attracting the opposite sex cannot be relieved by a flying saucer (even if it is remote-controlled).

Sharper Image

www.sharperimage.com

Unless you go to "view" at the top of the screen and set "text size" to "largest", you may easily mistake the ionic conditioning hairdryer for the ironic conditioning hairdryer. And there's nothing ironic about this American site, where gadgets are not a means to an end but an end in themselves. The site does deliver outside the US but repeated inspection failed to reveal on what terms. The site has an auction section and invites you to get in touch in if you've got a great new product. Before you start sending off your all-in-one telephone, cocktail shaker and global positioning system, the site says, "DO NOT SEND SAMPLES." You can tell from the capital letters that they're serious.

The Gadget Shop is one offline retail brand which has not fallen flat on its face by moving into cyberspace

Propagangsta

www.propagangsta.com

Contrary to the images conjured up by the name of the site, you can't buy meat hooks and trench coats here. It's not immediately clear which icons lead to something. Useful features include a select by price option, a top ten chart (that Billy Bob Fish again) and a date reminder service. A brief log-in and registration screen speeds up the buying process.

 Conspicuous consumption at its most flagrant

Fundamental

www.fun-damental.com/

This wacky site tries to put the "fun" into "fundamental" although you may decide that the emphasis is firmly on the "mental". Amid all the frat humour of the farting teddy bears, there's the toy backseat-driver which you can set to say amusing things like, "Yo Sherlock! Since when are stop signs optional?". You can email orders and for once there is even a UK distributor.

Kitsch

www.kitsch.co.uk

The home page of this award-winning site has clear category headings making it easy to find what you want. The range of real gadgets is small but there's stacks of tack so you can't fail to be impressed. The buying process is secure but also simple and fast so you won't have to wait any longer than is strictly necessary for your *Wonder Woman* mouse mat.

Q-Link

www.qlinkworld.com

A site dedicated to the Q Link pendant which is described as "a modern day antidote to the modern day world". That's if you think the modern world's problems are all to do with negative magnetic fields and their effect on your good self. Ordering looks like it's going to be simple but isn't.

Games

Looking for the perfect antidote to Nintendo? You can try a game of Burmese billiards, backgammon or Flibble, all of which are merely a hyperlink away

Big Game Hunters

www.gardengames.co.uk

Traditional garden games like croquet and skittles are joined here by oversize lawn chess and Snakes and Ladders sets. The stand out is the Hi-Tower, a large-scale version of the table game Jenga, which comes very smartly presented in its own wooden box. All items are durable and beautifully made. Delivery is free within the UK and your order should arrive within a few days.

The Chess Shop

www.chess-shop.co.uk

It's chess and chess accessories only from this Scottish site. They range from wood and stone carved sets to an expensive novelty set depicting characters from the battle of the Alamo. Delivery is by regular post or Parcelforce.

David Naylor

www.backgammon-boards.co.uk

Make your opponents feel inferior with one of these gorgeous handmade leather backgammon boards. There are even custom-made dice rollers to make sure every throw is as random as possible. They come in various colours, a choice of sizes and prices start at £495, so it's not a game to shove under the sofa when you're not using it. There's an online order form which you can either email or print and send with a cheque.

Discount Games

www.discountgames.com

If you're after the unusual at outstanding prices, the extra shipping might be worth it from this US-based site. Their vast catalogue of games, from traditional to video (including 28 different kinds of Monopoly) will keep even the most fanatical competitor quiet, although the site would have been even more fun with more pictures of the games. International shipping is via courier (plus $4 handling fee), so it certainly won't be cheap, but hey, if you want to get your hands on a Spanish edition of Scrabble it's waiting for you here.

Dominoes
www.dominoes-highstreet.co.uk
In the traditional games section of this traditional toys shop, there are several odd games for sale. Carroms (Burmese billiards) might be just the ticket as a gift for the person who has everything. Delivery costs £2.50 within the UK.

Fleming Bridge Supplies
www.bridgesupplies.com
Bridge addicts need look no further for Contract and Duplicate bridge kit. Playing cards, score cards, boards, wallets and even tables are available here at extremely competitive prices. You can email them the online order form and then they recommend you phone or fax your credit card details through.

Gibsons Games
www.gibsonsgames.com
Stuffed full of fabulous Nintendo antidotes. Mini-croquet and table top pinball are here, as well as stacks of old board games (Escape From Colditz, anyone?) and newer family games like Pass the Bomb. Not a full shopping site but there's a fast link to their mail order branch where you can make a secure order that will be delivered within four days for £2.99 p&p.

Masters Traditional Games Shop
www.mastersgames.com - secure
If you can play it in a pub, you can buy it here. Loads of traditional table-top games like Shove Ha'penny (the set includes a set of old half penny pieces), outdoor games, chequers, and table bowls. All made to a very high standard and likely to last a lifetime. Shipping costs vary but are calculated for you online before you pay, and delivery is within three to four days for the UK.

Kevingston Boardgames
www.kgames.demon.co.uk
Very basic site with only a few items but worth mentioning because of a brave effort to support small independent games manufacturers who make the kind of board games your gran used to have in her front room. Like the vastly underrated Flibble. Orders are by cheque only and prices include shipping.

R. Somerville (Playing Cards)
www.playing-cards.co.uk
There are some 2000 different packs of cards to choose from at this site, being renovated when last visited, with traditional and novelty shapes and designs like characters from Dickens. Online ordering is in its early stages and the site is not secure, so you can also phone through credit details or send a cheque. Delivery costs £1 for the first pack and 50p for every pack after that.

Whether your personal Eden is a
few geraniums in a windowbox
or a designer job complete
with uplighters and
the obligatory water
feature, it's time to get
those green fingers clicking

Birstall Garden & Leisure
www.birstall.co.uk
Everything you would expect to find at a large garden centre, plus a garden
diary and links to furniture and garden-feature websites. There are project
instructions for things like installing a pond, and you can buy all the
equipment you need online. Delivery prices vary, depending on your order,
seeds being rather cheaper to post than stone fountains.

Capital Gardens
www.capital-gardens.co.uk
Online store for South East garden centre chain. This is a huge site for
equipment including fencing, mowers, and composters – everything for your
garden, in fact, except the plants. There are also tips on cultivation and
with gardening problems. Delivery costs are calculated online right at the end
of the ordering process, but are sometimes free to addresses within the M25.

CMS Gardens
www.cmsgardens.co.uk
Everything for the serious gardener, from propagators and watering systems
to greenhouses. There are excellent savings to be made in the Specials
section. Order online or print out the order form to send with a cheque. You
will be emailed an order confirmation and delivery date, as some items come
from the manufacturers. Al goods can be returned within 14 days for a refund.

Crocus
www.crocus.co.uk
The big attraction with Crocus is that it has its own vans, driven by trained
gardeners, who will plant out your purchases for you. This service currently
covers 65% of the UK with evening and weekend delivery possible too,

otherwise your order will be sent via courier. It's a huge site, devoted to gardeners at every level. Plants are clearly photographed and come with care notes. There's also plenty of quality garden accessories and equipment, plus a section where you can buy discount and sale items. You have to register to be able to buy. Delivery costs depend on the order value and start at £3.95.

Designs in Wood

www.designsinwood.co.uk
Small family firm in the Peak District making delightful planters and window boxes from solid wood. All the timber used comes from managed forests and is treated, stained or painted to make it last a very long time. There's an order form on the site to print out and fax or post to the company, but they assure us they are working on a secure shopping basket.

Dig It

www.dig-it.co.uk
If you're staring at an empty flowerbed and wondering what to put in it, Dig It can help you with one of their border kits containing the plants, food and instructions that you will need to create an instant impact. There are lots of other garden products here, mainly chosen with an eye for design and satisfying results. The postage charge is £3.95 (double that for Saturday delivery) and if you order before midnight on Wednesday and you'll get your plants the same week; otherwise you'll catch the next week's delivery.

Direct Garden Supplies

www.directgardensupplies.co.uk
Very basic, no-visuals site offering a good selection of plants, shrubs and bulbs at prices far below those of your local DIY store. There's no online shop at the moment – you have to print out the order form and send it with a cheque – but if you know what you're looking for this could be a good place to save some money and find some quality plant varieties. If you're not happy with your order when you receive it, you can have a full refund.

Bad case of mildew, thrips or carrot fly? Draw the screens round the affected plant and call in Dr G

Doctor greenfingers

www.drgreenfingers.com
Great site, winningly laid out like a hospital with an isolation ward for garden pest inquiries and a maternity ward for growing plants from seed. Lots of tips for the novice and amateur garden-

er and well worth a visit if you're planning a new look for your garden, or just hoping to solve some existing problems. There's nothing to buy, but the abundant recommendations for plants and kit, as well as the regular equipment tests, are worth their weight in well-rotted manure. Other useful sections include tool care and a diary of gardening jobs.

E-seeds
www.eseeds.com
There are plants to buy here too, but since this site is based in Canada, you're more likely to have a few packets of their unusual seeds delivered successfully to your door. There are excellent photos of most plants and seed packs offered on the site, plus comprehensive links to information on plant care. International delivery has to be arranged via email.

Exhibition Seeds
www.exhibition-seeds.co.uk
North Yorkshire company specialising in vegetable and herb seeds via mail order. Lots of lovely ideas like a seed mixture for sowing a wild flower meadow, or to grow medicinal herbs, but since the quantities they sell are fairly large in some cases, you either have to have a large garden, or be sharing with a friend. Some products are not priced on the site, but most can be ordered online using the encrypted order form.

The Garden Shop
www.thegardenshop.co.uk
Turn your patio into an outside room with some fancy seating, outdoor heaters and lanterns. This beautifully designed site sells quality garden furnishings at outstanding prices – it offers a folding hardwood table that can seat 12 for only £249. Add a parasol, a hammock and a barbeque and you've got the perfect summer's day. There's an online order form to email through and once they have received it, someone from the site will contact you for your credit card details.

GroGro
www.grogro.com
Official shopping site from the Royal Horticultural Society, selling a wide range of garden supplies, decorations and tools, as well as books, gardening-themed gifts and tickets to RHS events. Delivery time and costs vary but all larger items have this information included in their description.

Hortus Ornamenti
www.hortusornamenti.co.uk
If your garden currently suffers from a lack of self-esteem, you can certainly boost its confidence with a few purchases from this glorious selection of handmade tools, planters and other garden accessories, all made from the finest materials to the highest specifications. Most items are available to buy

online, although a few of the larger ones require you to contact the site separately for full details, and there are also gift wrapping and engraving services if you're feeling extra generous. Delivery depends on the weight of your order and will be calculated when you go to the checkout.

Rose Cottage Nursery

www.hyperstore.co.uk/roses

Specialists in drought-resistant plants for busy people who would like a beautiful garden but can't keep up with the watering. There are no photos on the site, but the descriptions are good and there are plenty of annuals, perennials and shrubs to chose from. You have to send a cheque in with your order, but delivery is free on orders over £60, otherwise it's £5.50 for orders up to £30 and £7.50 for orders from £31 to £60.

Gardening 365

www.oxalis.co.uk

Horticultural portal with speedy and impressive links to loads of plant and garden shopping sites as well as gardening articles and green-fingered know-how. If you're looking for even quite specialist plant varieties or propagation equipment, you're likely to find them somewhere here.

Plantland

www.Plantland.com

Great source for mail order plants – despite looking slightly hectic, it's worth finding your way around. All plants are the size you would get from a garden centre at considerably reduced prices. Most plants have clear photos and there's a minimum order of eight plants with a £4.95 delivery charge to anywhere in the UK, whatever you order.

West Lindsey Growers Ltd

www.wlg-ltd.com

Save a tons on bedding plants – buy them as baby plugs from this simple but comprehensive site. Prices are excellent compared with buying older plants from a nursery later on, and they even have money-saving plant collections for people starting a border or patio from scratch. Prices include postage and delivery, and you can order online, but the form is not secure so you can also phone through your card number.

WATER FEATURES The Charlie Dimmock Effect

Thanks to Charlie & Co not even the tiniest bit of outdoor space, can be without some kind of pond, rill or fountain. Water features come in all shapes and sizes, from the simplest bowl to a full-on replica of the Brandenburg Gate. These sites may inspire you to do a Dimmock.

Groundforce (of course); www.bbc.co.uk/ground-force

Chorney Studios - Mad selection of fountains. www.chorney-studios.com.au

----

iGarden. Archived advice on building a small, self-contained water feature. www.igarden.co.uk

Golf

From links to hyperlinks, the Net is the obvious place to buy that club, jumper or get advice on improving your swing. But can it make you into the new Tiger Woods? Sadly, for that you need his Dad, Earl

Ace Golf Discount

www.acegolfdiscount.com

There is some fairly amateur site design here but the information is good. There are categories for ladies, gents and juniors all of them subdivided by item and brand. Online buying is simple and secure and, as you might expect with a name like this, the prices are, well, ace would not be too strong a word. Delivery costs £5 if you spend up to £50 but is free in the UK if you spend more than £150.

Easygolf.co.uk

www.easygolf.co.uk

The site is orange, the name has Easy in it, there's a phone number with an 01582 STD code but amazingly this isn't yet another province of the EasyJet empire. There's an auction section where you can search through classified ads as well as an extensive online catalogue of new equipment. The information section could really do with more information in it. If Easygolf really is Britain's "most established online golf retailer" it should be able to discuss shipping and delivery on site rather than in an email. It would also be a good idea if the site map had an option to take you back to the home page.

Golf4less.co.uk

www.golf4less.co.uk

There's not much on this homepage other than red and green text but press on and you'll find what looks like an electronic version of a mail order catalogue with a picture and namecheck for each category of product. Golf4less is a Which? Web Trader. The way the site is structured is not ideal for beginners because it takes a lot of clicks until you see (and get reasonable amounts of detail on) the product you want to buy. Ordering takes a while and there's plenty of small print to get through but one excellent feature is the detailed online golf tutorial, "Ask the Pro."

Nevada Bob

www.nevadabob.co.uk

The Nevada Bob brand is huge in the US but not so here. The company's dedicated UK site loads up with some cartoon graphics which sets the theme for a site which is really easy to navigate except, bizarrely, the product list, which seems foolish. The range is vast though and you can search by item or brand. Ordering is simple and safe but details about delivery are elusive.

PGA Tour

www.pgatour.com

The official site for the tour attracts zillions of hits from golf fans so it needs to be good. Presented in the patented American sports format you find on sites for American football teams and the National Basketball Association, the site has an online store which you access by clicking on a toolbar icon. The range of merchandise is huge but it's still easy to find the item you want. There's a price match guarantee but for delivery to "4,000 cities in the UK" in two working days you will have to shell out $40-60. The other thing to bear in mind is that you could pay another 20 per cent on top in tax.

Proshop.co.uk

www.proshop.co.uk

Proshop is the UK's biggest online retailer and this site has all the obvious signs of quality that savvy online shoppers look for: a Which? Web Trader guarantee, clear statements on privacy and shipping costs flagged on the home page, a massive online catalogue to inspect and free delivery within the UK.

St Andrews Golf

www.standrewsgolf.co.uk

The home of golf on the Net doesn't let the game or the club down. There is a useful golf clinic and plenty to buy from branded apparel to books. If you click to buy equipment you're referred to International Golf Outlet Inc. The site is secure, so there are no worries from that point of view although you do worry about the shortbread tartan on the homepage.

UKGolfdiscount.co.uk

www.ukgolfdiscount.co.uk

The homepage of this site is full of flashing brands and products. The main USP of this rather run of the mill site is the range of ladies golf wear.

Health & fitness

The quest for the perfect body, on the inside
and on the outside, continues online. Whether
you're after sleek muscles, clear skin or
regular bowels, you'll find something here
to cure whatever ails you. Or so they claim

Health stores | Fortified with vitamins and minerals

Bomiso
www.bomiso.com
This site is beautifully laid out and a pleasure to use, with a welcoming wish
for a "healthy body, mind and soul". The natural health section offers vitamins
and minerals, flower remedies, herbs, homeopathy and aromatherapy – the
range of oils in the latter is particularly extensive. Most prices seem to be
below the RRP and the accompanying Health Guide is helpful for deciding
what remedies to try for different conditions. Bomiso sells to the UK and Eire
only and will ship your order within 48 hours. Postage and packing costs
£2.15 for first-class mail.

Earthsense International
www.earthsense-international.org.uk
Just looking (and, unfortunately, listening) to this site will give you a headache.
Earthsense is horrifically designed. It offers a range of herbal tinctures for
anything from colds to cancer. These are said to be prepared under
conditions of "minimal geopathic stress", geopathic stress being the cause of
"95 per cent of all illnesses" according to founder, designer, tincture-maker
and researcher Dr Karen Stevens. The site offers numerous other services,
such as free iridology courses and psychic readings. The many pages of
health advice are badly written and, on the whole, dubious. Delivery of the
tinctures, which are reasonably priced, costs £1.20 anywhere in the UK.

EMC Health

www.emchealth.co.uk

This is a homey natural health shop, offering vitamins, minerals and herbal supplements. The range is limited to just a few brands, however, and the choice of supplements on offer is far from comprehensive, but with very good product descriptions and a number to call to check on suitability for children. Prices seem competitive and EMC offers free delivery, within the UK, on your first order and for all orders over £30, and promises to get your order out within 48 hours.

Frank Roberts

www.herbal-medicine.com

This pretty site is the online version of a herbalist's shop established in 1946. Frank Roberts makes its own remedies, 30 of which are licensed by the UK's Medicines Control Agency. Nearly 200 different formulae are on sale, and prices are claimed to be lower than both high-street and online competitors. All orders are dispatched by return of post and there is a range of postage and packing charges – from 95p for orders up to £14 and no charge for UK orders over £50.

The Garden Pharmacy

www.garden.co.uk

The online store of London's Garden Pharmacy, this site offers a comprehensive range of products, but no prescription medicines. You can, however, buy hair-loss treatments, contraceptives and anti-smoking aids, as well as a wide variety of cosmetics and toiletries. Complementary treatments include vitamins, minerals, homeopathy, Bach flower remedies and herbs. The price for Rogaine, for example, is similar to other online pharmacies at £60 for three months' supply. Ordering is easy and delivery is worldwide, by first-class post which costs £2.95 to UK addresses.

Goodness Direct

www.goodnessdirect.co.uk

Online shop for Leicester-based healthfood store, selling a standard range of vitamins and minerals at high-street prices, with regular special offers. The site's strength is in classifying its products to show which are safe for

QUACK WATCH

Questionable marketing, fraudulent claims, dubious side-effects and general health scams are investigated by this US site run by American alternative health scourge, Stephen Barrett, MD

Dr Barrett sides firmly with Western conventional medicine (that's where he gets his income from, after all) and the site would be improved by a slightly more open mind, but there are some very good investigations here, along with excellent advice on what should ring warning bells in a practitioner or product.

Particular scorn is heaped on some cancer therapies and badly trained chiropractors.

----

www.quackwatch.com

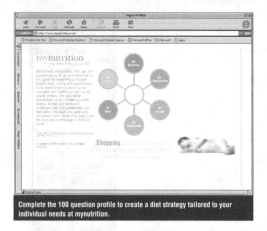

Complete the 100 question profile to create a diet strategy tailored to your individual needs at mynutrition.

diabetics, or are kosher, gluten-free or dairy-free. It also has a good selection of sports drinks and supplements for healthy athletes. Delivery is free on orders over £20 which will be dispatched overnight if received before 11am.

Healthtree
www.healthtree.co.uk
Healthtree offers a rather limited range of own-brand vitamins and supplements such as cod-liver oil, ginseng and St John's Wort. Simple and straightforward by virtue of its small product range. The delivery charge is only £1.15 within the UK or £1.75 elsewhere in Europe for any number of items, but you have to allow up to 28 days for your order.

Health Wisdom
www.healthwisdom.co.uk
It may sound like a science-fiction film, but The Thione Complex™ is actually a patented blend of synergistic antioxidants that work with your body to scavenge for free radicals and help prevent degenerative conditions like cancer, heart disease and arthritis. There's plenty of information about the complex on the site and you can order supplements and other products online although delivery charges are annoyingly hidden until you buy.

HerbalNet
www.herbalnet.co.uk
HerbalNet offers aromatherapy oils and herbal remedies. The site is very text-

heavy, but easy enough to get around. The range is rather limited, although the quality looks very good. There are also books, some interesting gift ideas, plus prize draws and competitions, free gifts, health tips, and a 10 per cent discount scheme for regular shoppers. Postage and packing in the UK costs £1.50 and shipping of the order is within four to five days of receipt.

Magnetic Therapy

www.magnetictherapy.co.uk

Magnetic Therapy is credited on this site with the ability to help any number of health-related conditions from arthritis to seasickness. There are impressive testimonials in many of the product descriptions, but the site could benefit from more information about what each item is designed to achieve. If you're interested, there's a range of books about magnets and even a section on therapeutic products for your pets. Delivery is free within the UK on orders over £15 (otherwise it's £2) and your goods should reach you in 2-3 days.

Medicine Cabinet

www.medicinecabinet.co.uk

Elegantly laid out, this site automatically inspires confidence. Medicine Cabinet offers a range of vitamins, minerals, homeopathic remedies, aromatherapy oils, diet/weight loss and sports nutrition supplements and other natural health products, many of them at discounted prices. Information is hazy on each product, though the selections are comprehensive. You have to register before you shop, which is annoying, but there is also a health e-zine, a news section and an excellent encyclopedia to look at. Shipping is by first class or special delivery within the UK only.

mynutrition

www.mynutrition.co.uk

mynutrition claims to be the only UK website to offer users a free personal consultation and to provide nutritional advice tailored to their needs. You can either fill in a detailed questionnaire and an eating plan will be designed for you, or choose from a range of over 1000 specially selected supplements, such as vitamins, minerals and diet aids, easily searchable by brand or medical condition. There are also lots of health-related articles on the site. mynutrition delivers anywhere in the world, with orders sent out within 48 hours of receipt, with postage and packing a reasonable £1.50 for the UK.

Nutravida

www.nutravida.co.uk

This is a lively site with a wide range of vitamins, aromatherapy oils and other health products on offer. You can also search special categories such as women's health, green foods and lifestyle formulas. Nutravida has some good offers, such as a number of "buy one, get one free" items, and claims that many prices are below the RRP. You do have to go through a few pages to get to the products, and illustrations are small, but you can pick up some interesting health tips along the way. Orders are dispatched on the same day and postage and packing are free within the UK. According to customer comments, this is an excellent online store.

Planet Botanic

www.planetbotanic.com

This site is heavy on green (the colour and the ethos). Planet Botanic sells a wide range of herbal remedies, backed up by well-written and comprehensive fact sheets. There are also a number of appealing environmental and spa products on sale here, such as a sick-building room spray and de-stressing bath-oil concoctions. Loads of information on each product can make buying a long process, but it is reassuring. Online chat with the company's founder, herbalist Douglas Schar, is available, together with a library of herbal information for those who want to research their products in more depth. Planet Botanic ships by first-class post to the UK, with postage and packing charges depending on the cost of your order.

Simmonds Herbal Supplies

www.herbalsupplies.com

Simmonds has been making its own herbal formulae since 1982 and a very good range of these is on offer here. There is also lots of sensible advice and information on natural health, using the remedies, and other lifestyle tips. The testimonials page is equally impressive with praise for many of Simmonds' formulae. This site is very easy to use, but heavy on text and clashing colours – its design could use a little streamlining. Most orders are shipped the same day to UK addresses by first-class post.

ThinkNatural.com

www.thinknatural.com

ThinkNatural scores highly as an attractive, easy-to-use online store which offers thousands of natural health products. The shop is backed by an excellent Health File, packed with information from expert contributors. Reassuring to some, hypochondria-inducing to others. Savings are only a few pence compared with the high street, but new products are highlighted and there are regular special offers. Delivery is promised within two days, and charged at £2.50 for UK orders under £15, and after that it's free. The site can deliver worldwide at higher rates.

THE XENON CENTRE AND PSYCHE'S GARDEN

If flower remedies are a little mainstream for your taste, why not visit the Xenon Centre in Fife for a spot of spiritual healing or other holistic therapies? The Soul Retrieval service begs the question "how did you lose it in the first place?", but there are a handful of tarot readers, crystal therapists, esoteric astrologers and humanistic counsellors on hand if rebirth sounds too much like hard work.

Owner Stephen Layton was prompted to open the Centre during a Vision Quest in 1995, since when he has developed its services and opened a retail shop selling crystals, incense-burners and tapes to promote meditation. Mail order is via an email address on the site.

----

http://members.aol.com/xenonctr/index.htm

ThinkNatural offers 10 different kinds of nettle supplements that won't sting your pocket.

VitaGO

www.vitago.co.uk

VitaGo is an attractive site with clear graphics and directions, offering many of the products you'd find in a high-street chemist. Medical care, beauty and personal care, plus baby and child products are all here. The Healthy Living section offers a good range of vitamins, minerals, aromatherapy oils and homeopathic remedies, many being priced below the RRP. It charges £3.95 for delivery on orders up to £30 (free thereafter) and goods are dispatched within two working days. The site also has a series of e-zines packed with useful information on fitness, nutrition, beauty and healthy living.

Vitamin Shoppe

www.vitaminshoppe.com

Vitamin junkies can save a fortune on all their supplements with this comprehensive US site. All the usual health-helpers are here, along with some you won't have heard of yet, at prices far lower than those found in the UK. The site also provides a newsletter and health articles if you're really interested in keeping in tip top shape. International delivery is via DHL which takes around seven days, or United States Parcel Service which takes up to six weeks, and charges will be calculated at the checkout. Remember, this will bump up the your costs, so buy in bulk to really save.

Web Direct Condoms

www.condoms.co.uk

Top of the list of modern health and safety products has to be the humble condom, but keeping stocked up can be pricey, not to mention the girl-in-the-chemist or slot-machine traumas of buying them. Solve your problems in one go with this straightforward site. Prices are excellent, delivery is speedy (often overnight) and free, and your order arrives in a plain brown package. As if it was anything to be ashamed of.

Alternative Therapies | Find information

Association of Reflexologists
www.reflexology.org
Take the link from this US site to learn about reflexology in the UK and how your natural healing process can be stimulated by specialist foot masssage.

British Acupuncture Council
www.acupuncture.org.uk
Get details of accredited training courses, find a registered acupuncturist, or read the comprehensive information on one of the oldest methods of healing. Needle-phobes are reassured too: it doesn't hurt.

British Homeopathic Journal
www.homeopathyhome.com
Read cutting-edge articles like "Homeopathic E-Mail: Can the 'memory' of molecules be transmitted via the Internet?" or get guidance on how homeopathic treatment might help you, with links to online suppliers.

Foundation for Traditional Chinese Medicine
www.ftcm.org.uk
Plenty of articles and news about specific research projects undertaken to strengthen the position of Chinese Medicine alongside conventional practice.

International Federation of Aromatherapists
www.int-fed-aromatherapy.co.uk
Smell your way to good health with essential oils and soothing massage. This site has details of courses and accredited aromatherapists throughout the UK.

The National Federation of Spiritual Healers
www.nsfh.org.uk
Information on healers attuned to universal forces who use peace and love to get your body working properly again. They claim.

The National Institute of Medical Herbalists
www.btinternet.com/~nimh/frameacc.html
Website for the oldest association of practising herbalists in the world, with information on members, campaigns, herbal suppliers and training.

Osteopathy in the United Kingdom
www.osteopathy.org.uk
If someone's going to manipulate your back and neck, you want to be sure they know what they're doing. Find a properly trained osteopath through the search facility, and learn about how they can help more than just bad backs.

The Society of Teachers of the Alexander Technique
www.stat.org.uk
Learn about how FM Alexander's methods can improve your posture and your health. The site offers guidelines for choosing a teacher, how much you should pay and information on courses in your local area.

 Go for the burn

Dieting, Weight Loss and Nutritional Supplements UK
www.weightloss-supplements.co.uk
Busy and in-your-face, this site offers a limited range of herbal and mineral concoctions which are meant to aid weight loss by either burning up fat or stopping carbohydrates being deposited as fat. There is little scientific evidence supporting their use – although the site lists many glowing testimonials from supposedly satisfied (and slim) customers. Each supplement costs £19.95 for a one-month supply and there are some discounts on offer if you buy three or more products. Postage is £1.50 for one item within the UK.

Fitness Options
www.fitnessoptions.co.uk
Gung-ho home fitness equipment for the serious trainer. Treadmills, rowing machines and multi-gyms, demonstrated by depressingly sleek-bodied models, are all selected for being top quality as well as possessing the power to make you feel guilty every time you look at them. For the unreconstructed slob, there's also a comfy-looking electronic massage chair. You can't buy directly through the site, but you can email for prices and further details or request a catalogue sent to you.

Newitts
www.newitts.com
This large sports site has an excellent Health-Related Fitness section where you can buy heart rate monitors, body fat scales and all sorts of hi-tech equipment to measure muscular strength and cardio-vascular fitness. They also sell home gym equipment and free weights to help you improve your scores and buff up your bod. Delivery appears to be free on UK orders, although check if you're buying a large item as you have to get a long way through the buying process before it tells you about shipping.

CONTACTS DIRECT
Contact lenses and specs supplied at about 40 per cent less than you would pay at an optician. You have to fax the company your prescription, so get a decent eye test first, but everything else can be done through the site.

Designer frames are also on offer, just enter the model number of the ones you like, plus a variety of lens solutions, including Ciba Vision and Bausch & Lomb, can be ordered direct. Delivery costs £2.50 and your order will be with you within 10 working days.

www.contacts-direct.co.uk

Hi-fi

Whether you just
want a steam-
powered radio,
the latest in MP3
technology or
the racks of silver boxes
so beloved of hi-fi 'enthusiasts', the Net
is ready to separate you from your money

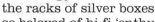

General | Separates, personals and portables

Audio Vision

http://ws.safestreet.co.uk/audiovisualsuperstore

Specialising in amplifiers, speakers and power amps, this is one for the hi-fi
enthusiast rather than the average punter. The limited visuals and single-line
additional info sections (that aren't really worth the time it takes to connect)
hardly suggest sophistication, but the brand names include Marantz, Acoustic
Energy and Toshiba, along with less well-known names recommended by the
experts at *What Hi-Fi?* Cheaper prices than the high street are a plus point.

Barclay Square

http://catalogue.barclaycard.co.uk/cgi-bin/audio.storefront

With a dull, silver-grey design and vast expanses of plain white space instead
of information about the item, the site struggles to retain interest. You can
choose from complete systems, separates, personals and portables, and
wade your way through top brands including Panasonic and Sharp. Both
descriptions and images are poor but competitive prices make up for this
oversight. Useful if you've already got a particular beatbox in mind.

Electrical Discount UK

www.electricaldiscountuk.co.uk

This looks like a discount bargain basement site, but there is no real sign if
the prices quoted here are world-beaters. Search for hi-fi systems, separates
and MP3 players, read the brief report and place your secure order. Delivery is
free unless you want the Saturday service, which costs an astronomical £30.

Electronics On-line

www.electronics-online.co.uk

Standard buying system on a standard site, though it's sub-categorised to make searching through page upon page of silver boxes that little bit simpler. You can select from personal mini-disc, compact disc and cassette players, mini-disc hi-fi's and CD mini hi-fi's (got all that?). Brands include Panasonic, Sony and JVC, but there's no indication about discounts, so shop around.

Hi-fi Bitz

www.hifibitz.co.uk

Another nondescript site with a tiny side bar indicating the sub-categories, mostly comprising hardcore hi-fi items: amplifiers, receivers, turntables and subwoofers – definitely one for those already babbling audio facts and stats. The level of information provided varies according to the price, with a few lines for a £100 CD player and full pages for £5,000 AV Processors. The 'more info' link generally finds its way to the manufacturers' site for the hard sell.

Richer Sounds

www.richersounds.com

Select a section on this warehouse site and scroll through. The pages are long but many items are either not in stock or are only available in store. What they do have covers every pocket, with CD players from £50 for a standard Ariston to the Alto, said to be the sexiest stereo system for £500. Best of all, the price reductions come thick and fast with scoops, sales, factory direct items and the price challenge, with many items reduced by hundreds of pounds.

Enough is enough It's the music that counts

While we'd all like megamoney systems, drawing on electronics and speakers with five-figure price-tags, the whole purpose of buying a system is to listen to music. Isn't it? If you're constantly worrying whether a new amplifier or that piece of black sponge you put under a CD player would make all the difference, you're not enjoying the music – just indulging in electronic masochism. So what's the answer? A large part of it is to buy right in the first place: when you're auditioning a system or a component, only buy something that blows your socks off with the improvement it makes to the music. We're often asked what is the best single upgrade anyone can make to their system, and the answer is invariably more music. Music is relatively cheap – especially if you buy online – and the thrill of discovering something new via that system on which you spent all that money is hard to explain. But one thing's for sure: it beats hearing a CD player maybe a tad better than your current one any day.
Source: www.whathifi.com

Value for Less

www.valueforless.co.uk

Bargains galore. The promise of big names at low prices is true for once.
Pick up a Panasonic portable CD player, or ghetto-blaster as they used to be
known, for £50, a Sony CD walkman for £30 and a complete Sharp mini-hi-fi
system for less than £90. The pictures and descriptions are poor quality but
that's perhaps no surprise with discount warehouses.

 In-car systems Cassette players and CD systems

Blue Spot

www.bluespot.co.uk

In-car cassette players rub shoulders with top of the range Blaupunkt CD
systems. If cost is the main consideration, head for the product guide section,
where price points lead to descriptions and the buying link. The range is limited
yet covers brands and prices across the board. If you don't understand the
technical information, the owners have at least had the foresight to include
further explanation; if this is still information overload, you can head for the
specification comparison chart. Most stereo prices are cut by 25 per cent.

MP3 The brave new world of music on the Internet

MP3 Players

www.mp3players.co.uk

Who would have thought there were so many MP3 players? Begin with the
news, reviews and beginner's guide to get you started, and then move on to
the online shop. Latest models displayed include Sony, Jaz Piper, Hango and
the Diamond Rio, each coming with reviews, spec sheets and images. Prices
range from £100 to £600, including free next day delivery, insurance and
parcel tracker. The site may lack imagination and effort, but fortunately far
more effort has gone into the content. An excellent all-round MP3 universe.

Premier Direct

www.premierdirect.co.uk

Scroll past the health and automotive sections of this e-store and head
straight for the future of portable music. Although limited to a choice of five
brands (including top dog Diamond at £209 and the less familiar Yelo, £115),
there should be a price to suit all pockets. If you're an MP3 novice, the
additional information at the beginning of the section should answer all your
MP3 queries, such as what 32Mb or 64Mb actually means, and encourage
you to make that leap past that free portable cassette player you received
when you joined the Britannia Music Club. A useful starting point.

Radios Still alive and kicking, despite the video star

Roberts Radios Direct
www.wesellradios.co.uk
You can't buy online but the radios are funky enough to deserve a mention. Roberts have been producing their brand of kitsch radios since the 1930s (they have a royal warrant, you know) but have now at least embraced email. Browse through the Classic, Revival, World and Lifestyle designs and you'll find a Ferrari-yellow, leatherbound, 1950s-style model for £130 or a plain old plastic pink-and-sky-blue design for £100. Make your selection and either email them or telephone, and your chic radio will be with you within 48 hours.

Simply Radios
www.simplyradios.com
The older it looks, the more expensive it probably is. Make your search by brand – Roberts, Grundig, Freeplay – or select by design and function. A 1950s-revival, claret-coloured model will set you back £130, compared to the personal or pocket compact designs for £25. They can even supply your bathroom needs – dolphin-inspired designs or one of those shower-resistant models resembling a Lady Shave – if you really can't do without those up-to-the-minute traffic reports. Standard ordering and free UK delivery.

The following sites are also worth checking out:

Best Buy Appliances
www.bestbuyappliances .co.uk
Everything mini and midi in the audio department from top names such as Sony, Philips and Samsung. High street prices apply.

Beyond Hi-Fi
www.beyondhi-fi.com
Got your hi-fi system? Now get all the essential accessories, from CD and mini disc wallets to speaker and amplifier storage racks.

Comet
www.comet.co.uk
Just like your high-street store.

Dixons
www.dixons.co.uk
Find of the day! A space-age Matsui CD ghetto-blaster can be yours for just £30.

Downloading music is the future of portable music, so where better to buy an MP3 player than the Internet?

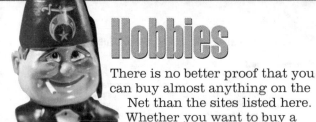

Hobbies

There is no better proof that you can buy almost anything on the Net than the sites listed here. Whether you want to buy a meteorite, pick a lock or go bird-watching, read on…

Antler Art

www.wic.net/antler

Some web sites leave you stunned by the powers of invention exhibited by homo sapiens. Whoever thought of taking antlers off a live deer and making a chair and ottoman out of them obviously has more imagination than taste.

Bird-watching

www.birdwatchers.com

For those to whom "attracting birds" has different connotations, this online store from Michigan covers most bases, from suet feed to houses and even a curiously-named jazz water sprinkler. The selection of bird seed is slightly disappointing as it doesn't include any architectural experiments with our feathered friends' food. You have to email for international shipping costs.

Boccerball

www.boccerball.com

Table football with marbles (but no players) hasn't caught on yet here and this site is strictly US-only. The inventors claim it's like table football, table tennis and billiards all rolled into one. Others might say someone's lost their marbles.

Boxes

www.worldofboxes.com/

Whoever decided to call this site "the enchanting world of boxes" has never worked in a warehouse. These boxes are made in the Tatra mountains of Poland and are, if not quite enchanting, certainly tasteful. The alchemist's box seems the pick of the bunch at $56, even if it does look slightly sinister.

Juggling

www.jugglingstore.com

"We're glad you're here" announces this site in such a cheery fashion you feel you ought to reach out and shake its hand. The Dube Squosh bean bag kit is billed as "the best bean bag kit on the market", and other delights include a book on the art of juggling, three hard juggling balls (not for beginners) for $20 and, for the master or the foolhardy, juggling knives. It does deliver overseas but can't tell you how much this will cost until the items are weighed.

Kites
www.kiteshop.co.uk/cgi-bin/kiteshop
Shopping here is 100 per cent safe, says the home page, which makes it several per cent safer than actually flying a kite. The selection varies from beginners' kites for less than £20, all the way up to the "easy to assemble and virtually indestructible" Flexifoil range of power kites. Free delivery in the UK.

Lock-picking
http://lock-picks.com
If lock-picking is one of your hobbies it suggests, at best, you are congenitally forgetful. But if picking locks is important to you, this is the place to be. A "pick set" could cost as little as $25 plus $7.50 shipping but if you're ordering bona fide locksmith's tools you have to sign a declaration that you are either in the business, a cop or a car dealer. Wary of having its own software picked, Lock-Picks.com asks you to print out the online ordering form and fax it over.

Magic
www.magic.co.uk
For wired wizards everywhere, this online magic merchant offers such mouthwatering tricks as the "bewildering floating bank note" and the "Easter Island mystery". The Amazon-associated site offers secure shopping and promises to deliver goods ASAP, although it does add the caveat "we are occasionally flooded with orders so please allow 28 days for any eventuality".

Meteorites
www.geocities.com/~meteorite/catchafallingstar.html
This is the place to come to if the obscure object of your desire just happens to be a Sikhote-Alin meteorite from the eponymous mountains of eastern Siberia. You can buy just five grams for $50 (plus shipping outside the US) or spend $25,000 on a rock which is good enough to be on show in a museum.

Model Rockets
www.suborbital.com
Airfix schmairfix – the people at Suborbital have much loftier ambitions. But if you like the idea of launching your own high-powered rocket, heed the site's reminder that "You are now flying really big, potentially dangerous aircraft loaded with large amounts of propellant!". If you're interested in buying a kit, you want to know they're guaranteed "fat free and dolphin safe". Strangely, such a high-tech organisation doesn't take credit cards. For those who prefer to do their rocketry over sea or pond **www.nerdsinc.com** is worth a peek.

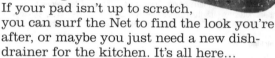

Home

Interior design is the new rock 'n' roll, or something like that.
If your pad isn't up to scratch, you can surf the Net to find the look you're after, or maybe you just need a new dish-drainer for the kitchen. It's all here...

Inspiration Ideas for improvements

Improveline
www.improveline.com
This site's main service is to hook you up with professionals in your area, whether they're architects or plumbers, who are interested in quoting for your home improvement project. There are lots of inspirational pictures and ideas in the design gallery, as well as articles on how to get the best out of your home and any improvement you want to make to it.

Interior Internet
www.interiorinternet.co.uk
An impressive design portal with links to lots of interior sites. There are sales sites as well as Web pages representing designers and their work. Well worth a visit, especially if you're planning a real household overhaul.

Furniture From futons to Harley Davidson barstools

Adrian Reynolds
www.adrianreynolds.com
This beautifully laid out site represents a bespoke wrought-iron furniture-maker in Shropshire. Details of his standard designs for dining tables, chairs, beds and other accessories are all available to view, and you can contact Reynolds through the site if you have a commission in mind. By shopping direct you can save a fortune over the retail prices of his designs in the shops.

Conran
www.conran.co.uk
Not as impressive a site as you would expect from Mr Conran, although it is
relaunching so judgement must be reserved. When we visited he seemed, for
some reason, to take great pride in his vast selection of ashtrays. Hopefully the
relaunched version will offer a better online shopping experience.

Furniture Busters
www.furniturebusters.com
Heavily discounted prices on brand-name furniture ranges. There's not much
here that's cutting edge, but Jaybe does some groovy sofas and for basic
beds, you can't go wrong. Delivery is free within the M25; if you're outside
that area they will email you with delivery charges.

Furniture Web Store
www.furniturewebstore.co.uk
Basic ranges of traditional furniture, delivered direct to your door. There are
some good designs in the bed section, and all the prices are very competitive
compared to many furniture superstores. Delivery is free on all items unless
you've requested the "express bed service" (same-day delivery if ordered
before noon – cost £14.99) for people who have nothing to sleep on.

Futons Direct
www.futons-direct.co.uk
This Oxford-based company offers futon sofa-beds and mattresses. The
range and information to accompany each futon isn't particularly detailed but
then there's only so much you can say. A three-seater will set you back about
£250, and delivery is charged at a flat rate of £20 for a mattress and £30 for
the whole package. An amateurish-looking site but it does the job.

Habitat
www.habitat.co.uk
Given its reputation for cutting-edge design, this is a disappointing site from
the high-street furniture giant. First, you can't access some areas of the site
without Shockwave. Then, when you do get into it, quite often there's only a
photo of one item from each range with line-drawings of the rest. All very chic,
but no use to shoppers. The site doesn't say if full online shopping is planned,
so for now you'll just have to keep visiting the shops.

The Iron Bed Company
www.ironbed.co.uk
Excellent sales site from a made-to-order bed retailer, though not all the beds
are iron – Shaker-style wooden beds are also available. (Their future plans
also include bedding and accessories.) Beautiful photos, size details and
careful descriptions make this a happy shopping experience. Beds are
delivered in around four weeks by the company's own vans.

Looking for a real jukebox or classic Coca-Cola machine? Vintage Vending offers restored 1950s memorabilia or reproduction items

Sofas And Sofa Beds

www.sofabeds.co.uk

As the URL suggests, this site sells a wide range of sofas, all of which are also available as sofa beds. Choose your base, then the fabric, and order online with a minimum of fuss. Alternatively, you can request further information or fabric swatches. All items are made to order, so getting your sofa can take a while, but the site will contact you to arrange delivery.

Sträad

www.straad.co.uk

A Birmingham-based online department store, Sträad offer art prints, lighting and executive gifts along with furniture and home accessories (there was an exotic line in loo seats when we visited). A simple system of clicking on a small image produces a larger version along with the usual information. Unfortunately the blurred and tiny images can make it hard to recognise what you're clicking on in the first place. There's a large selection of items on offer but not everyone will race to order the glass Homo Sapiens Valet, also known as a clothes horse, for £858. Pricey but unusual.

Vintage Vending

www.vintagevending.com

This US site sells restored 1950s furniture, juke boxes and vending machines. The diner sets are particularly glorious and if you're looking for a touch of bad-boy glamour, what about a Harley Davidson barstool for $129? The site can arrange shipping to the UK, but you have to email or call for full details and delivery could take as long as ten weeks. Worth it though.

Decoration & DIY — From strimmers to seagrass

B & Q

www.diy.com

The slow system can probably be put down to the multiple sub-categories, which offer everything from flooring and tools to gravel and the proverbial kitchen sink. Added information and images are available, but not for all products, and standard prices apply with no indication of online discounts. Delivery is free if you go wild and spend over £250; otherwise it's charged at between £10 and £20 depending on the distance from your local store.

Cooksons

www.cooksons.com

Hand tools, power tools, engineering tools and even tools for the ironmonger. Top brands include Black & Decker, Stanley and Dewalt. Head for Special Offers first – there was a B & D Strimmer for £26 when we visited – with most sale items half price and free delivery if you spend more than £45.

Interior Connections

www.interiorconnections.net

This is a New England-based company selling wallpaper and stencils for the home decorator. The designs veer towards a country style, but there are some simple and unusual ones too. Prices are very reasonable, although you have to allow for international shipping which they can arrange by special request.

The Original Seagrass Company

www.original-seagrass.co.uk

If you can't decide between wooden floors or carpet, this stuff is a good compromise. Natural matting, sometimes blended with wool to make it easier on the feet, is featured in a range of styles at reasonable prices. You can order samples of any of the products through the site, or ask for someone to get in touch about giving you a full quotation.

Walking On Wood

www.designerwoodfloors.com

Straightforward site offering photos and technical specifications for quality hardwood floors, which range from traditional parquet to more modern styles. There's an online enquiry form if you want further details of any of this London-based firm's products and services.

Wallpaper Online

www.wallpaperonline.co.uk

Bored with plain walls? This easy-to-use site can search through its database of 20,000 papers and borders to find exactly the right one for you. Whether your choice is contemporary, traditional, floral, geometric or textured, you can specify your preferences until you reach what you're looking for. You can ask for samples to be sent, or buy the whole lot using their useful calculator to make sure you get the right amount. Delivery is free within the UK.

Kitchens & Bathrooms   Pots and pans

The Cook's Kitchen
www.kitchenware.co.uk

Competitive prices on a vast range of kitchen equipment from specialist utensils (such as crème brulée torches) to picnic hampers. The site is easy to use, if a little dull, and it's a good pace to look for gifts for keen cooks. UK delivery costs £2.95 and orders should arrive within 14 days.

Culliners
www.culliners.co.uk

If you're following the trend for all things industrial, this site will help you kit out your kitchen with a range of professional catering equipment, whether it's oversize baking sheets or indestructible knives. Note that prices do not include VAT – which is calculated at the checkout – and delivery costs £2.95 unless your order is over £80 after which it's free.

Doors Direct
www.doorsdirect.co.uk

Overhaul your old kitchen for far less than the cost of getting a new one by simply changing the cabinet doors. This site has a selection of both rustic and modern styles – choose from standard sizes or their made-to-measure service. There's also a good choice of handles. For a deposit of £20 you can order a sample door so you can check that it's definitely what you want, or just take the plunge and order the whole lot with a detailed email, to which they will respond with a firm quote and delivery time.

Dryden Aqua
www.drydenaqua.com

Save a fortune on bottled water and have filtered drinking and cooking water whenever you turn on the tap. Dryden Aqua sell a range of filter and water treatment systems which can remove almost all the gunk and bacteria that water companies allow through. All filters come with easy installation instructions and prices include three-day delivery.

The Life-Enhancing Tile Company
www.letco.co.uk

If your house is blessed with beige tiles featuring harvest mice, you might like to look at this site for some more contemporary ideas. Products are not yet available to order directly through the site, but you can order a brochure or, if you're artistic enough to design your own tiles, email for further information on their customised tile service.

Pots & Pans

www.pots-and-pans.co.uk

After taking so much care to highlight their Scottish heritage with a beautiful tartan banner, it's a shame they didn't concentrate their efforts more on the visuals of their products. Using hand-drawn images to encourage you to buy a single pan for £35 is neither helpful for shoppers nor good business strategy. We were also confused to find a bright blue Seahorse bathroom radio on the Special Offers page while searching for a bargain wok. Ordering is simple.

Scott & Sargeant, The Internet Cookshop

www.scottsargeant.com

High quality branded kitchenware such as Portmeirion, Global and Le Creuset at extremely good prices. You would be hard pushed to find this amount of choice in any high-street store and there are usually some good special offers

Kitchen Design From budget to bespoke

All the designer tableware in the world isn't going to help you if your kitchen is on its last legs. Kitchens are where everyone hangs out these days, so it's only polite to make it as cool and user-friendly as possible. Few people have the serious cash it takes to remodel the whole thing completely, but with a few ideas nicked from the professionals, even the saddest of cabinets and mouldiest of fridges can be persuaded into a new lease of life. The following kitchen-design sites, ranging from cheap'n'cheerful to gasp-inducingly pricey, might provide some inspiration for your own kitchen ambitions:

www.chantrykitchens.co.uk	Bespoke units at factory prices.
www.kensington-kitchens.co.uk	If you have to ask you can't afford it.
www.magnet.co.uk	Affordable prices with a surprisingly stylish choice of designs.
www.mfi.co.uk	Low prices and special offers on a wide range of kitchen cabinetry.
www.moreland-classic-kitchens.co.uk	Family firm offering kitchen design and installation.
www.nonamekitchen.com	Limited range of designs, but top quality without the designer prices.
www.ps4kitchens.co.uk	Delicious contemporary and traditional designs.

to be had, along with wedding gift ideas. Future plans include a recipe section so you can try out all your new kit. There's a 30-day money-back guarantee on all items and delivery costs £3.95 on orders under £100 (it's free over that). Goods should be received within 7-10 days, often sooner.

Shower Rail
www.showerail.co.uk
This site offers a fun choice of shower curtains from glam to country, along with other bathroom accessories, most of them with a nautical theme. They have occasional online competitions to help them decide their future lines, and you can also have a go at the fun quiz while you're deciding what to buy. Post and packing costs £2.95 for all orders and you can expect to receive delivery of yours within four working days.

Thomas Crapper & Co.
www.thomas-crapper.co.uk
We couldn't leave this one out, could we? Traditional Victorian and Edwardian-style toilets and sinks from the sanitary-ware supplier to Edward VII and George V Crapper's ranges of toiletries, bathroom towels and accessories are available for secure ordering through the site; alternatively you can place a provisional order for any of their toilets or sinks and someone from the company will get in touch with a full quote and delivery details.

 **Designs for living**

Danish House
www.triptrap.co.uk
Just in case you thought all Scandinavian design came in flatpacks with impossible-to-understand assembly instructions, this is the place to look for well-made furniture and accessories that embody the traditions of good Danish design. Navigating the site is easy, and you can also request one of the catalogues to be sent to you, but it's hard to find out anything about delivery charges without starting the buying process.

Lakeland Ltd.
www.lakeland.co.uk
This Lake District family business publishes a range of hugely successful catalogues featuring high-quality, great value-for-money household basics and accessories. You may find some designs a little on the twee side, but there are many things here, especially in the storage section, that will gladden the heart of even the most minimal interior decorator. This easy-to-use website is a recent launch and continues the business's emphasis on excellent customer service. Post and packing is free on orders over £35 and deliveries usually arrive within a few days.

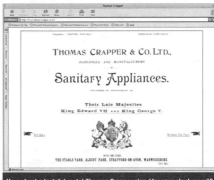

How about a tasteful metal Thomas Crapper sign "for your cloakroom"? No? Perhaps you'd prefer "bathroom preparations and useful requisites"

Manners

www.mannersmailorder.co.uk

The fact that this site is laid out like a tour of a country manor, including a library and a lily pond, should give you an indication of what kind of items are here. There's not much in the way of modern design, but there are plenty of decorative and well-made accessories, including lead statues for the traditional look, as well as some excellent gift ideas. Delivery costs £3.95 (more for heavier items) and your order will be with you within 14 days.

McCord

www.mccord.uk.com

This site offers well-made products for all over the house, selected with an eye for contemporary design. There are several useful services available, such as a fabric swatch request service if you're nervous about committing to a sofa without seeing the cover. Postage costs are £2.95 per order, but they do ask that you allow 28 days for delivery, which seems excessive these days, although apparently most deliveries arrive earlier.

Ocean

www.oceancatalogue.co.uk

Delicious but sometimes pricey furniture and accessories for the modern home. If chrome, frosted glass and pale wood appeal to you, you'll love this stuff. Delivery costs £5.95 for a three-day service or £6.95 for next-day, although our next-day order turned up two days late and with half the items missing, so it's probably not worth the extra pound.

Contemporary Design It's the new retro

Blue Deco
www.bluedeco.com
Lovely homewares, many of them handmade, from a selection of modern
designers. The oak furniture is particularly attractive, but even if you're only
after placemats there's something here for you too. Delivery costs depend
on the size of your order and are calculated on site, but there doesn't seem to
be any information on how long your items will take to reach you.

Deco Deli
www.decodeli.com
As the name suggests, this is a treasure trove of delicious accessories for the
contemporary home. Broken down into subsections such as Kitchen, Frames
or Light, the products are stylish and often a little unusual. P&P costs £2.95
per order and your goods should arrive within two to three working days.

Desaster
www.desaster.com
Whether it's an inflatable UFO for your playroom or a set of glass scales for
your bathroom, we defy you not to find something quirky and hugely desirable
on this fun and easy-to-use site. There are larger items of furniture as well as
accessories for all over the house, all of which have been given good photos
and descriptions so you know what you're getting before you click to buy.
The site offers a gift-wrap service and all items come with a 14-day refund
guarantee. Delivery is promised within two days.

Surprisingly these fancy
Czech chandeliers are only a
couple of hundred quid plus
taxes. Go on, we dare you

i4orm
www.i4orm.com
Comprehensive modern household goods site with a vast range that goes
from a bathroom tumbler at £1.50 to a designer chaise for £31,000. The
photos on site could be better – even enlarged, some of them don't give a full
idea of the item – but there's lots of good stuff to browse. You have to register
and wait for an email password before you can buy, however, and there are no
details about delivery times or prices until you reach the checkout, which is
doubly annoying. Otherwise, this could be an excellent shopping experience.

Ochre
www.ochre.net
There's some fabulously pretentious language on this site which invites you,
for example, to "get beyond the initial stage of the identification of an object",
but the site is saved from being ridiculous by the fact that its collections of
furniture, accessories and especially lighting are truly outstanding. The prices
vary from reasonable to jaw-dropping, but you're unlikely to come across any
of this stuff in the high street. Delivery costs vary (you have to email them for
details) and goods can take up to six weeks – six weeks! – to arrive.

Unit 26
www.unit26.com
Beautifully designed site full of stunning examples of top quality modern
design, including furniture, ceramics, lighting and textiles. This is definitely not
IKEA, so don't faint at the prices, but if you're looking for the antiques of the
future, this is the place to start. The costs shown include packing and
shipping for mainland Western Europe, which implies there may be a
surcharge for the UK, so it's best to email them first just in case. Delivery
times will vary according to where your goods are coming from.

 **From Czech chandeliers to Greek rugs**

Bedding World
www.beddingworld.co.uk
Poor quality images let down this otherwise simple but well thought out site.
Thankfully they've put the money into the products rather than tacky graphics,
offering a variety of bedding designs at reasonable prices (around £40 for a
double bed duvet). Delivery takes only three days and the maximum shipping
cost seems to be 55p. The site also offers the chance to specify delivery
instructions, so your new sheets can be left with the neighbours if you want.

Chandeliers
www.chandeliers.co.uk
Glamorous chandeliers at reasonable prices, delivered direct from the Czech

Republic. All the designs are fairly traditional and they will also supply wall sconces and lamps to match if you want the complete bordello look. The site is secure for credit cards, but delivery takes up to 28 days.

Chiasmus
www.chiasmus.co.uk

Don't be put off by the wordy homepage: this site is full of funky housewares and gifts to add a little originality to your home. The site is easy to navigate once you get past the opening blurb and you don't have to register to order, which will be a winner with those concerned about privacy issues. Funky items include Mr & Mrs Salt & Pepper pots which resemble baby space-hoppers, and inflatable table lamps (a snip at £26). No one will ever mistake you for an IKEA shopper with that on your side-table.

Clickdeco
www.clickdeco.co.uk

The site is quite random in its layout and you don't get a list of categories until you've already looked at one item up close, but there's lots of fun and groovy stuff here for every room in the house. Prices are reasonable and there's a bumper section for lovers of all things kitsch, including da-glo nodding doggies and Indian sun-god candle-holders. Delivery takes around 14 days and all items come with a money-back guarantee.

Essentially English
www.essentially-english.co.uk

Much of the stuff here is toe-curlingly twee, but once you get past the busts of Henry VIII, there are some things which are definitely worth a look, especially the funky ceramics and handmade wooden storage chests (all made in England). As most items come from different suppliers and are often made to order, delivery times and costs are usually included in the description, but if you're unsure, the site will email you the full details.

The Feng Shui Shop
www.feng-shui-shop.co.uk

This site offers all the kit you need to balance and harmonise your home according to ancient Eastern principles. Books on feng shui, as well as such accessories as three-legged frogs (very

important) and windchimes, are all available, although if you're a beginner, you might want to start with one of the kits they have thoughtfully compiled with you in mind. Despite championing pared-down simplicity in the home, the site is a hectic mish-mash, but you should be able to find your way through it as long as you read all the instructions carefully. Delivery is £3.95 in the UK, but they don't specify how long it will take.

The Forge
www.eshopone.co.uk/OnlineShopping-TheForge.html
Wrought-iron accessories for the home, handmade in Derbyshire. There's a good selection of curtain-poles and some very funky candlesticks, although the pictures are a little small. Buying direct makes the prices a bargain, and as a bonus, delivery is free. Goods are usually dispatched within two days.

Handles Direct
www.handlesdirect.com
Sleek and stylish door and cabinet handles to give your house that just-had-the-architect-round ambience. You won't find these at your local DIY store and prices start at a reasonable level before heading off into the realms of interior design fantasy. A range of light switches and plug sockets is also on the launch schedule. Delivery costs £5 plus VAT and as long as the handles are in stock, you'll get them within seven days.

Holding Company
www.theholdingcompany.co.uk
Although small, the Holding Company offers a vast collection of products with mesh, bamboo and chrome featuring prominently. They pride themselves on being able to mould any fabric into anything you desire, but they may have gone a little OTT with the denim shoeboxes and Perspex tissue-dispensers. They do offer more practical items, however: £60 for a woven-grass folding screen is cheap compared to what you're likely to pay in John Lewis, and they only charge £4 for delivery. Stylish, yet practical and easy to manage.

Inhabit
www.inhabit.co.uk
Yet another site offering wacky novelties. This one is easier to navigate than Chiasmus but it lacks that site's variety, with many products listed under multiple headings. Particular favourites were Harry Mobile Holder and the Bubblo placemats, both of which can be bought with Beenz points. On the down side, however, they ask you to register before they'll tell you about any discounts, and postage and packing more than doubled the original cost of an aqua door-mouse doorstop to £8.98.

Mythology
www.mythology-rugs.co.uk
Rugs are notoriously expensive, given that most people just wipe their feet on

them, but this site has excellent prices on a range of decorative rugs direct from Greece. Don't think that this means they'll be covered in pictures of minotaurs or prancing naked warriors as these designs are colourful and contemporary, with a mostly abstract slant. Delivery is free within the UK but you have to allow 28 days for your rug to arrive.

Nice Irmas
www.niceirmas.net
A luxurious site with an equally lavish purple homepage, held together by the products themselves. The home accessories include cushions in tactile velvet and beaded fabrics from £16, with beaded napkin rings and tea-light-holders from £2.50. Unfortunately not enough thought has been put into the buying process, with poor images and a faulty link to the checkout letting the site down. Persistence is needed here but the products are worth the wait.

Nubold
www.nubold.com
Hot contemporary designers like Nic Wood and Bodo Sperlein sell their accessories through an excellent site that does them full justice. The lighting department is particularly irresistible, and there's even a wedding list service for brides with seriously good taste. They offer 10 per cent off your first order,

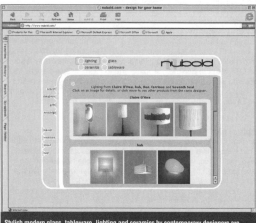

Stylish modern glass, tableware, lighting and ceramics by contemporary designers are what's on offer at Nubold's site. It even lets you search by material, colour or price

although many of the prices are surprisingly reasonable anyway. Delivery is calculated at the checkout and your order should arrive within seven days.

Out Of Afrika

www.outofafrika.co.uk

Truly lovely wood, ceramic, metal and glass accessories for people who want a touch of Africa. The site is beautifully laid out with easy-to-view photos, and all products are bought at a fair price from small co-operatives (five per cent of each order is donated to a children's home in South Africa). Orders over £150 are carriage free; otherwise it's £3.50 for delivery within 3-5 working days.

The Roman Blind Company

www.roman-blind.co.uk

A simple and straightforward site offering Roman blinds, with full measuring guidelines and examples of previous commissions. All blinds are made to order with fabric that you supply, and you can pretty much cover any window. Email the site for further details and prices.

Ruana

www.ruana.com

Fair-trade site selling goods from Central and South America made by local craftsmen and small co-operatives. The household accessories section has, among other things, a selection of delightful clocks and windchimes, plus colourful wall tapestries all made from sustainable resources and using traditional designs. Postage and packing varies depending on your order and is calculated on site. UK orders are sent by Royal Mail.

Web Rugs

www.webrugs.co.uk

Huge selection of floor coverings to choose from here, including oriental and modern styles, natural rugs or cartoon ones for children's rooms. Prices are competitive, particularly since they include delivery, and the availability of each design is specified with its description. All household sites should be this informative and easy to follow.

Jewellery & Watches

Easier than trudging the streets, but can any computer screen stir the soul like a jeweller's window?

Jewellery — From catalogue to contemporary

Argenteus
http://argenteus.co.uk

Contemporary and modern designer jewellery at high-street prices. All the additional information you need is provided on the opening page, and you can search according to the product you want and the price you want to pay: under £50, under £100 etc. Silver dominates both extensive catalogues, and designers include Julie Ann Comley and Iain Henderson. If these names mean nothing to you, you can read about the inspiration behind each collection to gain a better idea of what they sell. Among the more unusual items are a wavy square ring set with gemstones from the Ming Collection for less than £100.

Bijoo
www.bijoo.com

French company Bijoo sell a limited selection of fine gold, white gold and gem set jewellery. Contemporary ring, necklace and earring designs set this apart from its competitors, but the prices are steep for the simple designs: £200 to £350 for rings and £75 for gem set pendant necklaces. Insurance is included and shipping is free for a limited time to celebrate their recent opening.

Copyist
www.copyist.demon.co.uk

Imitation antique jewellery may not be everyone's cup of tea, but Copyist offers five compact pages, displaying anything from Edwardian to gypsy-style rings and earrings. You don't need to stick to the exact designs as you can customise them with your choice of gemstone. At under £50 for any item, the only complaint is the poor browser connection which makes buying difficult.

Half Price Jewellers

www.hpj.co.uk

This amateurish-looking site makes no bones about its bargain basement nature: they obviously feel the products will sell themselves. Traditional items, t-bars, torque bangles, signet rings and traditional-style engagement rings – every item is half price, with wedding rings the most expensive at just over £50. With simple navigation and inexpensive postage, this is the on-line equivalent of the high-street jeweller.

Icon

www.icon-jewellery.com/st

Each item that Icon sell is handcrafted – many by up-and-coming designers – and you can regulate the expense according to which carat of gold or gem you choose. The price also depends on the designer, but a ring will set you back anywhere between £30 and £400. With beautiful and original designs, Icon is a good choice if you're looking for something that little bit different that won't break the bank.

It Sparkles

www.itsparkles.com/cgi-bin/Itsparkles344.storefront

Despite the name, you won't be dazzled by anything at this site. The catalogue is limited – generally to 12 items per category search for diamond and gemstone gold rings, crosses, pendants and earrings. Diamond rings are between £250 and £600 depending on the carat, and the remaining items are anywhere from £50 upwards. In style terms these are traditional pieces, with nothing as modern as a piece of silver or a Tiffany cross, but delivery is free, so this is a useful site if it matches your tastes.

The Jeweller

http://the-jeweller.com

With over 250 items under one category alone, The Jeweller can be forgiven for lacking inspiring site design. Standard Ernest Jones/H. Samuel items make up the extensive catalogue, but at half the RRP. It's advisable to make your search as specific as possible, but this is easily done by choosing a style and price range to suit. Enlarged images and advice on size are also available.

Jewellers

www.jewellers.net

This busy catalogue-style site offers gold, silver and luxury items, along with cheap and cheerful fashion novelties. Multiple sub-categories allow you to narrow your search, and if you're looking for something with a gemstone, they also offer additional information about what that stone represents. Prices range from £20 to £200, but you can't search according to price range.

Tateossian

www.tateossian.com

This stylish site sells unusual and contemporary jewellery items, making it a refreshing change. There's only a small collection of fibre-optic glass jewellery and silver and zircon designs, and £40 for a pebble design necklace and £80 for a zircon cross may seem quite steep, but the designs are one-offs.

What She Wants

www.whatshewants.com

The items featured here – from earrings to body-jewellery – range from £2 to more than £1000 but they're categorised by product, making it quite difficult to search by price. But this site does offer a more up-to-date range than most of its discount rivals, and there's a free gift if you register.

Watches From club-style to computer-buff

Apple Watch

www.applewatch.co.uk

Apple's dedicated watch site has only a few offerings, but there's an iWatch available in iMac colours for £42, and a counter-clockwise watch for £29.95. Details of shock resistance and waterproof capabilities are provided.

Face for Watches

www.faceforwatches.com

Brands include ultra-trendy Spoon and AKA in styles dubbed club, tech and sporty. Prices fall around £100, but the futuristic designs are unusual. Extra information is available, and insurance is included in the £4.95 postage.

Storm

www.storm-watches.com.au/index.html

The site seems to comprise the entire Storm range, but prices are in US $ (they do offer a link to a currency converter, however). At $100 – $200, there are few bargains, but you may find something unusual. Check delivery prices.

Watch Heaven

www.topbrands.net

Pages of Swatch watches (better than the problematic official site), brands including Seiko, Casio and Baby G at prices anywhere between £20 and £150, a separate bargain section and free delivery make this an excellent site.

Whether you're looking
for a publication about
carp or something more
obscure, you'll find it on the Net

British Magazines Direct

www.britishmagazines.com/

"The UK's largest online magazine store" is the boast here, although W H
Smith might dispute that. Still, extensive interrogation did suggest that the
catalogue is pretty vast (the site says it has 3500 titles in stock). A good swift-
to-download site with a fast search mechanism and secure ordering either of
one issue or a subscription. Database includes seven magazines about carp.

English Magazines

www.englishmagazines.com/

This site claims to offer over 3000 titles. The home page is not that appealing
and the search mechanism can be laborious at its worst. But there is a very
good range of magazines and an email form for when you can't find what you
want. Database includes six magazines about carp.

Magazine Café

www.magazinecafe.co.uk/

You can search this site by title or browse by category, although the selection
is not exactly huge. Database doesn't include any magazines about carp –
possibly because the titles here are all international magazines and the rest
of the world doesn't find this particular fish quite as fascinating as the British
evidently do. This site does, however, stock the tattooist's bible, *Skin & Ink*.

Magazine Shop

www.magazineshop.co.uk/

Database includes only one magazine about carp, aimed at anglers who
consider themselves "advanced". That lapse apart, this is a decent site,
sensibly structured to make it as easy as possible to find the title that
interests you. You need to subscribe to order but there are some good offers.

W H Smiths

www.whsmith.co.uk/

Apparently driven by a compulsive need to offer online customers 50 per cent
discounts, this site is well worth checking out. Customers can order a single

Dr Mag can prescribe the right kind of magazine whether you're into marlin or fur fish

issue of a favourite magazine or subscribe to it. Database only contains one title about carp but it does also link to Dr Mag.com, an international (ie American-based) magazine store which didn't seem to have any magazines about carp but stocked one title about marlin and another about fur fish, whatever they are. If Dr Mag doesn't list the international oddity you're after, you can email them to find out if they have information on it. www.DrMag.com

Yahoo Auctions
http://search.auctions.yahoo.com/search/auctions?p=magazines&alocale=1us&acc=us

Thousands of magazines are on auction here at any one time which makes it a must for collectors, whether they're after a copy of a gay magazine starring a nude Sylvester Stallone or a 1951 edition of *National Geographic*. Among the items on sale were four magazines about fish.

The Net also plays host to countless e-zines – magazines that don't exist in printed form. Here are some of the best:

The best of the general e-zines is probably *Salon* (www.salon.com) which, although it has fallen on harder times of late, is still the nearest thing to an online *Vanity Fair*. Its range is astonishing – from the minutiae of technology and health to a report on American marketeers who hypnotise consumers to find out what they really think about products.

The Onion (www.onion.com) is justly famous for the sharpness of its wit, although it hasn't been as funny since the Clinton impeachment hearings ended. *Modern Humorist* (www.modernhumorist.com) is the latest launch by a *Salon* writer who outed Tinky Winky as a joke – a joke which the American Moral Majority took seriously. This site's 'downloading MP3 equals communism' poster is truly wonderful. No e-zines about carp yet, but it's only a matter of time.

MAGAZINES ON THE NET

Some magazines make all or some of their content available online. Others generate new material. Just try keying in *www.* and the magazine title and *.co.uk* or *.com*. Among the more unusual titles in cyberspace are: *www.cranestoday-magazine.com* about lifting devices, not birds *www.ctmmag.com* for "correction management" *www.nailpro.com/new/main.html* for "nail professionals" *www.pitandquarry.com* serving the non-metallic mining industry

Motorbikes

Head out on the information superhighway and you can do everything from buy a bike to book a holiday on the open road

Accessories Helmets, leather and spare parts

Mad About Bikes
www.madaboutbikes.com
Bright and well-organised, this site sells accessories, magazines and security equipment. Every section is sub-categorised by brand or product type. The additional information is adequate and links to the checkout are fast and secure. Slightly cheaper than its competitors, but only a handful of named brands (including Shoei and Sidi). A useful site for those on a lower budget.

Motorcycle City
www.motorcycle-city.co.uk
No bikes here, just leathers, waterproofs, accessories and helmets. Huge discounts make up for lack of stock, with some items reduced by as much as £300. The clothes are more dark avenger than the colourful biker, but this is worth a look if you're a beginner looking for safety rather than fashion.

Rainbow
www.rainbow.co.uk
BMWmad site with bikes for hire, used bikes to buy, spare parts, leathers, boots and helmets. Additional information is sparse so you need to know your bike to ensure you get what you need, although it does offer a sizing guide when you buy a helmet. Clothing wise the catalogue contains everything from all-in-one leathers at prices starting at £350, to kidney protectors for £48.

Urban Bikes
www.urbanbikes.co.uk
Standard clothing and accessory categories, plus multiple visor tints, tyre sizes and boot colours. Top brands include OGK and Caberg helmets, Sidi boots and PowerBronze screens. Prices range from £99 to £400 for helmets, £50 to £100 for tyres and £70 to £500 for luggage. Something for all budgets.

Before you empty your wallet...

Bike Trader

www.biketrader.co.uk

This online relation of *AutoTrader* looks the same and provides exactly the same information as the traditional version. Make a basic search stating your preferred price, model and the distance you are prepared to travel, and it will list the models matching your criteria. The results will include a picture of the bike, a brief description and contact details. You can also make advanced searches, but registration is required, and there's welcome advice on buying and finding the best insurance. A useful directory.

 Bikes with attitude (and without)

TPC Motorcycles

www.tpc.motorcycle.hire.mcmail.com

This Southampton-based, family-run business hire motorcycles for business or pleasure. Despite their limited range of six models, they have bikes to suit all needs, from a bike with attitude – the Retro GSX750 – to the racing TL1000R. Bikes can be hired on a daily basis (from £55 to £90) or at a weekly rate (£310 to £400), depending on the model. Descriptions and pictures are available, and though you can't finalise the deal online, you can make provisional bookings.

SCOOTERS ONLINE

Want to do as the Italians do and travel everywhere on a scooter? Scooter Zone is one of the few scooter sites to sell online but it hasn't quite got things right.

It's an adequate enough site, dealing in Peugeot, Italjet and Malaguli, with prices ranging from £1700 – £2000 for 50cc and 100cc models. With pictures, descriptions and technical specs of each model, making a selection is simple, and your choice will be with you within two weeks for a mere £4.50 delivery.

Unfortunately you can currently order only by email. It's not really advisable to send your credit card details along unsecured lines, so order at your peril.

www.scooterzone.co.uk

 **On and off the road**

Grass Routes

www.grassroutes.freeserve.co.uk

Holidays and weekend breaks to suit both the experienced biker and those just wanting something a bit different. Choose from on and off-road tours of Britain, Ireland and shortly, America and Canada. Though amateur-looking, the site is easy to navigate with all the information you'll require, with prices, duration and accommodation details all on the same page. Prices begin at £195 for a weekend off-road trail, including bike hire. You can't finalise your order online, but you can make enquiries and be contacted.

Museum shops

Desperately seeking a mini Roman duck oil lamp? A Freud-styled Brainy Beanie Baby? Or maybe a gold-plated pocket watch (a snip at £700)? What luck! You just happen to have come to the right place…

Armagh Planetarium

www.armagh-planetarium.co.uk

There are three fundamental problems with this site. Once you connect, it offers you the option of searching the online shop via their secure server or not. Fortunately an announcement popped up on screen that their security certificate had expired and anyone could read the buyer's details. Secondly, there is no customer services section nor any hint of delivery costs and times, and thirdly, it remains a mystery how much any item in their extensive catalogue costs until you click to order. If none of this puts you off, they do sell some interesting items, particularly the Astronaut vanilla ice cream for £2.

British Museum

www.thebritishmuseum.ac.uk

Britain's premier museum hosts an equally interesting shopping site, with replica jewellery and collectibles alongside standard hieroglyphic-printed tea towels and the inevitable mugs for the tourists. Some of the more interesting items include replicas of historical jewellery, with prices starting at around £40 for a gold-plated snake-ring traditionally used to ward off evil and to ensure fertility. For the kids, wean them off Pokémon toys with Egyptian Prince and Princess dolls or the Mancala counting game which dates back to the time of the Pharaohs. Novel gifts with a real history.

Cutty Sark Museum

www.cuttysark.org.uk

This traditional British tourist attraction (the Victorian merchant ship, that is, not the whisky) has embraced the future by offering an online shop. The design and navigation are basic, and the products are for die-hard Sark fans only – everything from Cutty Sark tea towels to sweat shirts. Slightly classier items include the traditional ship in a bottle and a knotboard, both at £24.95, and a mini ship's decanter for £25. Perfect for the nautical fanatic.

Freud Museum

www.freud.org.uk

Freud would probably have his own interpretation of why this website is so sparse, dull and unsophisticated but it sells gifts for every taste and age. Replica statues of those which adorned Freud's own hallway can be bought for £34, although it's unlikely the Freud picture mugs (£9.50) mirror his own kitchen collection, and one can only guess what he'd read into the Freud-styled Brainy Beanie Babies for £17. The most annoying thing is that you need to write down the details of the items you want to buy, as there are no direct links to the order form. No straight answers from the genius even in death.

National Maritime Museum

www.nmm.ac.uk

In terms of price this is far from your average museum gift shop. Only the extravagant will be tempted (or able) to afford a gold-plated pocket watch costing anywhere between £300 and £700, or a Hoggett crystal decanter for £200. Even the cheapest globe comes in at £100. With no indication of delivery charges until the final tally, it probably assumes you're not bothered about a few more pounds extra expense if you can afford such treats.

Victoria & Albert Museum

www.vam.ac.uk

An attractive, well-designed site in imperial purple, offering jewellery, books and art nouveau gifts. All the information you need is contained on one page, with enlarged images, descriptions, history, costs and delivery times. Pewter, William Morris, decoupage and tulips feature strongly and you should be able to pick up a delicate decoration for under £20. Search the V & A Gifts section rather than a sub-category to appreciate the full range.

Westair Reproductions

www.westair-reproductions.com

Westair produce gifts for museums around the world, but they also sell from

their own online store. Another dull grey site, it sells mostly miniature models of planes, cannons and soldiers. A Battle of Britain fighter complete with box and historical account will set you back £7.50; American Union and Confederate soldiers can be yours for £3 or, if you prefer, there are cannons for £1.

Grey is good at Westair. Even the pewter reproductions are grey – classy, but grey

Music

From acoustic guitars to zithers, from JS Bach to Beatles on the organ, it's all there in cyberspace

Sheet Music — You can download this too

Amazing Music World
www.amazingmusicworld.com
If you have Adobe Acrobat you can use this site to buy and download sheet music direct to your computer, thus cutting out any tedious waiting for the postman. Search by composer or instrument and then follow the step-by-step instructions and you'll have your music in a jiffy. Prices depend on the piece.

G&S Works Inc.
www.gsworks.com
If you yearn to be a pirate of Penzance but lack the resources of the D'Oyly Carte Opera Company, this site can provide scaled-down scores of Gilbert and Sullivan classics for production by small theatre companies and bands. You can attempt *HMS Pinafore* with just seven musicians (and presumably even fewer sailors), and there's a list of companies who have successfully used the scores. Email through the site for rates and further details.

Look Music
www.lookmusic.com
There's no excuse for murdering the same show tune over and over again when there are so many pieces to chose from, no matter what instrument you play. Prices here are very reasonable and the site aims for user-friendliness at all times. There's even a clever "sounds like" search facility for hesitant spellers, although results can be random – it came up with a Dire Straits track when we asked for the *Concierto de Aranjuez*. Delivery charges vary, but are very reasonable and you should receive your order within three days.

Music For A Song
www.musicforasong.co.uk
Learn new tunes and save a packet at the same time by buying used sheet music and music books for far less than they cost new. It won't always have what you're after, but it's worth a visit. The site is easy to use as it's little more

Music

than a basic list searchable by composer or instrument, and you can email to reserve your selection, then phone through your credit card or send a cheque.

The Music Room
www.musicroom.com
Whether they're after the Bach *Lute Suites* or a book of Beatles hits rearranged for the home organist, budding musicians can happily surf this easy-to-navigate site for hours, just looking at the huge stack of sheet music available to buy online. If you can't find what you want, you can email them and they'll try to find it for you. All orders are sent out by first class mail; the first item costs £1.50 and then £1 for every subsequent one.

 **If you were born to play the noseflute**

All About Sound
www.guitarsales.co.uk
Acoustic, semi-acoustic, electric, steel-stringed or classical – whichever guitar you're looking for, you can drool over it here. Parts of the site are still under construction, but a full-service online store is promised soon, with drum kits and amps also on offer. It's everything you need to make an almighty racket.

Dawsons Music Store
www.dawsons.co.uk
This impressive store sells a wide range of instruments ranging from tenor saxophones to Fender guitars, all through their secure server. You can apply for store finance online if you're looking to get the band back together and buy the instruments at the same time, and delivery costs will be calculated at the checkout. There's also a monthly competition with some very cool prizes, or if you're fed up with the life of a struggling musician, you can offload your old kit in the classifieds section.

The House of Musical Traditions
www.hmtrad.com
Lovely online store offering a great selection of unusual musical instruments from around the world. Decorated mandolins, ukeleles and zithers rub shoulders with such esoterica as noseflutes and panpipes. There's a secure ordering system, but since the company is based in the US, you will have to email for full shipping costs. These will vary greatly, depending on whether you're after set of bagpipes or a harmonica.

The Newcastle Drum Centre
www.newcastledrum.freeserve.co.uk
Indispensable for those who really hate their neighbours, this site offers a full range of percussion instruments from a beginner's drum kit to samba band

bongos. There's a good selection of sale items and a special service for schools. Online shopping is not available yet, but if you email the store through the site, they'll do their best to get you what you want.

Phuture Sounds
www.phuture.co.uk
Small online store for analogue synthesizers and drum machines. There's not much information about each model on the site but if you're in the market for such things, it's likely that you know what you're looking for. Just email your order through and they will contact you with final cost and delivery options.

The Piano Man
www.pianoplus.co.uk
Thankfully this has nothing to do with the Piano Man himself, Billy Joel. This site offers new pianos at discounted prices as well as second-hand ones, especially unusual and decorative instruments. The Piano Man also buys old pianos and will quote for restoration, repair and removal work if you email them. There's not a lot of stock to look at online, but a detailed enquiry form is provided for you to describe what you're after.

The Virtual Piano Shop
www.pianoshop.co.uk
Directory of advice and links for people in the market for a new piano. Useful guides on what to look for and how much you can expect to pay, as well as contact details for piano shops, removers and tuners.

The Wesson Accordion Company
www.crosswinds.net/~zydeco/
Serving as a sales page for Castagnari Melodeons as well as the home page for the Joe le Taxi Zydeco Dance Band, this site offers a range of traditional squeeze boxes at varying prices. You can email Rees Wesson for an up to date stock list and he accepts credit cards and cheques in payment.

Yamaha
www.yamaha.co.uk
This is not so much an online store, more a fancy sales brochure for Yamaha's comprehensive range of acoustic and electronic musical instruments from portable keyboards to euphoniums. You can email for further details or just check out prices online to compare with your local retailer.

PIANOLA ROLLS

Once again proving our assertion that you can get anything over the Internet, what about some new music rolls for your pianola?

If you're lucky enough to own such a treasure, you can visit The Keystone Music Roll Company (in Bethlehem, Pennsylvania) at www.keystonemusicroll.com and discover new tunes from Irving Berlin to Ludwig van Beethoven.

If this whets your appetite still further, you can always surf on over to www.leedyrolls.com where you will find links to The Automated Musical Instrument Collectors Association which also devotes considerable hyperspace to nickelodeons.

Net stuff

Thousands of web sites say
they can make your surfing
more productive and enjoyable.
But only a few actually deliver

Software Try it, buy it or download it

Dave Central Shareware Archive
www.davecentral.com
This may sound like someone's dodgy home page, but it's actually a brilliant
portal for finding software downloads for Windows or Linux platforms.
Whether you need conferencing software or a graphics package, you'll find
something to link to here, with many downloads reviewed by techies.

DemoNet
www.demonet.com
Try before you buy. Many of the 47,000 items of software available here have
demonstration versions for you to play with before you take the plunge. To
keep you informed while you browse, the site also contains updates on the
Nasa Mission to Mars, and they are planning a new venture, DemoNet TV,
which will broadcast information and instructions for all kinds of software.

ZD Net Downloads
www.zdnet.com
You can find software downloads for Mac, PC and even Palm from here.
There are free downloads, as well as costlier programs that will enhance your
computer, make surfing more fun, or just provide you with some new games.

E-Greetings Save trees, handwriting and pandas

Blue Mountain Arts
www.bluemountain.com
Missed someone's birthday? Quick, send an e-card as though that's what you
intended to do all along. Blue Mountain offers a huge range of cartoon cards

to personalise and send, from the silly to the soppy. They even have cards for events you never knew you had to celebrate, like Kiss and Make Up Day.

E-Cards
www.e-cards.com
Send an e-postcard to anyone with an Internet account. This site, run by three Netheads in San Francisco, generates revenue for a variety of wildlife and ethical charities and many of the cards feature stunning photos of the natural world, including endangered species and rare flowers. You can also send video cards if you're feeling really ambitious.

 Decorate your desktop

Celebrity Desktop
www.celebritydesktop.com
Customise your screen with a favourite star of the screen or sports field. Loads of celebs to choose from as either wallpaper or full screensaver, as well as links to many other celebrity sites. It should make coming to work just that bit more bearable.

Dead Can Dance
http://wkweb5.cableinet.co.uk/brilliant/free.htm
Screensavers for the morbid and macabre, where animated skeletons and dissected body parts float around your screen when it's idle. Particular applause goes to the skeleton who rides around on a spacehopper (they also go pogoing and parachuting). Not that many to choose from, but certainly something different, or gross, depending on your point of view. If you really like chilling your colleagues' blood, you can download "Day of the Dead" startup and shutdown screens.

Screen Savers Bonanza
www.bonanzas.com
When you get bored of the selection of screensavers that came with your computer, this site can help you out with over 450 different screensavers for Macs and PCs, all arranged depending on your operating system. Anything you might possibly want, from a tribute to Frank Sinatra to an Egyptian mummies cube to bounce around your screen, is here, and you can also download a free version of WinZip to open the files.

FLASH HARRIES

When you're surfing the Net, you will doubtless find sites, even basic shopping sites, that tell you they are best viewed with Flash, or Shockwave, or any of the many video and graphics packages.

This can be annoying if you don't have them installed, but basic versions of all these are available for free, or, if you're seriously into downloading video and graphics, you might want to buy an upgrade.

Often you can download the software through the site you're looking at, but the URLs below might help you learn about what you're downloading.

Flash
www.macromedia.com
QuickTime
www.apple.com/quicktime
RealPlayer
www.real.com
Shockwave
www.shockwave.com

Office supplies

Let the Internet be your very own personal digital assistant even if all you really need are some new pages for your Filofax, a rubber stamp and some more business forms

Action Office Supplies
www1.action.com

Specialising in computer supplies, hardware, software and peripherals, Action's online store is a boon for busy offices. Customer service is outstanding. They will also help you with office design. Prices are always low and delivery is next day for most of the UK with a same day service for panicking customers in central London.

The City Organiser
www.cityorg.demon.co.uk

For those Luddites refusing to get on the PDA bandwagon, this is where to come for accessories and inserts for your trusty Filofax. Diaries, pads, pens and other useful additions are all here to keep you organised. Some complete binder systems are available for one hour delivery in Central London, or you can choose your delivery method and cost which starts at £2 for first class post. For some reason, the site also sells a selection of cufflinks.

NEBS Business Forms
www.nebs.co.uk

You can buy from their stock of standard forms such as invoices or purchase orders, including ones compatible with software packages like Sage, or email the company for a more personalised job. They can also print company T-shirts, mugs, pens and so on, as well as Christmas cards and calendars.

Polka Dot
www.polka.co.uk

All the top brand names are here, from Avery to Xerox. This site is best for large, expensive orders as there is a £7.50 delivery charge no matter what you have bought. And don't worry, the yellow dots vanish after the homepage.

Print Mountain

www.printmountain.com

Excellent site for people who need professional printers but don't know where to start to get quotes. Register here and enter the details of your job, including deadlines and finishes, and then wait for different printers to quote for your business. You can then follow the transaction through online or contact the printer you most like the sound of.

Solid Stamps

www.solidstamps.co.uk

Rubber stamps and self-inking plastic stamps at prices way below high street. The site is pretty basic, but there are detailed online order forms if your needs are simple, or you can email them for a personal service. Stamps are usually dispatched the next day and listed prices include postage and packing.

Toners.Co.UK

www.toners.co.uk

Whether your photocopier is bang up to date, or has seen better days, you'll most likely find toner and supplies here. If yours is not listed, email the company and it will try and track it down. Delivery costs depend on the item and VAT is not included until you reach the checkout. Orders received before 3pm will be dispatched the same day.

Viking Direct

www.viking-direct.co.uk

Stock up on Post-Its and paper clips at this online warehouse. New users are offered a free gift with their first order and the site is very simple to use although you do have to register to shop. Prices exclude VAT, but delivery is free on orders over £30 and most goods will be with you by the next day at most.

Willett

www.willett.co.uk

Give your control freak side full rein with Willett's range of label-making printers. You have to register with this site in order to look at many of the products, but there are solutions here to labelling everything from hanging files to large shipments, including the printers, software, labels and other accessories.

SORT OUT YOUR HOME OFFICE

Be of good cheer. Your working space may be a rickety table in the corner of your living room but try some of the sites below and you could soon have a home office to be proud of:

Interior Motives

www.int-motives.co.uk
Glamourous desks and chairs for any office location

Posture Point

www.posture.co.uk
Ergonomic chairs and seating designed to be as easy on your back as they are on the eye.

President Office Furniture

www.president.co.uk
Impressively versatile desk and storage systems for growing companies.

Space 2

www.space2.com
Groovy, tough, desks and computer workstations to satisfy the most design conscious home-office worker. Online shoppers may get discounts.

Work All Hours

www.workallhours.co.uk
Designer office kit, with a particularly great selection of desk lamps.

Outdoors

Boomerangs, black magic women and men with beards - you'll find them all in the great outdoors which, confusingly, you can access from the less-than-great indoors thanks to the Internet

Airways

www.airways.uk.com

The sky's your limit at this Derbyshire-based site. Paragliders, hangliders, harnesses and accessories (including compasses, sunglasses and perhaps a rather more essential range, parachutes), are all for sale. Browse by manufacturer, but make sure you visit the Paraglider Chooser if you're not already sure exactly what you want. This is a straightforward site to use, with pictures of every product, and postage and packing according to Royal Mail rates. If you're not convinced by the paragliders, you may prefer to browse Airways' decent range of kites.

Climb Limited

www.rockrun.com/

Although it's billed as Climb Limited on some search engines, the homepage bears the brand name Rockrun which spins off the company's two Rock and Run shops. A member of the Which? Trader scheme, the online shop on this site can take a while to load. Depending on the time of year, you may also be disappointed by the clearance sale which only had two items in it when this the site was last checked. These minor flaws are more than compensated for by some of the discounts on offer on the rest of the site (with 50 per cent marked off some sleeping bags), the secure ordering, and by the range of products from Black Diamond gaiters to Terminator crampons. There's also a telephone helpline from 9am to 5pm weekdays.

The Complete Outdoors

www.complete-outdoors.co.uk

A large range of big brand trekking, rambling and camping gear, including a separate kids' section, and accessories and gizmos (pedometers, cooking equipment, Leatherman tools and much more) make for a packed and useful outdoor site. There's a distinctly above average online magazine to inspire your choice and a few special offers to tempt you. Delivery is guaranteed within 48 hours and costs £3.95, but VAT is added only after you arrive at the checkout. The tents look like a particularly good deal.

Ellis Brigham
www.ellis-brigham.com

Plenty of photos of bearded men dangling off cliff faces and smiling couples barely breaking sweat as they hike through the wilderness are the order of the day at Ellis Brigham's striking but oddly arranged site. Quite why visitors should want to wander through a virtual store, complete with floors and product zones really isn't clear – and it does make browsing very time-consuming. You can opt to search by brand and you will find a great selection of outdoor clothing, footwear, rucksacks, camping and ski equipment – even a Snowboard Asylum. There are loads of clearance bargains available, but irritatingly, despite all the general pics, many of the products on offer aren't accompanied by photos. You'll have to trawl through the list and just guess what that K2 Black Magic Woman might be.

Explorers Online
www.explorers-online.com

Over 5,000 products are for sale at this great Stockport-based site. If you're after Swiss Army knives or Maglites (and their associated accessories – you might be surprised...) this is definitely the place to come. If not, you'll still find good prices on climbing and camping equipment, first aid kits and more. The site could do with a few more pics to brighten it up, but it's admirably easy to use. You have to register to buy, dispatch is within a few working days, and postage is based on Royal Mail rates. Buying something requires progressing through a seemingly endless succession of screens, but is still fairly straightforward. If you have any comments about the site you can send them along with your order.

Eyewood Designs
www.eyewooddesigns.f9.co.uk/

Despite the nudge-nudge pun in the company name, this is a serious, intelligent, website about the boomerang, a slice of Australiana which, in the UK, has generally been regarded with all the gravitas normally reserved for Rolf Harris and his didgeridoo. The first boomerangs didn't come back at all, they were hunting aids used in Poland. It was the aborigines who came up with the idea of

PRACTICE, PRACTICE

If you want to go climbing, you don't have to head for the country. If you;re in London, you can find a castle wall to climb on a grade 2 listed folly in Stoke Newington. You can find Stoke Newington's finest residence on www.castle-climbing.co.uk/

The Castle Climbing Centre has a counterpart in Glasgow. Called Cliffhanger which you can find on www.glasgow climbingcentre. co.uk.

If you need to brush up on your kayak skills try the Vive La Montagne consultancy on www.vimadventure consultants.co.uk/. Even in the wild, you can't escape consultants.

making them return to sender. Eyewood sells four basic models which range in price only slightly from £20 to £25 including the cost of recorded delivery, Ordering at the moment is via post, cheque and postal order although the company will confirm your order by email.

Oswald Bailey
www.outdoorgear.co.uk
This is a great outdoors site absolutely packed with products – everything from tents and boots to mosquito head nets and waist wallets. You'll find decent product descriptions, very reasonable prices and an order tracking facility. But, though prices supposedly include mainland UK delivery, a £1 "carriage" charge will be tacked on to your final total. What makes this seem unforgivably underhand is that it's done only after you've entered your credit card details. Pity really because the rest of the site seems to support the boast on the homepage about how well loved this outdoor shop is.

Pennine Outdoor
www.pennineoutdoor.co.uk
Don't fancy the latest Berghaus fleece? Think you could improve on Patagonia's shorts? Then this site is for you. Pennine Outdoors sells a staggering range of specialist outdoor fabrics – everything from fleeces and breathable waterproofs to heavy duty neoprene-coated fabric (perfect for running up your own bivi bag). You can also buy patterns for outdoor gear, including one for a not very natty but no doubt functional Mountain Jacket, and even a child's hooded ski jacket. Freezing-temperature zips? No problem. Seam waterproofing? You can buy it here. Ordering is fairly straightforward (it's the choice that will be hard) and low-cost delivery takes 72 hours to most of the UK. The only complaint: there's simply too much information running down the left hand side of the home page.

Waist wallets? Don't be misled by the Ovaltiney colours, Oswald Bailey's is a great outdoor site

Pro-Line Sports

http://shop.proline-sports.co.uk

If the mind's willing but your flesh is weak, this is the place to come. Pro-Line Sports specialises in shoulder braces, knee supports, calf protectors, kidney belts, toe warmers... in fact, a whole range of outdoor body aids. The site has a brilliantly simple shopping system: simply skim your cursor over thumbnail product images for a description and price. Ordering is easy, delivery is free and there's a 30 day refund. Internet shopping should always be like this.

Simply Scuba

www.simplyscuba.co.uk

Billed as the UK's biggest online dive store, this site has everything the scuba diver or snorkeller could need. This excellent site has a phone back facility, order tracking, and a highly detailed chart matching dozens of body measurements to equipment size. Second-hand kits are for sale – details are on the message board, where you can add your own if you have something to sell.

Snow and Rock

www.snowandrock.co.uk

It isn't too hard to guess this site's speciality. Big brand skiing and climbing gear is arranged into categories (including a section for kids), but frustratingly, you can't cross-brand browse for a particular item. Delivery depends on cost, but though orders up to £100 supposedly incur a £2.50 charge, you may well find £4.50 added at the checkout. Rather unhelpfully, goods are dispatched only "as they become available". Plenty of pictures make the site pleasant to browse, and you'll find the usual range of clothing, tents, backpacks, etc, but you may prefer to buy from a site with delivery guarantees.

Stif Mountain Bikes

www.stif.co.uk

"Register – it's free" may not be the best invitation to splash across your homepage, but if you're into mountain biking, you'll find this site truly indispensable. There's a big selection of bikes on offer, plus associated "software" - bags, Oakley glasses, drinking systems (just so you know they're serious), jerseys, helmets – even replacement bike parts. Well designed, the site also features plenty of biking news and views to soften the sales edge.

Wild Spirit

www.wildspirit.co.uk

It might not have the most sophisticated website in the world, but this Northumberland-based store does offer a reasonable selection of outdoor clothing and equipment for everything from trekking to camping and mountain biking, and web customers get 10% off every order over £200. Downsides? You'll find your clicking finger aching by the time you actually access the shop, delivery can take up to 28 days, and there is no secure ordering system. You'll have to e-mail those credit card details if you're keen.

Parties

Let the Internet sort it all out with a bouncy castle, security cards, a tour on a double-decker bus and a Jane Asher cake only a few clicks away

General All you need for big kids and little ones

Dr Party
www.drparty.com
Fabulous site that will get you in the mood to party as soon as you reach the home page. Whether it's a raucous bash or a kiddies' tea party, there's plenty of advice and help here to make it all run smoothly so you can enjoy the event too. There are loads of links to party sites in the usual categories, plus a few you won't have thought of. Don't get on down without it.

Just For Fun
www.justforfun.co.uk
There are loads of fancy dress here for kids and grown-ups alike, along with decorations and joke items. Need the biggest afro you've ever seen? There's one here for just £9.99. The site is user-friendly and well-designed with a good help section if you get lost among the bunting. Delivery is within two days, but next-day service is available if you order by phone.

Party E-Time
www.partyetime.co.uk
Suppliers of party goods for children's parties and other celebrations, with some great time-saving theme packs containing items like banners, table cloths and napkins, based on kids' favourite characters or movies. There are also dress up items like masks, or you can email for details of full costumes.

The Party Store
www.thepartystore.co.uk
Huge selection of party goods with almost any theme you can think of catered for, including pirates or the Roaring Twenties. The pest novelty items include *pinatas* for kids parties and inflatable guitars for a rock'n'roll themed event.

There are helpful suggestions on each page of co-ordinating products for you to consider, plus lots of planning tip and ideas for harrassed hosts. Standard delivery time is three to four days and the costs are £3.50 on orders up to £70 (after that it's free), or you can arrange a next day service for £6.50.

Party Time

www.partytime.co.uk

This is a helpful planning site to remind you of all the things you need to really make a party swing. There are links and contact details for party suppliers, entertainers and caterers, plus ideas for games and general good times.

 From fireworks to restaurant tours

Balloons

www.webshops.co.uk/shops/The_Balloon_StoreD

This simple, easy to navigate site offers a range of party balloons from adorable heart shapes to balloons for modelling, along with more standard shapes and colours. If you're after a lot of balloon décor for your bash, you should save money here. There's speedy, secure online ordering and the goods are promised to reach you within five working days.

Balloons

www.kentballoon.co.uk

Secure online ordering was not yet up and running when we visited but the hassle of ordering by phone or e-mail is worth it if you're after personalised balloons for a special celebration. All styles can be printed with a message of up to five words and you can even rent helium gas equipment through the site so your guests can giggle in Mickey Mouse voices later in the evening.

Fireworks

http://208.185.197.122/fantfire.html

You can request a display to be created for you at this outstanding (and very noisy) fireworks site, or simply buy one of their ready packs to use at home. There's information on each kit which tells you how much space you need to be safe with the display and how noisy each of the rocket packs will be.

Party Express

www.partybus.co.uk

If you're looking for something a bit different for your party, why not consider a tailor-made party outing on double decker buses? This site offers nightclub or restaurant tours of London, Newcastle, Brighton and Blackpool. Costs vary depending on the tour (most are around £40 per person) and the number of people in your group. The online booking service was still being set up when visited, but you can email through the site to make your reservations.

Hired help | From bouncy castles to security

Accessories
www.hss.co.uk
Disco lights, smoke machines and bouncy castles are available to hire here, along with catering equipment and glass and plate hire if you're planning a really big event. Prices are reasonable and HSS will deliver all items to you on the morning of your party as long as you give them enough notice.

Entertainment
www.mmssoft.force9.co.uk
For a touch of the kitsch you can always hire an entertainment act to liven up your evening. Acts from stand-up comedians to puppeteers and from after-dinner speakers to The Fraud Monty are profiled on this site and you can e-mail or phone their agents for further details and prices.

Jane Asher Party Cakes
www.jane-asher.co.uk
Impress the socks off your birthday boy or girl with a flash cake from Jane Asher's shop in Chelsea. You can chose from fruit cake or sponge cake and there are a number of fancy designs to choose from, including one in the shape of a Game Boy. The speed at which this reviewer's cake disappeared is a glowing testimonial to how good they are. Use the online order form to send them your request and then phone your credit card details through, but remember that they do need seven days notice to get the cake to you.

Jane Asher's site now includes a home baking page for those of you with six months to spare to recreate one of her designs

Security
www.idcband.co.uk
For those who are getting into party organising in a big way and are concerned about security for their event, this site can supply ID wrist bands, hand stamps and stewards' vests to guard against gate-crashers and other party trouble. They can also supply a range of table-top party bombs which can be themed for your event. You can email them for further details and request a sample of most items through the site.

Pets & pet supplies

Evening primrose vitamins for cats, pizzas for dogs – amazing what you can find on the Net

Animail

www.animail.co.uk

With quick and simple registration and a bright, inviting cartoon homepage, you can't help but be swayed into spoiling your pet. Luxuries range from the extravagant pine cat-bed for £129.99 to the more modest furry cat-tunnel for £7.99, or a pizza specially created for your pooch. Unfortunately difficulties with broken links and poor directions left this visitor searching for a more organised venture. The free gift for new customers was partial compensation.

Pets on the Brain

www.petsonthebrain.com

This run-of-the-mill site offers food, toys and equipment for your animal, whether it's a cat, dog, horse, or common garden-variety lizard. With items such as a large heated rock for reptiles costing £30, it's advisable to join their club for discounts on everything. The downside is that once you've registered, it asks for your credit card details for you to be eligible for the discount.

Pet Emporium

www.petemporium.co.uk

Resembling *Gardeners Weekly* rather than a pet site, the cat- and dogalogue are limited, with an obvious range of cat baskets, scratching posts and dog homes. The most unusual item is a zebra-print duvet cover for £26.75. Most annoyingly, you need to view a separate page to find out prices and you can only empty your entire basket as opposed to removing items one by one.

Pet Mad

www.petmad.com

A multitude of colours and categories makes this site seem a complete nightmare at first glance. Once you're in, however, it's easy to use, offering pet food, beds, toys and ailment remedies, plus the option of searching by animal, product or category. Some brand-name foods are available at around half supermarket prices – e.g. 11 Whiskas Singles at £2.20 rather than £4.50. Best of all, for those who remain wary of ordering over the Internet, Pet Mad will take you step by step through the ordering process and send you and your pet a free gift, no purchase necessary. If more sites offered this kind of facility, maybe they'd get more sales.

Petz Online
www.petz.co.uk
Once past the dull, sterile homepage, you'll find the extensive category list holds endless varieties of dog collars, cat combs and varieties of chipmunk food. Prices are reasonable, but poor descriptions and a lack of images lets this site down.

Pets Park
www.petspark.com
Pets Park may opt for the same headache-inducing colours as many other sites, but it offers the natural way to pamper your pet. Organic catnip toys and Evening Primrose vitamins for your cat were new to this visitor, but the strangest feature was one on the pros of acupuncture treatment. It even offers food for less domesticated animals, such as the hedgehog or rat. This unusual site is easy to navigate, cheap and informative, with reasons why you should be feeding your pet vitamins, rather than just saying you should.

Pet Planet
www.petplanet.co.uk
This site offers news on pet services, particular breeds, vets and pet passport information. The shopping offers the usual dog, cat and bird items, along with more innovative ideas such as a thermal bed or grooming mitten. The free pet goody-bag after you've registered is one bonus, as is the promise that if you order before noon they'll deliver the same day if the product is in stock. If it isn't, your new account is credited with £10. The lost pet service is good too.

Pets Pyjamas
www.pets-pyjamas.co.uk
Pets Pyjamas have revamped their site recently, so this visitor can only pity those who tried to shop here before. A sister site to Animail, it may offer hundreds of of items of pet paraphernalia but the type is too small to read without getting a headache, the category links don't always work and the key-word search is too non-specific. One for the dedicated pet-owner only.

Phones

Whether you're after a
fashion accessory, something you
can use to access the Internet or
just a tasteless novelty to appal the
neighbours with, the Net can help

Brands The hippest way to say you're on the train

Alcatel
www.alcatel.com/consumer
Alcatel's bubblegum-design mobiles are distributed through French company
Walkyries, so you, *l'internaute*, are protected by the French Code de la
Consommation. You can also pay in euros – a One Touch 300 will set you
back around e252. Colourful and attractive, but it's a pity the navigation isn't
better – essential phone specs are hidden away at the bottom of the site.
Prices start at around £120, but you will need to sort out line rental elsewhere.

Siemens
www.ic.siemens.com/mySiemens?world=MW
Titchy phones, including the latest M35I and the C35i, plus the incredibly
svelte and well-designed IC35 Communicator. Warning: you won't manage to
successfully link to the checkout facility if you're going there via a firewall.

Networks You've got the hardware, now hook up

BT Cellnet
www.btcellnet.co.uk
BT manages to demonstrate once again why it is way ahead the field with
its simplistic yet comprehensive shopping site. Choose from the very latest
mobile models from top brands Ericsson, Nokia and Siemens, and select
either Pay As You Go or monthly tariffs to suit your budget. Unlike a number
of outlets, here you can choose your own combination to suit your needs,
and if you're not sure what these might be, simply answer a few questions
and the site will come up with the best package for you.

Phones

Orange
www.orange.co.uk
Blissfully uncluttered and clear. Orange offers four different tariffs and a choice of the latest phones. Descriptions of the tariffs are available alongside a choice of phones, or go straight to the product range.

One2One
www.one2one.co.uk
Fancy but fast to download, with easy-to-spot buttons to navigate with, this is a slick info-packed site but repeat visits suggested a few technical glitches.

Virgin
www.virginmobile.com/mobile/
The bearded chap's site easy to use, and also also allows you to check whether the phone you have is compatible with their network.

Vodafone
www.vodafone-retail.co.uk
The site is zippy to navigate and the choice of mobiles is excellent, but the tariffs aren't exactly in yer face and their layout is cramped and hard to read.

Re-sellers Hot deals from your friendly salesman

Carphone Warehouse
www.carphonewarehouse.com
An excellent, non-scary site. If you're an old hand, opt for the express service, simply choose a tariff and a phone and buy. If you're a mobile virgin, opt for the interactive service. Said to take around 30 minutes, it took this visitor only 15 to find a network, tariff and phone tailored to individual needs.

Direct Phones
www.directphones.co.uk
Once you move past the initially confusing homepage, the site is easy to use and buy from. It's a case of choosing from three of the five networks, several tariffs and popular models from Siemens, Panasonic and Ericsson. Direct Phones throws in freebies such as £50 cash back with its Simcards.

Just Phones
www.justphones.co.uk
Alongside the usual selection of new contract and pre-pay mobiles, this busy and happy site lets you choose a second-hand model, with prices ranging from £15 to £250 for the latest Panasonic GD92. Or you can bid in the auction and pick up a Motorola V.3688 for less than £100. If you already have a phone going spare, sell it online or buy a Simcard package from the usual networks.

A WAP rap

So who wants to phone for a pizza?

You know those irritating types who wave their spring-loaded Nokia WAP phones around in bars, acting as though they have access to a really hip and exclusive variant of the Internet that us common mortals can only dream of?

Well, all they can currently do with their fancy Keanu-in-The-Matrix fashion accessory is buy pizza. Or maybe the odd bunch of flowers and a cinema ticket. Not exactly going to save the earth from unnameable evil, is it?

The fact is that although WAP (**Wireless Application Protocol**) has been the cause of much excitement, and has spurred techno manufacturers to produce some rather lovely phones (such as the aforementioned Nokia 7110, the svelte, grown-up Ericsson R320, the Motorola L7389, the Sony CMD Z5 with its rather weird not-all-there screen cover and the virtually wearable Alcatel 300 series), the WAP world is still gravely lacking in the actual-things-to-do-and-buy department. And, even more humiliating for the WAP fashion victims, we can reveal that it's currently actually faster (and certainly cheaper) to order your pizza via an ordinary phone call.

That's partly down to a **lack of agreement** between the big players over which **delivery platform** to use – in fact, the jury is still very much out on the topic of whether WAP is the way to go. Most of the networks' early WAP services have been provided courtesy of GSM (Global System for Mobile Communications), although Orange has boldly forged off on its own with a technology called HSCSD (High Speed Circuit Switched Data), which makes you dial up any time you want to download something. GPRS (General Packet Radio System), expected to be more widely available early in 2001, is better as the line is always open and you pay only for the data you download, but this technology requires you to spend your Christmas cash on a new handset. There's much excitement over **iMode**, DoCoMo's Japanese mobile technology, as it appears to be more efficient than the European solutions and has been snapped up by an astonishing 10 million happy Japanese subscribers. But as **adopting it** would necessitate **trashing everything** the industry has developed so far, it'll probably stay in the land of the rising sun while the rest of us muddle through in the land of the rising phone bill.

So it will probably be **nearer Christmas 2001** before there's meaningful **shopping** to be had **via WAP** (supermarkets are expected to get in on the act soon). By then, retailers will have cottoned on to the fact that it's best to leave out the 'Mobile Internet' pretence and serve up straight data feeds with the information you want. It'll be faster, cheaper and if companies don't get snitty about making their stock information available, will mean that you'll be able to suss out which store has the style or model you want in the colour and size you want, at the right price, even as you saunter up the high street.

In the meantime, price your pizza at www.iobox.com, www.checka price.com or www.gelon.net's **Wapalizer** while you dream of joys to come.

Talking Shop

www.talkingshop.co.uk

This site operates as a supplier for every network, tariff and phone manufacturer, so it's easy to see how things have become complicated. Once you get over the retina-crunching design, the site itself is easier to navigate than you'd expect, but in-depth information is lacking. It's often not clear what you're actually going to be charged for, and though some of the deals that sound great value, the lack of reassuring small print leaves you with the feeling that they could be too good to be true.

Novelties "All in the best possible taste"

North Coast Phone Center

www.phonecenter.net/

If you fancy a phone which really makes a statement, why not have one styled to look like R2D2, a bag of golf clubs or even a pair of red pouting lips? You'll find all these and more here – but you may not find instant e-gratification, as it was impossible to confirm whether they delivered to the UK. Of course, if you really like the sound of these phones you could do a Victor Kiam and buy the company, as when this visitor logged on, there was a small sign on the home page which read "This business is for sale"…

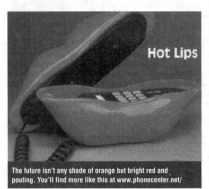

Hot Lips

The future isn't any shade of orange but bright red and pouting. You'll find more like this at www.phonecenter.net/

Property

Finding your home sweet home can be a doddle (well, almost) if you take a look online

Buy & sell — Track down the home of your dreams

Asserta Home
www.asserta.co.uk
You'll find 100,000 or so properties listed here, from estate agents throughout the country. Each entry comes with a handy, if sometimes depressing, estimate of how much a mortgage would cost on that property. Other excellent features include directories of local tradesmen in each area.

Easier
www.easier.co.uk
You have to register as a user first and the search engine can be temperamental but this site does have a huge database of properties up for private sale. If you're looking for anything from an ex-council flat near Harrods to a barn conversion in Herefordshire, there are online brochures to be viewed and printed out, plus plenty of instructions and tips for both sellers and buyers.

08004Homes
www.08004homes.com
Property portal with excellent choice of channels, including one for interiors and another for the experts' view of what's happening to the housing market. Properties for sale are registered by estate agents: buyers can search through the thousands listed and link to the agent's pages for more info.

Home Check
www.homecheck.co.uk
Not a sales site but definitely one to check before you buy. Enter your postcode and it gives local information on potential problems like pollution, subsidence, flood risk, landfill sites and air quality. Some of these might come up in your Local Authority search or your survey. No Northern Ireland, Scotland or Isle of Man coverage yet, but it's coming, so they say.

Property

DOING IT YOURSELF

Dreaming of a self-built mock-Tudor dream, or a gleaming homage to Le Corbusier? ebuild (www.ebuild.co.uk) is low on visuals but is well designed, as you'd expect, and is a source-goldmine of architects', legal help, products and services directories. If the story of the Three Little Pigs never struck home try www.mayabooks.ndirect.co.uk/selfbuild.html for how to build your very own straw house. More practical souls should try www.mw scaffolding.demon.co.uk/selfBuild, or www. housemag.net, for help on project planning and planning permission.

House Net

www.housenet.co.uk

Dealing with both private sellers and estate agents, this site has a vast number of properties on view, from seafront flats in Hove to a traditional farmhouse with stables and barns in Warwickshire. On this site, however, small classified listings are free. This means very few people have gone for the option of paying £17.63 to have a photo added to their page, and almost no one has gone for the full-details option for £29.95, so the browsing process is incredibly frustrating. Links to regional estate agents are more useful.

Houseweb

www.houseweb.com

Launched in 1996, this site really is user-friendly, with 150,000 properties and features like auto-notify to let you know when a property matching your criteria comes up. Specify either a wide search, with hundreds of properties to browse, or narrow it right down if you know you won't be happy without a fireplace, gas cooker and a garden.

London Home Net

www.londonhomenet.com

London-only site aimed at private sellers and landlords, with a special section for flatshare listings. There's a one-off sales payment of £45 (£29 for lettings, free for flatshares) for which you get a full web page that will stay on the site until you sell your house, plus a photographer to snap the property if you live in Zones 1-4. All sellers and landlords who register a property are sent an information pack with tips on stumbling blocks like price negotiation and legal aspects of the sale or let, putting this service a cut above the rest.

Property Broker

www.propertybroker.co.uk

A site aimed at private sellers within the M25 looking to sidestep the estate agent's fees. For a flat £58 fee, the site will send a photographer to take quality digital pictures of your home, list your property details and photos on the website, and they'll put up a sale board if you want one. Buyers can search or browse, then e-mail or phone sellers to make an appointment.

Property Finder

www.propertyfinder.co.uk

Search engine for sorting through the thousands of properties on estate agents' books. Using your specified postcodes, bedroom requirements and whether you want a flat or house, the site will come up with all matching properties plus easy links to contact the agents they are selling through. Fast and efficient with distractions kept to the minimum, but there's no browsing and the selection of properties at last glimpse was just 32,000 nationwide.

Really Moving
www.reallymoving.com
Practical, well designed and fun to surf portal that guides you through the whole house moving process with skill and reassurance. There are just 20,000-ish properties to look at, but the real benefits of this site are things like the email service to remind you of all the things you must do when moving house, from commissioning a survey to forwarding your mail. There are also online quotes on services like removals and spring cleaning your new home.

Under One Roof
www.underoneroof.com
Stylish site for housebuyers. Listings include information on new developments as well as estate agent-registered homes, with some fancy extras like a quick mortgage calculator and 3-D tours of some properties. The best item on the site is the Home Check service, where you can pay to have a dossier compiled on any property to check such things as noisy neighbours, if the street is used as a rat-run for local traffic, if a drug dealer lives upstairs… all essential details that no one will tell you before you buy.

Up My Street
www.upmystreet.com
The ultimate information site, containing demographic details for the area you are considering moving to, often in graph form. The data is usually incredibly detailed, offering insights on everything from average house prices, school performance and contact details for local tradesmen to which newspapers your new neighbours read. Vital for those relocating over any distance, but interesting if you're thinking of buying a new house and a fascinating browse.

Unusual homes Psst! Wanna buy a pyramid?

Pavilions of Splendour
www.heritage.co.uk
If you're longing to find a home that isn't a three-bedroom semi in a greenfield development on the outskirts of a major city, then Pavilions of Splendour may be able to help. This company specialises in unusual and historic properties, often listed and even more often in need of a great deal of TLC. Since many properties have had preservation orders slapped on them, you have to be prepared to fork out vast wads of cash and spend weekends raking through architectural supply yards just to repair a window (no self-styled Handy Andys need apply) but a look through their portfolio may convince you it's worth it.

Ken Lund's Islands for Sale

www.islandsforsale.com

Always dreamed of doing a Richard Branson and buying your very own island? Ken Lund's your man with plenty of dreams to choose from. He specialises in the stunning islands off the coast of British Columbia, but if you're after a slice of Caribbean or Pacific heaven, he can help you there too. A five acre island just east of Nassau will set you back a cool $259,000, but after a few rum punches, you're unlikely to care that much.

Greek property

www.parosweb.gr/house/

Included as a warning, because it's a good (bad) example of the kind of site you'll have to trawl through if you're looking for that dream Mediterranean home. The home page unfolds to reveal a picture of a property on the Greek island of Paros. A cheesy Mediterranean rock theme blares out and you're told to click on the picture to view the property from different angles. This proves, eventually, to be true. But your only means of getting hold of such trivia as "how much does it cost?" is to email the Webmaster. It's a miracle this site attracted even 6207 visitors in its first nine months. For a bona fide version of this type of site, try www.symi-island.gr/restate.html and check out the properties on the site belonging to Greek estate agent Doma.

Phi Designs

www.phidesigns.com

Eco-architecture practice in Oregon specialising in the construction of hugely funky solar pyramid homes which they reckon would work just fine in the South of England (sorry, Scotland: not enough sun). Lots of pictures and details on energy conservation and materials used. If you want to find out how to get one of your own, you can e-mail the architect through the site.

Tropical Islands

www.tropical-islands.com/

The Internet address which would most appeal to 21st century Robinson Crusoes. And don't worry if you haven't got the £6.7m in your current account to buy an island off the Bahamas, you can lease yourself 1.2 acres of tropical paradise for a year for a £6000 deposit and £6200 in rent. Mind you, Lord knows where you're going to live while the local builders knock up a quick eco-lodge. But after all, as the home page says, who wouldn't want "your own kingdom in today's developed world"?

Snake island

www.webwave.com/snakeisland/

The owners of this 53-acre island (less an island, more an "experience" according to the site) off the coast of California will listen to any offers. So even if you haven't got the $2.5m recommended retail price it's worth emailing them. The picture of Rattle Snake Island seems to indicate that you'll have your own private jetty. But the valuation does appear to be based on the idea that if you buy it, you'd want to build a casino, golf course, and health spa on your isle, which seems to defeat the point.

World of private islands

www.vladi-private-islands.de/home_e.html

Welcome to one of the most comprehensive island sites on the Net. While some sites offer you the island equivalent of a package

Why bother with the one-bed flat in Wandsworth, when you can afford a prime slice of Norwegian real estate?

holiday in Marbella, Vladi Private Islands has something for the more independently minded, like Flatholmen, 1.25 acres of "peace, relaxation and pure nature, off the northern coast of Norway," for £137,000. Millionaires of a sunnier disposition might prefer to lash out £5m on the 52-acre Isola Gallinara near Genoa. If islands really aren't your thing, you can also find a palace near Cologne or express and interest in viewing billionaire Malcolm Forbes' old estate in Morocco.

Finance Don't forget to read the small print...

John Charcol

www.charcolonline.co.uk

The Mortgage Wizard search engine scans the products from 45 different mortgage lenders to find the exact deal for you, some of which are exclusive deals done with the high street names and which can make amazing-value bargains for those who qualify. It can also offer you a mortgage if you're one of those people many banks won't touch – the self-employed, those with a poor credit history, or people wanting to buy to let.

Ashley Page and Veingard

www.consultant-insurance.co.uk

Buying insurance direct can seem like the way to save money, but sometimes, especially if you have some high-end kit you need extra cover for, using an insurance broker is better as you get a more individual approach, plus support if you need to make a claim. This site outlines the services the broker will offer you, and you can e-mail queries, after which you will be contacted to discuss your requirements further.

Direct Line

www.directline.com

Online arm of the TV-advertised insurance giant. Plenty of information here about Direct Line Household Buildings and Contents Insurance (including the whole policy document to download if you're really keen on small print). The basic outline of cover, including legal protection, leads you to a tailored quotation, which you can accept and purchase, all online. Mac users might find they have a problem with some of the quotation pages, but Direct Line assures us they are investigating the problem.

Easy Quote

www.easy-quote.co.uk

If you're concerned that requesting an insurance quotation online will bring a never-ending stream of sales calls, then this site is probably your best bet as Easy Quote promises no one will hassle you once it has provided a quote from one of the company's respected insurance partners, which include Northern Rock, CGU and Norwich Union.

Grove Insurance Services

www.grove-is.co.uk

Straightforward independent site offering quotations on policies from over 60 different insurance companies, along with advice on which one is likely to be the best for you. Fill in the detailed online form for a free initial quotation and you will be e-mailed information within a couple of days.

Promise

www.ipromise.co.uk

If you're looking for a new mortgage or to re-mortgage, Promise can offer you an online quotation in moments, followed by a speedy online application if you like what you see. It doesn't lock you in with redemption penalties and offers flexible products, some incorporating payment holidays and the chance to overpay. Mortgage virgins should check out the indispensable jargon buster, which explains financial terms in words everyone can understand.

Northern Insurance Direct

www.northern-direct.co.uk

A fast service, designed to get you a quote based on information you provide. Not much detail on what household policies cover on this site, but it lets you learn more about the policies and find one tailored to your needs.

Wise Money

www.wisemoney.com

Here, you'll find quotes offered on household insurance, mortgages and other financial products. You have to register in order to get a full quotation, but the site is easy to navigate and quick to respond, so if you're serious about looking for a mortgage lender or insurer, this is a good place to start.

Records, CDs etc

Music on the Net is a vast virtual treasure trove where you can find anything from the Farmer's Boys to the raw early recordings of Winston Churchill

General Sites where you can find (almost) anything

101cd.com

www.101cd.com

By autumn 2000, this store was boasting that it had over 1.6m titles online. It's easy to be cynical about such claims. After all, who actually bothered to count them? But there's enough stock on display to convince you that, for once in commercial cyberspace, they're probably not exaggerating. Probably the only criticism that you could lob at them is that although you can browse music by price and search by artist, it's not easy to browse by category.

Action Records

www.action-records.co.uk

The online arm of one of the UK's largest independent record stores covers most of the bases from country/folk through rock to ambient, dance and indie. You can download the catalogue, which is probably easier than trying to find your title on the site in the absence of any easy-to-use mechanism. There is a search button on the homepage but after repeated attempts, keying in artists known to be listed on the site, it just returned this visitor to the homepage. You have to know what you want because the description begins and ends with the artist, title, format and price.

Amazon

www.amazon.co.uk

Best known for books, Amazon's online music store is definitely worth perusing because you can find some good value on offer here. For example, in the site's exotica section, David Byrne and Brian Eno's acclaimed collaboration *My Life In The Bush Of Ghosts* is available for just £7.99.

Boxman
http://www.boxman.co.uk
Proof that online stores don't have to stun the visitor with flash graphics or in-your-face typography, Boxman's site design is so quiet it's positively reclusive. But whether you're into pop, soul, dance, jazz or country, there's something here for you. The FAQ is typical of the rest of this excellent site: clear, to the point and yet exhaustive.

British independent record dealers
www.birdpages.purplenet.co.uk
Don't be put off by the plethora of options and luminous coloured type on the homepage, this directory of British record dealers is a useful gateway to stores throughout the UK. You can search for dealers alphabetically, by location and by genre and there are some great links for collectors too. This site is so ridiculously useful that every other industry association should be forced to visit this URL to see how it should be done.

CD Now
www.cdnow.com
Not so much a distinctive homepage as a homage to Amazon, CD Now has a whacking great stock archive, including Japanese imports and the 23-track *Ultimate Collection* by Benny Hill, for just $6.37. Delivery charges vary but you are notified before you're asked to place your order. A damn fine site.

CD Wow
www.cd-wow.com
Not to be confused with the above and not to be confused with a really big music shop because many searches of the database suggested that the shop only sells the most recent or most obvious titles for many artists. That said, the prices are very keen (most of the top 75 CDs are on sale at around £8.99) and there's a neat guide to how to use the site.

Click Music
www.clickmusic.co.uk
You'll think you've been Tangoed from this vibrant orange directory with everything you could possibly

---

THE FAQs

How can I post my band's MP3 files? You could try any of: *www.clickmusic.co.uk*, *www.crunch.co.uk*, or *www.peoplesound.com*

Where can I watch bands online? You'll find details of RealVideo live shows on *www.virtuetv.com*

Which is the best newsgroup for musicians? Try *alt.music.makers.dj*

Where can I find out tour dates? There's a brilliant search engine/ordering site at *www.aloud.com*

Where is the best place to search for a band site? Probably *www.ubl.com* but *www.bigmouth.co.uk* is not bad either

Artists The stars can't leave home without a homepage

members.tripod.com/-tax4158/pepper.html	The Beatles
www.davidbowie.com	David Bowie
www.catatonia.com	Catatonia
www.bobdylan.com	Bob Dylan
www.bryanferry.com	Bryan Ferry
www.macygray.com	Macy Gray
www.jamiroquai.co.uk	Jamiroquai
www.bbking.com	B.B. King
www.manics.co.uk	Manic Street Preachers
www.bobmarley.com	Bob Marley
www.videoranch.com	Michael Nesmith
www.oasisinet.com	Oasis
www.des-oconnor.com	Des O'Connor
www.elvispresley.com	Elvis Presley
www.love4another.com	Prince
www.radiohead.co.uk	Radiohead
www.remhq.com	REM
www.stereophonics.co.uk	Stereophonics
www.supergrass.com	Supergrass
www.travisonline.com	Travis
www.robbiewilliams.co.uk	Robbie Williams
www.weirdal.com/home.htm	Weird Al Yankovic

want to know about the music world. See who's topping the charts, gigging and generally mincing around, with news bulletins every five minutes. John Peel's successor as music guru, Steve Lamacq, surveys MP3 sites and the shopping directory lists specialist shops as well as your high-street HMVs.

Crotchet
www.crotchet.co.uk
Idiosyncratic site which 'specialises', if that's not putting it too narrowly, in classical music, jazz, world music, film music and soundtracks. The site has a *Which?* Web Trader seal of approval for secure ordering and has a lovely ambience, almost as if you'd popped into your local independent store for a natter with the owner. The added attraction online is that you can search the database which contains, for instance, 92 items on jazz saxophonist Stan Getz.

Disc'n'Tape
www.disc-n-tape.co.uk
The site comes equipped with a huge but quirky database. You won't find all artists listed here – note the exclusion of Macy Gray and inclusion of Ann Gray

(and there's no Les Gray either) – but the directory is pretty comprehensive and easy to navigate. If you can't find the musical object of your desire you are invited to email the company with your request. While this kind of invitation can often be ranked in the top five lies of modern business (just above "People are our most important asset"), Disc'n'Tape says it can find every CD, LP, MC,12in, 7in, DVD and Mini Disc now available in the UK. High-street prices apply but immediate shipping is free in the UK.

Dotmusic
www.dotmusic.com
Originally an online extension of trade mag and all-round industry bible *Music Week*, this site is now visited by professionals and punters alike, not primarily to shop but for the latest news. The shop, which looks like it has been tacked on to the back, helps the site pay its way and is actually far more comprehensive than it might seem at first glance, so it's worth a try. Other mag sites with online stores include **www.nme.com** and the fast-improving (but still disappointing if you buy the magazine) **www.qonline.co.uk**.

Eil/Esprit
www.eil.com
Fancy that Japanese limited edition picture disc by your favourite artist which came out 10 years ago and was only sent to the country's DJs? Well, this is the place to begin your quest. Ignore the flannel about this being "the world's biggest and best online music store". This site is far better than such macho marketing posturing might suggest, containing, for instance, The Farmer's Boys seminal slice of East Anglian rock *Muck It Out* in its pig-shaped picture-disc format. But be warned: you can get addicted to searching this site. If rarity really turns you on, you could also try **www.vinyltap.co.uk**.

Big discounts are the star attraction at Music For Sale, but the vast catalogue is not to be dismissed lightly

HMV

www.hmv.co.uk

Nice-looking (using Elvis's favourite colour combination of pink and black) and well-organised, this site reeks of tender loving care. It covers all the usual categories, and highlights webcasts and free downloads from the likes of Peter Gabriel. Pity the search mechanism can be a tad slow.

Music 365

www.music365.com

From the people who brought you Football 365, this is a decent site which offers the visitor the latest news as well as an extensive CD shop and a nice little earner (for Music 365 and Boxman) called 2000 for 2000, where you can find reasonably authoritative reviews of top albums.

Music For Sale

www.musicforsale.co.uk

Some swingeing discounts on normal retail prices are the main attraction here, although the online catalogue is vast. Don't click on the covers of the CDs on the homepage unless you want to add them to your virtual shopping basket. In fact, the same happens if you click on the title of the album or the price! A good site to save money.

Purple Haze

www.purplehaze-records.com

With a database containing more than 100,000 entries and all prices below £10, it's a shame this Darlington-based site didn't opt for a more stylish design in its recent revamp. Catalogue entries range from the B-52's, Snoop Doggy Dog and the Black Crowes. But there are bargains galore here: many CDs are less than £5 and postage is £1.25 for the first item and 50p for each one after that.

Tower Records

http://www.towereurope.com
or www.towerrecords.com

If you want to increase your options, you could browse both the American and European sites. As you would expect, both are decently stocked, with a wide range of titles, sound samples and free

---

SLEAZY LISTENING

This top 10 of online music sales, from a random week in the Net's life, shows that surfers have no better taste than offline fans

1 Eminem
The Marshall Mathers LP

2 Britney Spears
Oops!...I Did It Again

3 Red Hot Chili Peppers
Californication

4 Carlos Santana
Supernatural

5 N-Sync
No Strings Attached

6 Moby
Play

7 Dr Dre
The Chronic 2001

8 Creed
Human Clay

9 Backstreet Boys
Millennium

10 Shania Twain
Come On Over

Source:
www.cddb.com

World domination **The world music giants**

Amazon
www.amazon.com amazon.co.uk
Awesome search engine which will pull up almost any US or UK release and much besides, often with audio samples, reviews from customers and (soon) Rough Guides' music books, making vast acquisitions dangerously easy.

Borders.com
www.borders.com
Borders is a nice, clean, browsable site very much like its terrestrial stores. There is a reasonably deep catalogue and array of sound samples.

cdnow.com
www.cdnow.com
Pretty good on Latin music and they have keen prices with lots of samples.

CD Universe
www.cduniverse.com
CD Universe's world music section is well laid out, browsable country-by-country, with an excellent search engine and a far-ranging catalogue.

Hearns Music
www.hearnsmusic.com
Global mail-order company which reckons it can lay its hands on more than 60,000 world music titles. All enquiries, however weird, are welcome.

Tower.com
www.towerrecords.com or
www.towereurope.com
Tower's US and European sites deliver impressive catalogue returns and they have sound samples for a huge number of discs. If you know what you're looking for, you stand a very good chance of finding it here.

downloads. Because of the absurd price of CDs in this country, you can find bargains on the US site, eg B.B. King's *Blues on The Bayou* is $13.99 on the US site and £14.49 in Europe. You don't have to find too many CDs you want to buy to pay for the cost of shipping from the US and still save money. (The same technique might also save you money if you're buying your sounds from Amazon.) The only criticism of the European site is that in busy times you might get a "sorry we're unavailable" message – the online version of the local post office shutting in everybody else's lunch hour.

Waterloo Records
www.waterloorecords.com
A rare curio amidst all the musical hypermarkets selling music over the Net, Waterloo is based in Austin, Texas, although curiously it uses the sign for the London underground station as its logo (a tribute to The Kinks?). You can find releases by anyone from Aaron Neville to Joe Cocker and Sarah Brightman, but the main attraction is the huge stock of Texan and rootsy music. If Papa Mali & The Instigators' *Thunder Chicken* does it for you, then you'll find it here. If you're not au fait with this kind of stuff, you might have trouble telling the name of the artist from the title of the album. The site doesn't (yet) accept credit card orders online but you can email them and phone in your details.

W H Smith
www.whsmith.co.uk
The music section of W H Smith Online is far more extensive than you might think from the rather mainstream product on display in some of its high-street branches. This site offers keen prices, a vast catalogue and a tickertape of names like Shania Twain and Morcheeba advancing across the screen. Check out also the sister site www.cdparadise.com/hme/hmepge.asp which has a wealth of stock at such unfamiliar (to the high street) prices as £7.99.

Waterloo Records: not very big on Abba but there's no better place to buy Papa Mali and the Instigators

Ferrets, dwarves, woofing cookies and suburban nightmares. It can only be Midnight Records

 For connoisseurs, experts and utter posers

BLUES

Midnight Records

www.midnightrecords.com

Midnight is such a great name for a blues label that you warm to this site at once and if you like the blues, you won't be disappointed. The site looks and reads like a fanzine but the catalogue is exhaustive, spanning blues, rock and rock'n'roll, and including such obscure acts as The Ferrets, Dwarves, Suburban Nightmare and the Woofing Cookies, some of whom are on Midnight's own label. There's secure ordering and delivery to the UK costs a B.B. King-sized $7.50 for the first item and $2.75 for each one after that.

CLASSICAL AND JAZZ

Classical 33

www.classical33.co.uk

This offers more than 8000 CDs and LPs of classical recording to browse through, although you have to download the regularly updated catalogue (in html or Microsoft Excel) to see what's on offer. We're not sure what to make of the Russian and Oriental brides agency advertised prominently here.

Counterpoint Music

www.counterpoint-music.com

Search for all kinds of jazz CDs, from Big Bands to solo artists, at excellent prices on this US-based site. There's lots of stuff here you won't find on the big commercial sites, and they can even try and hunt down a special order for you if you can't find what you want. International shipping costs start at $4.

LP Classics
www.lpclassics.co.uk
This is a basic site offering vintage vinyl recordings of classical music. You can download the catalogue and order through the site, although the form is not secure so you might prefer to phone. Delivery costs vary, and reflect the breakable nature of the LPs, so it may be best to buy more than one at a time.

Timewarp
www.tunes.co.uk/timewarp
An online CD store with a strong emphasis on unusual jazz and jazz-based music. Be-bop rubs shoulders with trip hop with titles searchable by artist or title. CDs cost 25p each to mail, LPs cost 75p and deliveries take two to three days.

COUNTRY
County Sales
www.countysales.com
From old-time banjo music to modern bluegrass and fiddle, this Virginia-based site is as country as grits. The extensive catalogue includes popular and rare work from Bob Amos and his new bluegrass sounds, to Druha Trave and their blend of country from the Czech Republic. Don't be put off by the fact that this is a US site: most albums cost $8-$13 and shipping is a bargain at $6 for six to eight CDs.

The Music Barn
www.themusicbarn.com
Asking you to get all nostalgic and remember your first barn dance in the same ilk as your first car may seem slightly extreme, but the CDs and cassettes on sale here are old skool country if there is such a thing. Vernon Dalhart and Lulu Belle & Scotty are among the limited onsite database, and if they have nothing to suit you can print out their complete catalogue.

DANCE MUSIC
Juno Records
www.juno.co.uk
This functional site is extremely easy to use but rather bland. No reviews, just the complete listings of new dance releases in the UK and the chance to hear

---

THAT'S CRAP THAT IS...

It's hard to resist a site called Collecting Crap Records. When you open www.78rpm.sonow.com/002/CRWHY.htm you see an album sleeve starring a fake Loch Ness monster for a record by The Improvisors called, appropriately enough, 'Loch Nessie'.

Nor is that the oddest record alluded to on a site devoted to pop music's dustbin. That closely contested honour probably goes (just) to an EP recorded by *Animal Magic* host Johnny Morris for Winalot.

For more in this line try http://franklarosa.com/$spindb.query.new.vinyl although the inclusion of the Banana Splits in this site's compilation of the musically disadvantaged does undermine its credibility somewhat.

them, then buy them. There's a secure shopping trolley and you'll know exactly how much your choice costs and how soon it will get to you.

INDEPENDENT

imusic

www.imusic.com

Apart from offering all the usual releases and reviews, this site entices you with a bargain box, the ability to buy and sell second-hand CDs, and the chance to give your view on the latest Travis song. There's a huge news section and an alphabetised board so you can go straight to your favourite band. Your details are kept secure and you'll get your CDs between three and 21 days after they receive your order, depending on your shipping method.

Indie music

www.cdnow.com

An excellent, easy-to-use site, even for online virgins. There's a page on every type of music you could hope for, but the indie/alternative page is tops. It has truthful reviews, new releases, interviews and a really good staff pick if you fancy chancing it. When we visited, their top 20 albums included Moby, Morcheeba, Limp Bizkit, Pearl Jam and Foo Fighters. Your details will be safe as houses and they'll ship you the CD of your choice, hopefully in two weeks. To find out how much it'll all cost, just log in to your account.

Unsigned

www.unsigned-indie.com

This site offers "the best unsigned and independent artists you've never heard of". Not a bad site and – and this is where thousands of would-be musicians get really excited – you can even put yourself on the list and hope for fame. It's easy to use, and you'll enjoy picking out the class tunes from the dirges.

NOSTALGIA

Past Perfect

www.pastperfect.com

All the good-time tunes you could want, with hits from the 1920s to the 1950s including jazz, swing, and big-band hits. Browse the art-deco-inspired pages for CDs and cassettes at high-street prices. Each CD is an original recording but has the clarity of today's sound. Noel, Gertie and Glenn (Miller, that is, not Matlock) are all there, along with Winston Churchill himself.

POP

Abbey Records

www.abbeyrecords.com

Such an original name for a shop based in Liverpool. Abbey Records sells everything from dance to punk, but with an emphasis on pop. The Queen of Pop herself warrants her own separate shrine and this is one of the few places you can pick up vinyl and CDs from such 1990s relics as Martika, Pepsi & Shirlie and Sonia. Discounted prices, many under a fiver, apply, plus shipping charges, and they'll be with you within two days.

Eureka Records
http://clara.net/eureka/eur.htm
Amateurish-looking, the directory of (mainly) pop artists is extensive if hard to browse. You need to scroll through the alphabetical catalogue, note the artist, record title, price and shipping charges and calculate everything yourself to use their secure Safepages server. The discounts make up for it.

ROCK

BURBS
www.burbs.co.uk
BURBS is an acronym for British Underground Rock Bands. Use this suitably patriotic site to read up on these underground luminaries, mark their gig dates in your diary and then browse the online store. It's pointless to list featured artists as they're so far underground, but albums can be bought online at bargain prices and you can download tracks as a taster before you buy.

The Music Index
www.themusicindex.com
The headline 'This Day In Rock' isn't entirely accurate, as you're not going to find any chart-toppers like Stereophonics or Bon Jovi here. It boasts a database of 26,000 artists selected from reviews featured in *Q* magazine, but

Read all about it The muzak press online

The Web is also a great place for intelligent comment about music.
Here are a few of the best:
www.blaze.com is a fine hip hop magazine
www.channel1.com/users/obscure is for the musical obscurantist and trivia champs
www.gramophone.co.uk is for the serious student of classical music
www.laritmo.com is for music fans who know they don't speak latin in Latin America
www.launch.com offers new music with lots of exclamation marks!!!
www.nme.com Nuff said
www.rollingstone.com is authoritative, occasionally worthy, comprehensive
www.webnoize.com is for insiders and professionals

Ozric Tentacles and Lawnmower R n B are as famous as it gets here. You can download MP3 files or head straight for the online store. Worryingly, Rick Wakeman is used as the example to describe how to search the catalogue.

WORLD SPECIALIST

Descarga
www.descarga.com
This Brooklyn-based Latin mail-order specialist is an awesome store with a vast catalogue on its superbly designed web site. It has a great search engine (it will direct you to 187 CDs featuring Celia Cruz, for instance), extensive track listings, reliable reviews, and includes the *Descarga* journal with features and interviews. A must for anyone into Latin music.

Digelius Music
www.digelius.com
Helsinki-based shop, specialising online in Baltic and Nordic music.

Mostly Music
www.jewish-music.com
All aspects of Jewish music from the great cantors to klezmer.

Sterns African Records Centre
www.sternsmusic.com
London's premier African music store is also pretty strong on Latin music. The team have years of expertise and are the UK distributors for many African, Latin and world music labels, so there are many desirable items in stock.

Trehantiri Music
www.trehantiri.com
Situated in the heart of North London's Greek and Turkish community, Trehantiri is a retail nirvana for anyone with more than a passing interest in all types of Greek, Turkish and Middle Eastern music.

WEIRD STUFF

Lama Gyurme
www.lamagyurme.com
You certainly won't find tracks named *Chenrezi Pure Land Prayer* on the next Spice Girls album. Despite its flashy appearance, this site sells just one album by Lama Gyurme and Jean-Philippe Rykiel. The hip Buddha-loving Lama sings prayers at a slow pace whilst Rykiel provides the sparse keyboard notes as accompaniment. Read about this unlikely double act and then buy their latest release online for £12.99, and the first 50 copies bought online are even exclusively signed. If you're still a little wary especially after viewing the duo, you can check out the downloadable samples before you buy.

The Loveliest Of Trees
http://marches.county.net/housman

You can't buy this eccentric album online but all the information is available for you to determine whether Nigel Hawthorne might have delved a little too far into the Madness of King George. To mark the centenary of the original publication of A E Housman's *A Shropshire Lad*, Sir Nigel and his chums in the Shropshire-bred Polly Bolton Band have collaborated to produce a haunting, if not disturbing, version of the poem through a mixture of readings and lyrical ballads. All this for just £12.50, all inclusive.

Self-Abuse
www.selfabuserecords.com/home.html

Not for the squeamish music fan or the music fan, Self Abuse owns the Abuse Label and releases stuff with titles like *Skin Crimes* or containing the sound of a 1khz test tone. You can buy online but why would you?

Sleep Machines
www.sleepmachines.com

First there was the Miami Sound Machine, then Tin Machine, now comes Sleep Machines – a Californian company which sells CDs with a single sound and which are guaranteed to help you nod off. The titles are equally stupefying – *Dryer* is a good example – and at $13.49, they're not cheap, but they guarantee there are no subliminal messages involved. Insomniacs might be better advised to buy Michael Nyman's soundtrack to *The Piano*.

 Only one careful owner. You hope

101 Records
www.101records.co.uk

If you're lucky 101 Records will still be holding their celebratory half-price deals to mark their launch, knocking the already bargain prices down even lower. This simple site uses alphabetised listings to scroll through and order. Acts run from the sublime to the ridiculous, with famous names including the Beatles, the Rolling Stones and Paul Weller, alongside Distant Cousins. Prices can be anywhere from £1 to £10 even without the half-price deal.

Bus Stop Records
www.busstop-records.co.uk

Preferring to refer to its collection as pre-loved rather than used, Bus Stop sells 1970s, 1980s and 1990s disco, soul, hip hop and house. Disco jives include Amii Stewart's *Knock On Wood* and *Bumper To Bumper* by the Avenue B Boogie Band, both for under a tenner. There was no online system when we visited but they list their entire catalogue in genre order. Click on the order form, submit a request and you could be jiving in a few working days.

Sugar Bush

www.sugarbush.u-net.com

This honey-pot of rare vinyl LPs includes the golden era of rock, progressive, psychedelic and soundtracks from the 1960s. Scroll through the standard alphabetical lists to find everything from The Mamas & The Papas to Wilson Pickett. Prices range from £5 to £25 and the list is comprehensive, but there is no direct link to the order form and the site didn't have a secure server when we checked, so it may be best to go for the telephone option.

Vinyl Records

www.vinylrecords.co.uk

Don't scroll down the entire homepage because it will probably give you vertigo. You can browse lists of the vinyl classics available but there are no direct links from them to the order form. However, the site does allow you to copy and paste your selections into the form, making it slightly easier than some similar sites, and the order form is secure.

 The hottest music format since 8-track cartridges

2look4com

http://en.sonico.com

Fancy downloading a few seconds of Uruguayan grindcore? Or maybe a quick sample of Ecuadorean death-metal? If the answer is yes, you will be sadly disappointed on this occasion, but the beauty of this site is that it allows you to search for any combination of type of music and nationality. Perhaps sadly, you're most likely to succeed with traditional Latin American genres.

Lycos MP3 search

http://music.lycos.com/mp3

This site offers one of the simplest and fastest ways to find out what MP3 files are available for downloading and for which artist. Lycos obviously know a thing or two about search engines and theirs fairly zips through your request. Worth bookmarking, especially if you're just starting out in MP3.

MP3.com

www.mp3.com

If you're going to join the hordes downloading music from the Internet, you are almost legally obliged to go this site. Apart from the fact that there are over 500,000 songs from more than 80,000 artists (to say nothing of 3500 classical recordings) available, you will also find an excellent FAQ if you're at that stage in your digital education where you don't know your MP3 from your Fun Boy 3. There's a payola (geddit?) section featuring shameless plugs for new songs and a Top 40 where, alongside names like The Doors and The Eagles, you'll find Frankenstein Drag Queens and The Muckrakers.

Shoes and boots

Sensible or spinally challenging, for the fell-walker or the horse-rider, the range of footwear available online is, er, staggering. And most of the time you can

Anello & Davide
www.handmadeshoes.com
About to be launched when we looked, this site promises that you'll be able to choose the style, colour, and heel height of your shoes, which will then be handmade for you in Italy. They specialise in party and bridal shoes and you can request a brochure and measuring kit so you know you'll get an exact fit.

Barratts
www.barratts.co.uk
Barratts have let themselves down on the design stakes with this tacky and amateur-looking site. The footwear from Barratts and Saxone is exactly what you'll find in the shops with no discounts and £3 delivery charge. On the plus side they do offer a direct link to Tall & Small (www.tall-small.com) where you can buy similar fashionable designs in the different sizes and at no extra cost.

Faith
www.faith.co.uk
If fuschia kinky koots and baby-blue go-party shoes are what you're looking for, Faith stock all the backache-inducing footwear you could ever want. After revamping their image, Faith now sell some of the best designer replicas on the high street. Prices match those offline but the sale selection holds styles you might actually want rather than stuff they haven't been able to get rid of. Delivery is free and will take 4-5 days, in time for high stepping at the weekend.

Office
www.office.co.uk
High heels, mid heels, low heels, ankle boots, knee boots: you probably didn't think there were so many varieties, but Office and their casual sporty partner Offspring have a shoe for every occasion. Bright, blazing graphics match the

In the 1960s, Kinky Boots was a single by Patrick Macnee and Honor Blackman; now it's part of Faith's online range

polka-dot kitten heels and pink snakeskin boots which typify the collection. Prices range from £20 to £60 and trainer brands include Adidas, Nike and the ultra-trendy Acupuncture. Ordering is simple and secure, with enlarged clear images of each design.

Nine to Eleven
www.9211.co.uk

Not to be confused with 911 (the swanky designer high-street brand), this rudimentary-looking site offers women's shoes, socks and hosiery in larger sizes, hence the name. Despite a limited range, each style is up-to-date in the fashion stakes, making a welcome change to the usual dreary specialist collections, and each item is only slightly more pricey than the average high-street 4-7 size range. It's a useful specialist site but it could be improved by direct links to the order form, rather than customers having to write the information down.

Schuh
www.shoe-shop.com

Despite resembling an American Internet mall, this is actually the on-line store for high-street trendsetter Schuh. With labels DKNY, Duffer, Red Or Dead and Diesel all at reduced prices (£10-£15 off RRP), free delivery and Price Watch (where they'll match the price of any of their on-line competitors), this makes a terrific site to buy your designer kit. You can shop without being a member but if you join they can send your order to your work address. They also have perfect shoes for the wider foot, as well as those that are larger or smaller.

Shaka Sandals
www.shaka.co.uk

Despite being based in Kent, this is actually a shop window for South African sandals. The 4x4 of footwear, Shaka sandals come in five styles – Fisherman, Hiker, Outback, Raider and Whitewater, all made from waterproof fabrics and following ethical and environmental guidelines. Despite the small selection, a great deal of thought has gone into each product and each has been tested by such tough users as a Navy Seal unit and a champion surfer. Up-to-date styles, and all at less than £40 including postage.

Shopeeze
www.shopeeze.com

A bizarre combination of men's and ladies' footwear alongside perfume and electrical goods, with everything at discounted prices. Although not all the styles are up-to-date in fashion terms, a stylish pair of sandals for £10 or a pair of men's hiking boots for £14 make this site well worth a look.

Tim Little
www.timlittle.com

Tim Little shoes are usually only found at Harvey Nichols, Saks Fifth Avenue and Harrods but now you can get hold of a £200 pair of Tim Little's from his very own web site. The stylish layout is initially let down by tiny images, too small to show clearly what you're clicking on. However the enlarged pictures are far better and a lot of thought has gone into the additional information, presumably to justify the cost. Shipping charges at £9 are price, but if you can afford the stock in the first place an extra £9 probably isn't a problem.

Specialist footwear For hiking and horse-riding

Cox The Saddler
www.saddler.co.uk

There's no excuse for a scruffy show at the local gymkhana as you can find smart riding boots galore here, from long leather boots to short waterproof jodphur boots. Postage costs are calculated as you add items to your shopping basket and delivery is via Parcel Force.

John Norris of Penrith
www.johnnorris.co.uk

The Rolls Royce of Wellington boots is sold through this straightforward site at reasonable prices. When we checked there was a special offer which lowered the cost of Hunter boots even further, making the green welly look accessible to everyone. Shipping costs are calculated on site before you buy.

Rock and Run
www.rockrun.co.uk

You'd look a prat wearing some of these boots to go to the pub, but for a hike up Ben Nevis they're just the thing. This is serious footwear for hill-walkers and rock-climbers, with a few more general use boots for sale. The shop is part of a large outdoor site and it may take you a while to find the boot section, but the shopping basket works well and customer service is good. A 2-3 day shipping service costs £5, and overnight delivery costs just £10.

Sports Shoes Unlimited
www.sportsshoes.com

If it's comfortable and fits on your feet, you'll probably find it here. Alongside all the usual trainer brands there are useful sub-categories like pool shoes (swimming rather than *Pot Black*). Prices are keen and they get even better in the mega-deals section. P&P costs £3 and orders should arrive in five days.

Snow sports

All the essential gear for the slopes, from the hippest clothing to the coolest equipment. Even beginners can look the part on their way downhill, not to mention keep up with the in crowd back at the ski lodge. Plaster casts not supplied

 For all you piste artistes...

Big Day
www.bigday.co.uk
Speedy online store for men's and women's ski clothing, with a small but attractive range of jackets, trousers, hats and gloves. Shipping costs £5 for any order and your goods are promised within seven days.

Braemar Mountain Sports
www.mountainshop.co.uk
These Scottish specialists in ski touring, cross-country equipment and accessories have been selling skis by mail order for many years. They will even send you boots on approval if you make a specific request. Some items lack photos, so this site is best suited to those with some degree of expertise and already know what they want. However, there's an excellent customer service line available if you have questions that are not answered on the site itself. You also get a ten per cent discount when you buy any complete package of skis, bindings and boots.

Ellis Brigham
www.ellis-brigham.com
The ski section of this well-designed and speedy outdoor sports site has an excellent choice of boots, skis and other accessories for secure online

purchase. There's sound advice on offer, especially when it comes to buying boots, which it recommends you definitely try on before you buy as the fit varies so much from make to make, and their customer service department can help you with enquiries about sizing. Prices are average, but there were some very good savings to be made in the Sale section when we looked. Delivery is via Parcelforce, and the reasonable charges are calculated when you reach the checkout. If you're not happy with your purchase, you can return it unused within 14 days for a full refund.

Facewest
www.facewest.co.uk
Hi-tech equipment for back-country skiers and boarders. If you're going off-piste, or anywhere you might encounter an avalanche, then this selection of transceivers, lightweight shovels and other rescue items might just save your life. Ordering is via email, so you might prefer to phone your card details through, and delivery is £3 for orders under £100 and £5 thereafter. As long as your request is in stock, it will be dispatched within 24 hours.

Rei
www.rei.com
Despite the hectic home pages, a wade through this American outdoor site will turn up a fabulous selection of ski gear at prices that make you vow never to shop in the UK again. As well as bargains on skis and boots, there are particular savings to be made on hi-tech clothing like Polartec fleece and thermal underwear. The checkout page gives you a choice of shipping within the US or outside, and all international deliveries are insured and sent via DHL. Charges start at $13 for surface mail and $19 for air mail, so you'll only save serious cash if you're after a fair amount of stuff.

Ski Net
www.skinet.com
When you're looking to buy skis or boots for the first time, how do you find out which ones are going to be the best suited to your needs? This vast ski resource site has nothing to sell, but its Gear section is packed with up-to-date product reviews and has a Gear Finder tool which can match your skill level against a database of different skis. There are also plenty of lively message boards where snow dudes argue about the relative merits of Atomic Beta V8.20s versus the Salomon X-Scream Series.

Snow And Rock
www.snowandrock.co.uk
It was high summer when we visited this site, so it wasn't surprising that they had little in the way of winter sports gear on offer. However, we are assured that they do sell their equipment and accessories through the site during the ski season. There's a Flash version of the store, which stubbornly refused to let us into the online store, but the non-Flash version works just as well.

MORE WAYS TO GET DOWNHILL

Resorts around the world are filling up with daring youngsters whizzing around on what look like two skis that have met with a terrible accident. Since they are still so new, blades are harder to find online, but the following sites are worth checking out if you're interested:

Blades In Action
www.bladinaction.com

Ski and Skate
www.skiskate.com

Lazer Blades
www.lazerblades.com

If just going downhill is getting a trifle dull, you can always try telemarking to enable you to ski uphill when needed (although it does beg the question "why would you want to?'). Learn more about telemarking and the kit required at:

TSS
www.tss-online.com

The Back Country
www.thebackcountry.net

Mountain Quest
www.mountainquest.ca/ activities/skitouring.htm

Prices are the same as on the high street and standard delivery costs from £2.50 (orders over £500 are carriage-free), although there is a rush service if you're in a hurry to hit the slopes.

Snow Shack
www.snowshack.com
Search this site by manufacturer or equipment type for good deals on many top brand skiing products. There are also a few excellent accessories which you probably won't find in the temperate UK – frequent snow-sitters should consider the thermal butt-muff for extra comfort on their next trip. Overseas orders are sent via US parcel post and charges are calculated online before you input your credit card details. All goods come with a 30-day money back guarantee.

Tack and Ski
www.tackandski.com
Another nicely-designed site that closes its ski shop during the summer, but there are still some fleece and Gore-Tex clothing items all year round. Postage costs £4.95 per item and most orders will be dispatched within 14 days. If there is going to be a significant delay, they will contact you to advise.

World Ski & Snowboard
www.worldski.com
The seriously committed can register with this US-based site and get discounts on kit and holidays.

You can get further technical information on the skis you're considering at the following manufacturers' websites:

Elan
www.elanskis.com
Dynastar
www.dynastar.com
K2
www.k2skis.com
Rossignol
www.skisrossignol.com
Salomon
www.salomonsports.fr
Völkl
www.volkl.com

Snowboarding
Be the dude who says "Eat my snow"

Big Deal
http://bigdeal.com
This American site offers cheaper-than-average costs at $96 for boards (well, it is an expensive hobby) and a matter of a few dollars for accessories. Pick a category and use the scroll-down brand menus to select an item. Each one comes with a full spec sheet and enlarged pictures, and the brands include Airwalk, DC boots, Vans and Gnu. A useful site for overseas bargains.

Complete Snowboarder
www.complete-snowboarder.com
Peaceful aqua shades fill the screen, putting you more in the mood for a relaxing holiday rather than flinging yourself down snow-covered mountains. Here you can search for flights, accommodation and last-minute packages to boarding resorts around the world. £300 for a week in Italy isn't bad going, and the site will make a booking when you find a deal that interests you. As for gear, you can search for boards, boots and bindings with the interactive gear-finder but unfortunately you can't buy online. They will, however, find the boards to suit your own level of skill, and rookies can read the gear guide to learn the difference between such techniques as freestyle and free ride.

Fusion
www.fusion.com
You can either browse through the usual categories of gear or search by your favourite brand on this US-based site. The tiny initial pictures are hard to view and the faint grey condensed type is hard to read, so it's best to stick to the enlarged images and extended information. Once again, you need to contact them for shipping quotes but the discounted prices are worth it, starting from $70 for boards and $40 for boots. A message board, entertainment (videos and a solitary CD when we visited) and even radio are among the extras offered by the site, which also has sections for surfers and skaters.

Jester
www.jester.com
The RRP's for top board brands Avalanche and Morrow are marked next to Jester's own hilarious price – generally half the recommended amount – on this American site. But it's best not to get too excited, because once you've added on $150 for shipping, you're often back to where you started. But note that board purchases, boots around the $100 mark and accessories only carry a $20 shipping fee, so they represent a better buy. This site also caters to surfers and skaters, and carries competitions, music reviews, contributions from participants and good articles by experts in their field.

Snowboard Asylum
www.snowboard-asylum.com
Most snowboard enthusiasts are looking for adventure and excitement
with a bit of style thrown in. If this is the case for you, don't be put off by the
dull black design or the Santa music playing as you enter – far more thought
has gone into the actual content. All the usual categories are there, ready for
you to search for your favourite brand (QuikSilver, Billabong and Airwalk are
all represented), and details of each item are available. For boards, prices
start as low as £140 and go all the way up to £500. There's also a handy
search section, whereby you input your skill-level and what your requirements
or interests are (beginner, big feet, tricks and flips etc)
and the site suggests a board to match your criteria.

MEANWHILE IN MONTANA

If you measure out your
life in ski holidays, you
might want to log onto
Resort Ski Network
(*www.rsn.com*).

The site has won loads of
awards but what really
makes it stand out is an
idea so simple it's pure
genius. RSN has put web
cams (little cameras
which feed images back
to the website) on the
slopes of 110 ski resorts
(109 in North America
and one in Chile).

So if you can't go skiing
today, you can at least
console yourself with
the thought that there's
no snow in Big Sky,
Montana, not today any-
way. But when you do get
set to go, you can check
the weather, buy gear
and even order your holi-
day (often at low prices)
through this site. Roll on
the day when they put
their web cams
on the Cairngorms!

Snowboarding UK
www.snowboardinguk.co.uk
A busy, busy, busy directory with news, snow reports
and resort guides, but best of all, snowboarding
auctions. Click on the link and be transported to
e-bay's Extreme Sports Zone, where you can pick up
everything from boards to snowboarding pants and
sunglasses. This reviewer came across boots for £60,
pants for £25 and, bizarrely, a Hello Kitty board for
£70. But don't be put off – the top brands are there
too: Vans, Airwalk Ridge and the mouthful Dub
Reverb. If you can't wait for the auction to end, you
can search the store directory and buy your kit
straight away either from an online store or from
your nearest high street stockist.

Snow Traders
www.snowtraders.com
A visit to this site begins promisingly enough. The site
is willing to ship to the UK – all you have to do is
contact them and they'll search through their shipping
partners to find you the best deal. Such service! The
shine begins to disappear when you start shopping.
They sell boards, boots and every other accessory
imaginable, and each item is discounted, but prices
are still high compared to their competitors – boards
remain around the $400 level. But even if you do find
something you want, you can't move any further until
you register all your details with the site and, although
they say they will ship to the UK, no one seems to
have told whoever set up their system – it requires
you to list a US state. A bit more planning – and possibly a geography lesson – is needed, it seems.

This snowboarders' newsletter also offers books, kit reviews, a directory of retailers, news of trips and humour. Why not try stairboarding? "Rule number 1: Use somebody else's kit…"

The Boarder

www.theboarder.co.uk

Nothing to buy but worth a look for the novelty factor. Read how plans for numerous snow sites across the UK are progressing, find the best dry and snow slopes in the country (Wycombe Summit features highly) and plan your TV viewing from now until next year for boarding programmes. You can even spend Christmas Day watching snowboarding from Austria on Eurosport!

The Board Store

www.theboardstore.freeserve.co.uk

This site offers simple graphics and organisation and enables you to view lists of prices before you go any further or waste time browsing through models too pricey for your pocket. Fortunately, the boards here range from £150 to £400, so there should be something to suit all types. If you select your board based on its trendiness or image, The Board Store will be heaven for you with its enlarged images of funky designs but with no specs. There's no online buying on offer, but as we went to press you could place your order and have a representative call you back to finalise the deal. They also offer a handy email service where you can send them a query (for example, how do I cut back edges without ruining my board?) and they'll get back with the answer.

Sports

Whether it's real tennis, astanga yoga or the triple jump, you've got to look the part. No grubby trainers here, just go-faster gear that will at least make you look like a sporting star even if...

General Outdoors, indoors, in the gym, on the pitch

Fitness Peak
www.fitnesspeak.co.uk
Leeds-based company offering an extensive range of gym equipment from exercise bikes and heart monitors to table tennis and treadmills. Basic but functional interface with useful site links to other manufacturers. Click on the product name and you'll get a comprehensive description with obligatory fit-girlie-in-action and close-up shots. Cost comparisons are given – prices are around £30 cheaper than retail outlets plus discounts (a few high-street prices may have been inflated for comparison purposes – check in stores to verify your "bargain"). Orders by email, phone or fax, Monday to Saturday.

Kitbag
www.kitbag.com
Visit one of the biggest and best known sports shops on the Internet and you'll find a huge range of football, rugby, Formula 1 and cricket kits, with accompanying accessories. A self-proclaimed "sports shop for the sports fan", this site is aimed at people who want to buy replica or retro shirts as worn by their favourite team. This being a male-oriented market, sizes reflect that. It's also excellent for extensive cricket equipment and souvenirs. Everything is clear and upfront. Get your order in before 4pm and you should receive it the next day, and delivery is free of charge for anything over £15.

Newitts
www.newitts.com
The largest mail order supplier of sports equipment in the UK has gone online

and offers a vast range of clothes and equipment for every sport from boxing to bowls and tennis to trampolining. But due to the sheer volume of goods available, products are initially listed without pictures, which makes shopping slower as you can't view anything at a glance. Special offers exclusive to online shoppers are available. Prices include VAT and there's free next-day delivery for all orders received by noon.

Simply Sports

www.simplysports.co.uk

This lively site offers more than most sports shops, including pretty much every net, hoop or goal post used in mainstream sports. It also has exercise bikes, a sports bookstore and a new medical section offering heart-rate and blood-pressure monitors. It's one of the best sites for outdoor or indoor games, with backgammon, chess, archery, croquet, table tennis and table football on offer. Navigating your way around the busy home page can be trying. Prices include VAT, but delivery time and cost varies, depending on stocks and the size of the product. Shipping is mostly free for the UK.

Sportsking Online

www.sportsking.co.uk

This is a bargain basement site and no bones about it. It's quite prepared to admit that the range might consist of "last month's or even last year's products", its USP is low prices and clearance lines. No-fuss, easy to use, and worth a quick rummage. Allow 3 working days for delivery at £2.95.

Sweatband.com

www.sweatband.com

When online stores were lining up for names, sweatband.com were clearly at the back. But it makes up for this with a well-designed site that's divided into tennis, squash, cricket, rugby and football shops. Each section has its own news updates for fans to dip into, and a whole host of special discounts and competitions. It's particularly good for tennis racquets and cricket bats, and you receive a free sweatband just for registering.

Sweatshop

www.sweatshop.co.uk

Online branch of high-street aerobic and cross-training specialists. A bright and colourful interface with user-friendly navigation button guides you through history, jobs, sports injury advice or straight to a "small selection" of equipment (although if this is anything to go by, their shops must be hangar-sized) of which much is very reasonably priced footwear. There are also heaps of sale items which you can check the availability of by email. Click on your specialist area – track 'n' field, running etc – select an item and a photograph accompanied by a decent description and sizes will pop up. Buy either by mail order or online – it's a secure site and all major cards are accepted. Delivery is by recorded snail mail within 5 to 7 working days.

Sportswear — From fashion brands to active wear

Discount Sports
www.discountsports.co.uk
Big on bargain prices, so not overstocked with the latest branded gear. Label-conscious individuals can use the drop-down menus to limit a search to their favourite brands, but if you're any more specific than that – say, "men's/Adidas/jackets" – you'll be disappointed. This is more a site for browsing in hope of unearthing a real bargain. Delivery is free and takes up to 7 working days, but a next-day service is offered for an extra charge.

FX99
www.fx99.com
This site claims that its products have adorned the limbs of Denise Van Outen, All Saints and Zoe Ball. The site's message is clear – looking good and feeling good during exercise can be one and the same. The original and good-looking separates are ideal for aerobic workouts, dance classes and gym sessions alike. In some places "tax to be added" notices misleadingly appear. Delivery charge is £2.50.

Hosana
www.hosana.co.uk
A Flash-happy baskets site with a community feel and a nice buzz about it. The visuals are great and Roger Hosannah's hip US college hoops gear, from mesh shorts and tanks to long-sleeve sweats, is the epitome of gotta-have-it cool. Ordering is by email and callback, shipping costs £2. You'll want some.

M and M Sports
www.mmsports.co.uk
The Internet arm of the M and M Sports Mail Order Company, this site is like the catalogue in that it offers a wide range of goods, but unlike the catalogue it's quite difficult to find your way around. Even selecting the specific sections doesn't seem to save much time, as all the products are listed in pages. However, its highly competitive prices make it worth checking out and it has a very good children's range. Delivery costs £3.99 and takes up to 10 days.

Sportackle.com
www.sportackle.com
An online shop of sporting briefs? Sadly not. In fact this has quite a small product-range of branded sports clothing, be they shorts, shirts or shoes. But it does have an ever-changing special offers list of items at reduced prices and it's particularly easy to navigate. Products are usually dispatched within 24 hours, and it keeps you updated by email on the expected delivery date of any item you order. VAT is not included.

Sports Connection

www.sportsconnection.co.uk

Here's a Scottish range that's ideal for anyone who is as interested in fashion as they are in sports clothes. Click on past the rather stylish home page and take a look at the affordable collection of urban-style leisurewear and you'll find that the latest gear is considerably cheaper here than elsewhere – everything on this site has 10 per cent already taken off the price. Delivery takes just one week and costs £2.99 for anywhere in the UK.

Get hip to the hoops with Hosana – top-quality US sou ern states college basketball wear with soul

 **From trainers to spikes**

Sportsshoes Unlimited

www.sportsshoes.co.uk

Sportsshoes Unlimited claims to be the largest sports shoe retail outlet in the world, with 4000 different styles of footwear. To see more, request a catalogue. There's an enormous choice for men, women and kids, including top brand trainers, specific sport shoes and even a Big Foot collection. Orders should arrive within 3-5 working days and all deliveries cost £3.

Specialist **Recreation over air, land and sea**

Acme Whistles

www.acmewhistles.co.uk

Acme Whistles is the online trading name for Messrs J Hudson & Co of Birmingham – purveyors of police, hunting, bird-watching, marine and sports whistles for over 130 years. Prices range from £3.25 to £30 – VAT and £1.50 shipping are added at checkout. Mastercard, Visa and Amex are all welcome.

Avalon Guns

www.avalon-guns.com

Here you can buy green wellies, cleaning equipment, protection togs, camouflage, books, videos, guns and ammo. Unlike some US sites, Avalon does not pander to survivalist sensibilities. No hysterical "blast 'em up" flashes here, only a sensible military green and brown interface advertising good deals for hunting and shooting enthusiasts. Orders for general equipment are taken by email or phone and are dispatched by Parcel Force. For shotguns and rifles, personal details, gun license and Police Notification forms must be provided by recorded delivery. Once processed, Avalon will ring to clarify and send completed papers to your nearest 'agent' – who will then only hand over on a face-to-face basis. Licence and Notifications are returned by recorded delivery.

Allballs
www.allballs.co.uk

Brand new site by Yorkshire-based company specialising in sports balls – even "educational" mega-size rubber ones for It's-A-Knockout type activities – and accessories – bags, handpumps and cleaning solutions. A cheery, user-friendly interface with lots of sparkly bits is undermined by low resolution photos but delivery, policy and returns details are precise. Goods are sent via Royal Mail or Business Post within 3 working days and there are no postage charges. Postage for returned goods is not covered unless incorrectly dispatched. You can pay by cheque or securely online via credit card.

Denney Diving
www.divingdirect.co.uk

If you're going diving, you'll find all you need under one virtual roof at Denney Diving. Excellent for all diving goods, it has an exhaustive range of fins, masks, protective clothing and technical equipment. Delivery is next day by courier; the cost depends on the weight of the goods you buy.

Diving Daisy
www.divingdaisy.freeuk.com

For a full review of this site see the watersports section on page 323 of this guide.

Encore
www.encoredw.freeserve.co.uk

The Internet is for everyone, as this site proves: it's run by an enterprising "dance mum" for other dance mums who wish to sell or buy unwanted or outgrown kids costumes. If you think the grey and pink homepage accompanied by a synthesised version of *Puttin' On The Ritz* is a killer, wait until you get to the catalogue – little girls in tutus appear to the strains of Richard Clayderman's rendition of the theme to *Titanic* (the James Cameron movie,

MASSEY ATTACK

What's the fastest-growing sport in the UK? No, not Beckham-baiting; tractor pulling. 'Invented' by our US cousins, the agricultural equivalent to F1 has now gone global. Britain has a Tractor Pulling Association (BTPA) and there are several magazines, notably the US's Full Pull. If you fancy a mud-fest while dragging a colossal John Deere along a 100 metre track, try the site below. And leave the kitten heels at home.

www.powerpulling.co.uk

not the Lew Grade one). Click on a photo and shoes,dresses, leotards *et al*,
modelled by aspiring Darcy Bussells, are revealed. Encore does fancy dress,
as well. No zoom facility for the pic and you can't actually buy online – but
you can phone or email Jan.

The Kite Shop
www.kiteshop.co.uk
Whatever kind of kite you're looking for – sports kites, power kites or kites for
beginners – you can't do much better than this, a comprehensive selection of
the best the kiting world has to offer, including visuals and full individual
specifications. There's no postal charge, but special delivery costs £3.50,
and UK customers should allow 7 days for their chosen product to arrive.

M Steel Cycles
www.msteelcycles.co.uk
Excellent online offshoot of over-a-century-old Newcastle company run by
former Commonwealth Gold Medallist Joe Waugh. Less a website, more your
friendly neighbourhood corner shop – because that's exactly what it is.
There's lots of proud text and photos of the store, staff and history. M Steel
stocks only four pre-manufactured bike ranges – TREK, (i)specialised(i),
Dawes and Peugeot – as the bulk is built in-house. Buy what you see or go
for a custom-made model (right down to the paint job and company logo).
Orders are taken by phone and paid for by credit card. Items are dispatched
by recorded delivery or Parcel Force (cycles come boxed and ready to ride).
M Steel will also check your bike after six months and a year – for free.

Martial Art Superstore
www.martialartssuperstore.procossax.com
The "first of its kind in the UK", this site is run by a team of inspired martial
arts experts who've thankfully resisted the urge to adorn it with the usual
'Oriental' gubbins. Instead what you have is a trendy, retro style, easy-to-
navigate interface offering everything an aspiring Jackie Chan could need:
Taekwondo, Kendo and boxing outfits, and even gifts – silk kimonos, wind
chimes and the like. Each product is accompanied by a small photograph,
a brief description, a price and, helpfully, a shipping time and how many are
currently in stock. It's a secure site with online orders by credit card. Prices
include delivery, regardless of size. Mail order is also available by phone or fax
and goods are delivered by first class post on receipt of payment.

Meridian
www.meridian-experience.com/stores/innovate/index.htm
For many sun-kissed beach babes and dudes, frisbee throwing is the be all
and end all of their sporting life. Any high street toyshop will sell you a plastic
model but from this general gadgets-you've-never-seen-before site you can
buy the worlds first programmable model. For £18.29 excluding VAT you
can send flying messages and abuse to all your friends and enemies. You

program the message into the frisbee and once thrown the message lights up in the sky. All round good or bad fun depending on how abusive you are. To find this gem head for the gift section of Innovate and scroll down. The site is painfully slow but it's worth it.

Ocean Sports Board Riders
www.boardriders.co.uk
Experience the colourful, laid-back world of surfing at a site that's designed to appeal to the whole boarding fraternity. Surfers, bodyboarders and snowboarders can get all the hardware they need here, along with the latest fashionable clothing, including some discount deals. Navigation is easy and ordering policies clearly explained. All UK orders cost £2 for delivery, apart from surfboards which cost £10. Next day delivery is around £6 extra.

Rock Run
www.rockrun.com
If hanging off sheer rock faces by your fingernails or striding through the Lakes in torrential rain is your thing then this is a must. Aside from mountains of outdoor equipment there's info on climbing, safety, weather (including Scottish avalanche forecasts), books, rocktalk forums and related sites. Zoom in on products or mosey round the bargain basement. Shopping basket sums are given in sterling and US dollars. Brilliantly, there's also a currency converter. The site is endorsed by Which? and shopping is secure. Major credit cards are accepted and if you place your order before 12 noon expect to receive it in 24 hours – otherwise it's 2-3 days.

Roch Valley
www.roch-valley.co.uk
The UK's leading classical dancewear distributor has a strangely secretive site. Each simple and stylish page – intro, garments, dance shoes, ballroom/Latin and information – contains a couple of photographs with very sparse text in English, French and German. Instead of buying online you complete what they call a "feedback" form for details on how to purchase, for a brochure or for your nearest stockist. Enquiries will be answered by the following day by fax, email or post.

Snookernet
www.snookernet.com
Recently awarded five stars by *The Net* magazine, this Lincolnshire-based site is more like an online encyclopedia than shopping mall. The site (decked out in, you guessed it, "baize green") has an image gallery – so you can drool over your favourite addled champion – discussion forums, a FAQ section and more. You can also buy everything bar the Benson & Hedges Cup. All prices are quoted in pounds and US dollars and are inclusive of VAT. Buy securely online with your credit card or mail order by fax or phone. If quoted delivery times change, you'll be notified by email before the order is processed.

Sporting Auctions

www.www.sportingauction.com

You can bid for almost anything here from a "Stearns Shorty wetsuit medium black and blue" to a Mizuno baseball cap. What's more, as it has been approved by US consumer review site BizRate, it's safer than many auctions. Remember to check with UPS how much they will charge to deliver.

Sporting Irish

www.sportingirish.com

A Dublin outfit dealing solely with Irish sports wear: rugby shirts and Gaelic soccer jerseys, all sourced from Irish manufacturers. The basic, no-frills interface features product photographs and a brief description of your chosen shirt. Orders can be placed securely via credit card or by mail order via fax or phone. Once you've placed your order you will be given a password for future buys or you can become a member, which guarantees a discount.

Tennis Nuts

www.tennisnuts.com

A site for tennis enthusiasts by tennis enthusiasts, and designed to mimic a salesman guiding you through your purchase. Having received your pep talk on choosing a racquet that's right for you, you can make the most of the 10 per cent discount available during the launch period. Also on offer are badminton and squash racquets and some sports shoes. Postage is £4 for orders under £100, free above that. Delivery is within 3-6 business days.

Trail Buzz

www.trailbuzz.com

This new internet retail outlet of Dorset's Shepherd Cycles (pedalling since the 60s) features a snazzy blue-and-orange interface offering deals on bikes, accessories, components, clothing and "specials" by every cycle manufacturer in the book. Contact details are repeated on every page and all major credit cards are accepted. It's a secure site. Prices include postage and delivery is by recorded snail mail within 3 working days – although, if in stock, they'll try to send goods the next day. Returned goods are refunded but unless they're faulty, postage is not reimbursed.

You can have any colour you want, as long as it's green: Sporting irish, purveyors of GAA, rugby and soccer gear

Television & video

The only place TV and the Web are really merging right now is in commercial hyperspace where you can get knockdown prices or spend a fortune on some plasma

General For those who want to merge with their sofa

Box Clever
www.box-clever.com
Beyond the flashy graphics, Granada has created a well-thought out and easy to navigate site from where you can buy or rent all your electrical needs. Narrow your search down to the exact model you want or search the entire catalogue of every TV set imaginable, portable, standard, widescreen and plasma, and the site comes up with a list of buying and renting options. DVD players begin at £299 or if you're flush and flash head for the 42in plasma widescreen display for a penny short of £9,000.

Digital Choice
www.digitalchoice.co.uk
A Which Web trader, Digital Choice makes a lot of promises, secure ordering, a no hassle returns policy, and a refund of the difference in price if you find the same item cheaper elsewhere. This is all in its favour, but the descriptions of the televisions, videos and DVD players are too brief, and the pictures poor quality. Top brands include Sony, Philips and Aiwa and you can search by model, manufacturer of price point. Not for the window shopper.

Dixons
www.dixons.co.uk
You know where you're at with Dixons. Choose a product category and scroll through the list of high street priced DVD's, videos etc. Basically, just the

virtual equivalent of their bricks and mortar outlets, with similar products, prices and discounts. On the downside, the added info is a bit simplistic.

Encore Direct
www.encoredirect.co.uk

Once you're past (or have skipped) the hectic home page click on the image of whatever DVD player, TV or DVD rental you're interested in. And pray. With the bargain DVD player for £170 we could read the spec sheet, but after many attempts the buy link still led back to where it started until we worked out that you have to click the separate rotund "basket" icon to continue the rather lengthy checkout. But delivery is free and the site offers useful DVD player-and-disks packages to get you started.

Hutchisons
www.hutchisons.co.uk

A dull bargain basement design, without the bargains. The extensive catalogue comprises every TV set, DVD and video player imaginable. Click on the image of the one you like the squint of and make your selection based on the limited info and tiny pictures. This is a shame because the range on offer beats any high street store and there are prices to suit all. Video recorders range from £99 to £500, although the site doesn't really explain why the prices differ so much.

Link On-line
www.linkonline.co.uk

If you bought one of the first DVD players, Link On-line specialise in DVD upgrades. The Paragon kit will allow you to make your existing model even flashier than it already is, although what exactly this entails isn't clear unless you link to a page of miniscule type. If you know why you want an upgrade, click on a kit code and see if your model is compatible. Most buyers pay around £30, unless you opt for the fitted price for double that.

New Era Antiques
http://neweraantiques.com/overview.cgi?televisions

Hard to believe the TV is now so old that you can buy retro models. And they don't come much more retro than this. For around $200 you can pick up retro portable TV sets from the likes of JVC and Hotpoint to General Electric and Admiral from this

---

BREAKING DVD'S CODE

If you're not a DVD expert yourself (and quite frankly who is?) but thinking of taking the plunge, log on to www.codefree.com.

DVD is not as universal a platform as, say, a CD player so if you buy a player from the USA it won't necessarily be able to play disks you buy in the UK.

That in a nutshell is why it's worth paying more (from £500 to £700) for a code free device.

Mail UK (which you will find on www.mailuk.com) works along the same system with slightly cheaper prices, £300 to £400 in most cases.

JUNK TV

Junk not as in the Jerry "I married a horse" Springer sense (that was the working title of one of his banned shows) but as in pay $4.95 for a 4in tall model TV set which plays Frosty The Snowman and Rudolf The Reindeer as sung by people you're too young to remember.

This can only be bought on Yahoo Shopping because the shop's own URL *(www. sterling. store.com)* links to a page about domains.

If you're intrigued by TV's future rather than its past, log on to www.flat-tv.com and let your eyes boggle.

American antique company. The *Happy Days* 1950s designs range from two-tone colour models to what look like astronaut helmets. No online buying unfortunately but you can make email enquiries to discover how to buy. If TV memorabilia tickles your fancy, you might also want to drop in on www.retrostuff.com which has an *I Love Lucy* toy TV set for sale for less than $20. It sounds horrendous, looks charming and will probably be sold on eBay for a small fortune 20 years from now.

Radio Rentals

http://radiorentals.co.uk

Annoyingly, only those with Shockwave already installed, or those that can be bothered to do the necessary just to shop, can browse. Once in, you might wish you hadn't bothered as the "rent this now" sticker leads you to a store locator rather than an option to rent there and then.

Remote Controls

www.remotecontrols.co.uk

No prizes for guessing what this site sells. With 30,000 replacement remote control units to choose from, the one you lost down the back of your sofa with the hamster should be there somewhere. Select the manufacturer and model number or code, which they help you to locate, and you're now completely rid of the need to indulge in your last remaining form of physical exercise, stumbling to the set to change channels

Satellite Shop

www.satelliteshop.co.uk

Detailed spec sheets, product guides and star ratings, plus discounted prices to boot. The scroll down menus for TVs, videos and DVD's makes the site far less cluttered than many of its rivals. Strangely, given the company name, the one button which didn't lead to any more info said "Satellite". It's probably worth another look when they get all the gremlins sorted.

Techtronics

www.techtronics.com

You won't find any dinky portable or 21in TV sets here, only your extra-widescreen, 50in plasma displays and rear projection monitors. Beyond the hyperactive homepage the site is easy to navigate with page long spec sheets and handy customer reviews. The cheapest set you're likely to find will still set you back something just short of a grand, but it'll satisfy the couch potato within you. The perfect site for your ultimate home cinema buys.

Tempo
www.tempo.co.uk
A basic site. Browse the store, read the standard spec sheets including the information you probably knew already, and buy. Delivery generally takes seven to ten days, and if you find the same item cheaper elsewhere they pay you the difference. Most items already offer savings, often around £30 off.

Unbeatable
www.unbeatable.co.uk
This online-only site is a neat alternative to the high street with competitive prices on top brand names, Panasonic, Sony and Philips. Click on a category and browse the long lists of TVs, video recorders and DVD's. The information is limited to a few features and pictures. Better for buying than browsing.

Web Electricals
www.webelectricals.co.uk
Comprehensive yet to the point. Search for TV's, videos and DVD players, or read the buyer's guides with their glossary of all those manual terms that have meant nothing to you thus far. The range is limited to four or five items in each category and if you can't drag yourself away from the home cinema units, there are finance plans to help you stiffen your purchasing resolve.

What TV & Video
http://catalogue.barclaycard.co.uk/cgi-bin/tv.storefront
Not to be confused with the offline magazine of the same name, this site is actually part of Barclaycard's cybermall Barclay Square. Instead of

This is as exciting as Satellite UK's site gets. After this, the pages plumb new depths of dullness nightingales or, indeed, tips on how to find the entertainment system to meet your needs and budget, you just get the usual list of models and the Barclay Square guarantee of safe shopping (if you're buying with Visa you get all your money back if anything goes wrong, if you're using any other card you get £50 back). The technical jargon here is easy to understand. Standard 21in and 28in models are on display at a site which feels like the independent TV and music shop you probably had in your town when you grew up.

 If your roof seems naked without a dish

Satellite Superstore
www.satelllitesuperstore.co.uk
The *La Bamba* music in the background is as much effort as the owners of this site have mustered up. Drowning in text, it's designed like a book. Head to page one of advice and essential tips before you buy and then scroll through page upon page of decoders, dishes and matching DVD players.

Satellite UK
www.satelliteuk.com
Once you get past the illustration, this sets new standards of dullness. Blue and red type on a dirty grey background with no visuals, just title headings to cover what is on sale, reviews and the essential FAQ's. The site is informative if you can stay awake, but at least you know they're not spending money on web design that could be knocked off their prices. Pick up digital receivers and accessories from the fill-it-in yourself online order form, and read up on Sky Digital, for example what "free set-top box" actually means.

Wizard Satellite
www.wizardsatellite.co.uk
Wizard Satellite has everything you need for satellite reception and the obligatory graphic of a rotating dish for those people who have trouble with the words "satellite dish". You can buy on-line but you might be put off by the fact that between pages the screen is filled by a blue Artex effect which looks suspiciously as if the site has crashed. It probably hasn't so just wait.

You might also find these sites of use. Then again you might not.
www.comet.co.uk
Standard site and prices from the high street king.
Co-op Electricals
Limited selection of Toshiba products at discounted Internet prices.
www.electricalwarehouse.co.uk
A sparse selection and too brief descriptions but keen prices.
www.teleview-direct.co.uk
Buy online or make a renting request and have them call you back to finalise.

Tickets

Not the kind your local bus conductor inspects, but the kind of ticket which earns you a spin in a Ferrari or a seat in a West End theatre which doesn't involve watching Michael Flatley

Events | General happenings and the Orient Express

Aloud
www.aloud.com
The opening homepage may be loud and fiercely busy, but this is a well thought out concert and theatre ticket site. It offers a comprehensive list of music events in the UK, right up until Christmas 2001, and you can search according to artist, venue or town. This site is easy to navigate, and they tell you on each page if an event is sold out rather than waiting till you've decided to purchase. Only the selling-fast marker is a let-down, as it seems to be more of a way to panic customers into buying than an accurate account of sales. The cost comprises the usual additional postage fee but you can track your ticket to see what stage of processing your order has reached.

Bigmouth
www.bigmouth.co.uk
A simple, alphabetical directory makes this site easy to search for information about tours, venues and travel. You can't always book on-line but postage is priced per total buy, not per ticket, so it may work out a lot cheaper than a number of their competitors (some sites charge £4 per ticket). This is more of a one-stop shop than an involving site, but useful nonetheless.

Latest Events
www.latestevents.com
Offering package events rather than simple ticket sales, Latest Events has some fabulous days out to choose from – if you have the money. Select their unusual events category and you'll find such tempting excursions as lunch on the Orient Express for a £414 (well, it's a five-course meal) , or the Ferrari

Experience, which offers Ferrari-driving plus lunch for £235. Concert and sporting tickets are also on offer, but again only as part of bigger packages. Despite the annoyingly slow system, this site is worth investigating if you're after that something extra-special.

Scene One
www.sceneone.co.uk
This cheery-looking site is one of the few to offer reviews and additional information about their featured artists and events to encourage you to buy from them. The site includes music, film, comedy and even television reviews, but you can only buy music tickets on-line. Ordering is simple but can be expensive with an added booking fee and then postage of £4 on top, but this site certainly offers more of a shopping experience than many of its competitors.

Ticket Master
www.ticketmaster.co.uk
The new look Ticketmaster site is slightly brighter than its predecessor, but it remains simple and well-categorised, offering sports, music, arts and family events. It's particularly useful for sporting events and theatre tickets, as you can specify where in the audience you would like to sit. You can also opt to collect your tickets in person to avoid extortionate postage fees. The only draw back is the lack of any additional information about the events on offer.

WHAT'S ON WHEN

Despite a distinct lack of on-line selling, 'What's On When' deserves recognition as the most comprehensive events directory around.

With the option to search continents and countries as well as cities and by type of event, you're pretty much guaranteed to find at least one event wherever you may roam.

If you're looking for a mind, body and spirit event in Egypt, you'll find it here. Each listing includes details of the event along with the when, where and how much. There are also links to official sites that often let you book online.

---

www.whatsonwhen.com

Film   Book tickets and receive 'personalised' info

Warner Village cinemas
www.warnervillage.co.uk
Warner Bros have moved one step beyond the usual online cinema-booking site, inviting you to register your details with their homepage and receive personalised information. If you live in the Reading area, for example, they'll send you the Reading Warner Village listings each week, along with those for one other cinema. Buying is as simple as it can be. Click on the location, film and time, and then hand over the money without having to pay a booking fee. They'll even tell you how to get there. Nothing could be easier.

From clubs and rock concerts to opera and ballet

First Call

www.firstcalltickets.com

Despite the user-friendly scroll-down menus, and the option of searching by artist, venue or date, First Call is frustrating to use because of the slow speed of the system they use. It takes too long to load a page, during which time you could easily find the information elsewhere. It's a pity First Call have this problem, because their coverage of sports, theatre and music events is comprehensive, and they guide you through the booking process. This is particularly useful if you're an online novice.

Raymond Gubbay

www.raymondgubbay.co.uk

Gubbay, a leading promoter of classical music, opera and ballet, offers a stylish and uncluttered site which is worth visiting, if only for the thought that has been put into it. Once you've specified the date and show which you want to attend, you can ask them to try again if you're not happy with the first selection of seats they come up with. They also offer additional information about each performance; there are extracts of reviews of the shows on offer, and there's also a mailing list that you can join.

Ticket Web

www.ticketweb.co.uk

Nothing flash in terms of design or contents, Ticket Web is a safe bet for all your UK gig and club tickets. You can search by venue or a particular artist, but booking fees apply despite their promise that the web is always cheapest. If you're reluctant to pay their high postage charges, you can pick up your tickets at the venue and you can also track your order as it is processed. This is, however, a very functional site which offers no additional information.

 Premiership football and "the sport of kings"

Aston Villa and other Premiership clubs

www.avfc.co.uk

Aston Villa are one of very few Premiership football clubs to use the Internet to sell match tickets. Although they have yet to set up their own box office, they offer a convenient link to Ticket Master to make your purchase. From here the standard Ticket Master rules apply. Other forward-thinkers include:

www.bradfordcityfc.co.uk	Bradford City
www.ccfc.co.uk	Coventry City FC
www.sunderland-afc.com	Sunderland AFC

Epsom, Sandown and Kempton racecourses all make it dangerously easy to watch the gee gees

Epsom Derby

www.epsomderby.co.uk

Epsom racecourse, along with Kempton and Sandown Park, offer a simple system from which you can buy tickets for race meets throughout the year. You can search by event or the approximate time that you would like to go, state whether you want to watch from the paddock or the premier area and that's it. You can pick up your tickets or have them posted out to you, either way it's free.

www.kempton.co.uk — Kempton Park
www.sandown.co.uk — Sandown Park

Newmarket

www.newmarketracecourses.co.uk

After making a good impression by offering an on-line ticket service in the first place, the Newmarket organisers lose marks for the inept system they use. Before you order you need to consult the price guide and then memorise exactly when you want to go, which tickets you want and how much they are, because once you go to buy they expect you to work out the cost yourself. Oh, and you can't book on-line more than two weeks before an event.

 London only – still at the rehearsal stage

What's On Stage

www.whatson.com

This dedicated theatre shop is one of the few to offer extra info about each performance, with news, reviews and regular thespian features. It would be nice to see them branching out of London and improve their range, they only have half-a-dozen options under each category, (typically the most popular shows). Face-value prices apply and you can specify post or collection. A good start with the potential to improve.

TheatreNet

www.theatrenet.co.uk

You can't buy here but you can join a club through the site which gets you discounts on tickets. Worth considering if you're a regular West Ender.

Toys

With more cuddly toys than the The Generation Game conveyor belt and more models than a Milan catwalk, the Internet means you have absolutely no excuse for buying gift vouchers for your nie ce

General Save money, time and tantrums

Etoys
www.etoys.co.uk
If you usually turn up at Christmas with an encyclopaedia for your nephew rather than a GameBoy, shopping at eToys may change the current plight of your relationship. For toys, computer consoles and games, as well as books and videos, search by whatever you know for certain about the child, whether age, the brand or toy character they like, or the particular toy itself. If you've been told to buy a Super Soaker but have no idea what one is, this could be particularly useful as each comes complete with a full description and age recommendation. High-street prices, if not slightly cheaper.

FAO Schwarz
www.faoschwarz.com
America's premier toy store will ship to the UK if you're desperate to get hold of an international Barbie or Furby but they charge 40% of the total of your order as a fee for the privilege, and you must order goods at least to the value of $200. If this hasn't put you off, the site is easy to navigate with brand and character shopping areas, and a number of items as yet unseen in the UK, including Gene, the Hollywood celebrity doll.

Funstore
www.funstore.co.uk
If your usual visit to the toy shop is typified by screaming tantrums and pleas never to have to leave their favourite haven, Funstore will be able to fulfil all

your child's toy needs and spare you a headache at the same time. Scroll through boys' and girls' toys, board and computer games, and construction and creative pursuits. Popular brand names include Action Man, Monopoly, Mr. Potato Head and K'Nex alongside unusual alternatives including Truth or Dare Jenga. Fast and easy.

In 2 Toys

www.In2Toys.com

Despite its bargain basement nature, In 2 Toys' site is well laid out with bargains, special offers, and boys' and girls' sections to browse. Alternatively, search by brand or price range if you have something specific in mind. Every item sold is reduced to some extent, many toys by as much as 70%, so you should be able to pick up a Super Soaker for £4.99 and a darts board for £1.

Toy Chest

www.toychest.co.uk

This family-run company sell fun educational and activity based toys and games for children 10 years and under. Search according to the age of your child, baby, toddler and so on, then browse though the toys on offer, each with brief descriptions and illustrations. Fun activities include candle making and mug painting kits for under £10, and Ocean Zoo Sea Monkey pets for £6.50. A particularly useful site if you happen to be a little late buying presents as delivery takes only two days.

Toy City

www.toycity.co.uk

A competent but uninspiring site, where you should find what you're looking for provided it isn't too unusual. You get off to a bit of clunky start in that the Europe-wide opening page asks you to choose your country, before taking you to the British page. There's a decent enough search facility, which you can use by age of the child in question, but the toys are very mass market. Goods are dispatched within 2-4 days and delivery is free if you spend more than £20.

Not so much a homepage, more a challenge to the human eye. Hope junior doesn't click on "mobile phone deals" by accident

Toys"R"Us

www.Toysrus.co.uk

Just as the shop itself is a lurid assault on the senses, this site isn't easy on the eye. But there are big benefits in shopping at such an outlet, the biggest bonus being that there is a huge range of toys. Customer service is excellent: any problems with orders and you're personally emailed with a £10 voucher as an apology. If you have loyalty points from the stores however, you can't use them here. Prices are the same as in the shops. Delivery takes 2-3 working days and costs £2.50 per order.

Toy Town
www.toytown.co.uk

This site is part of the Shoppers Universe mall. Search through the extensive catalogue of children's items to suit all ages, from cuddly toys and model kits for infants to roller blades for the older ones. Standard prices apply but delivery is free so it saves you having to carry the pool table back from the shop.

Toy Zone
www.toyzone.co.uk

Eye-catching primary colours fill this site selling toys predominantly aimed at toddlers and infants. Search by toys of the day, or recommended categories based on the age of your child, or use the fast search option for best sellers and toys under £20. In many cases it's cheaper than the high street; the only downside is you can't be certain you will receive the model shown in the picture so you may end up with a boy Furby and not a girl. Still, a fun site.

 **Modern** From Chicken Run to Pokémon

Aardmarket
http://aardmarket.aardman.com

Specialising in 3-D animation models, the Aardmarket sell toys and gifts, predominantly from the Nick Park stable: Wallace & Gromit, Chicken Run, Angry Kid, and coming soon, Morph and Creature Comforts. They sell the usual array of franchised merchandise, cuddly toys, watches, and back packs at high-street prices. Worth a look for gift to complete your child's collection.

Mail Order Express
www.moetoys.co.uk

Christmas can be a nightmare for those parents frantically trying to find the one Pokémon toy their child doesn't own. Mail Order sells every toy, game, piece of clothing and collector's card associated with such must-have brands as Lego, Scalextric, Barbie and Pokémon. Just click on the brand and then search the entire catalogue or cut directly to the price you're willing to pay. Another good site for late pressies, next-day delivery is charged at the unreasonably reasonable price of £5.99. Worth a look.

MR POTATO HEAD
Perfect play partner for everyone's favourite super spud. The star of Disney's Toy Story. Hat, eyes, ears and mouth – all 10 min and match face pieces store inside body for safe keeping. Age 2+

127434

INTERNET

Home : Toys : Video Games : Outdoor/Bikes : Home Entertainment
Nearest Store: Help and Advice: Services And Delivery: Gold Card: Free

Wade through all the stuff about nappies on Babies"R"Us and be rewarded by the appearance of Mr Potato Head himself

Up to toddlers   From the pram to the playpen

Babies"R"Us
www.babiesrus.co.uk
The baby version of Toys"R"Us offers baby products such as nappies, a range of gadgets and larger items like prams, car seats and high chairs as well as a pretty decent selection of baby toys like activity cottages, Mr Potato Head figures and a musical pop-up piano. The rattle-teethers aren't really pure toys. If any of us could remember what it was like to be that young we would probably insist they were a medical necessity.

Early Learning Centre
www.elc.co.uk
A good, reliable site, just as you'd expect from the Early Learning Centre, where you can shop by age, category and type of toy if you're stuck for ideas. Includes some decent discounts in the sale section, plus helpful categories such as Award Winners, Best-Sellers and What's New. The toys are organised into interesting sections such as Imagine, which includes dressing-up clothes as well as the more self-explanatory Sport and Activity and Discover. Deliveries arrive promptly within three days and cost £2.95 for goods up to £60; after that postage and packing is free.

PlayBug
www.playbug.com
A bright and uncluttered homepage lends itself well to this easy-to-navigate site. Search by age, price, product or department, each coming up with a

large range of toys suited to babies and infants. If you're worried about safety, read the ample descriptions for each item – every toy has passed the European Toy Safety Directive. Prices generally lie between £10 and £30 and you can take advantage of a next-day delivery option, a little costly at £15.

Toy Craft
http://catalog.com/uk/toy/
With toys and games on sale for as little as 40p this is a particularly useful site for children themselves to browse if they're looking to spend their pocket money. The section of the same name has cog puzzles for 60p and gliders for 40p. Old-school favourites include Fuzzy Felt sets for £3.99 and I-Spy, the board game, for £6.95. Pictures of the toys rather than text descriptions would go down well and they'd be advised to replace the amateur order form, simply a long lists of toys, with an automatic buying link.

 **As the slogan says, "For kids of all ages!"**

Action Man
www.actionman.com
Be warned, if you're visiting this site in the office you will become horribly conspicuous in a cybersecond as the arrival of the home page coincides with the kind of alert siren you used to hear on the good old *USS Enterprise*. When you've chosen the country you're browsing from, you'll be called to action stations. There's a link to a UK online store where you can buy the figures and the associated accessories. Well worth visiting, especially for thirtysomething men who can't believe the soldier of their youth is still doing the business.

Airfix
www.airfix.com
Another dream site for thirtysomethings. All the Airfix models you could ever imagine at cheap-as-you-like prices. Search by model type, classic ships, cars, war heroes and space models, and narrow your selection down to an era or type. Pick up Henry VIII or an Aston Martin DB for a mere £3.99, although the more advanced HMS Belfast and Cutty Sark sell for £7.99. Sizes and skill levels are included in descriptions alongside adequate images. Amateur-looking – but, be honest, that's how your models will probably end up.

Dawson and Son
www.dawson-and-son.co.uk
A delightfully old-fashioned specialist in wooden toys and games, this offers lots of quaint, romantic toys to dilute the Pokémon collection. Jack-in-the-Boxes, spinning tops and old fashioned pastry sets are usually still hits with small children, although the knitting sets and flower press kits are perhaps a little optimistic. The toys are quite pricey (the Jack-in-the-Box could be

yours for just £20), but they are beautifully made and built to last. Dawsons are a Which Web Trader.

Huggables

www.huggables.com

Gold, red and blue teddy bears, chimney sweep bears, mohair lambs, terriers and even polar bears. You may have guessed Huggables is a cuddly toy site, with prices ranging from £10 to £200. Not much you can really say, the only niggling feature being the lack of direct link to the order form. Another pen and paper job then.

Klikit

www.klikit.co.uk

Model kits for the serious builder. Choose from land, sea, air and off-world models including a Panther tank (£19.92), HMS Victory (£20.39) and the Hawker Hurricane (£31.44). View enlarged images of the constructed models but groan at the lack of additional information or history behind each piece. Prices include delivery and reductions on the recommended retail price.

Letterbox collection

www.l-box.co.uk

Presents, dressing-up clothes and a whole range of personalised items are on sale here, but steel yourself for some spectacularly un-PC costumes such as the Blushing Bride and Red Indian Chief outfits. Still, there's a decent range of goods focusing on fun and imagination rather than the practical, including birth announcement pictures and personalised pillows, towels and cutlery. These take 28 days to deliver and the non-personalised items take seven. Prices start from £2.35 for goods up to £19 and are free over £120.

Total Robots

http://mypage.ihost.com/totalrobots/

Obviously not your run of the mill toy selection, Total Robots sell robotic kits from which you can create your own walking or wheeled robots and artificial robotic lifeforms. Don't be put off by the stark homepage; images of each constructed model are available alongside details of what the robot is and the "hours of fun!" that can be had building and playing with it. You can also download many of the catalogues so you can inspect the full selection of robotic arms at your leisure. Prices depend on how advanced the robot is, and range from £8 for the solar powered Trimet to £250 for the Arobat.

Travel

It doesn't make any difference
whether you think it's better
to travel or to arrive. The Net
offers so much choice that it
has been known to induce a
state of analysis paralysis in
the indecisive or weak-willed

General Where to go and how to get there

A2B Travel
www.a2btravel.com
A2B contains information on every mode of transport possible. If you're in
a buying mood, you can log-on to the flight-finder to buy tickets online, or
rent a villa in France, Italy or Spain. The site doesn't offer its own package
deal section but it does offer hyperlinks to Bargain Holidays (see below) and
Escape Routes. Standard search systems apply, so just type in the wheres
and whens and see what they come up with. A2B is particularly useful as
an information portal for travellers, with insurance quotes, airport and
accommodation guides, and flight, ferry and train timetables.

Bargain Holidays
www.bargainholidays.co.uk
This is one of many sites where you can do everything apart from actually
book a holiday online. When we visited, it offered only flights for booking, but
this site stands out for its resort guides, weather information and brochure
request service, not to mention its regular competitions. A useful site to begin
with if you're not sure where you want to go, or how much you should pay.

Destination Group
www.destination-group.com
You can't always book online from this crowded, text-laden homepage. In the
majority of cases you search through the exotic package holidays, choose a
deal, click on it and they ring you back to make the booking. You can book

flights online, though on a few occasions you may find yourself linked to a separate site to book. Whatever the option, there are cheap deals to be had.

E Bookers
www.ebookers.com
Despite the automatic connection to the flight bookings section, you can also book accommodation, insurance and car hire online. For flights, type in your destinations, dates and details and it's guaranteed to come up with list upon list of flights. Once you've made your selection, however, the problems begin. You need to register before you can go any further, and this inevitably takes too long while you try to think up a password no one else in the world is already using. If you do have the patience, the step-by-step buying process does make spending hundreds of pounds that little bit easier.

Expedia
www.expedia.msn.co.uk
An easy-to-navigate complete travel resource, with online booking for flights, accommodation, package holidays, car rentals, resort and even airport guides. If you're booking a room, you can make as many specifications as you want: non-smoking, wheelchair access etc. Flights generally aren't cheap, but it's worth a look if price isn't your primary concern.

Late Escapes
www.lateescapes.com
If you've read Chapter 4 on auctions, you'll know that you really can bid for pretty much anything online. Late Escapes deals in holiday auctions, flights, packages, city breaks and cruises. Aside from the incredibly small type, which can make reading rather difficult, the site is well laid out and easy to navigate. All you have to decide is where you want to go. On a late-summer 2000 visit to the site you could pick up a flight to Menorca for £30, two weeks in Crete for two at £179, and two weeks for two in Barbados for £530. A good starting point is the Holidays for £1 section, which sounds to good to be true, but isn't.

Tel Me
www.telmeglobaltraveller.com
A useful all-round resource for business travellers, with online flight bookings and hotel reservations, as well as city guides and Tel Me miles to be collected by the frequent traveller. Follow the usual process,

selecting destinations etc. Prices are steeper than those of low-cost airlines, i.e. £400 for two flights to Barcelona. But then, if the company's paying...

The First Resort
www.thefirstresort.com
You should only use First Resort if you're definitely going to book that day and if you don't intend to travel for another ten weeks, as you can't book late or semi-late deals online. It takes too long to register – you have to give personal details and spend time choosing your favourite resorts. Otherwise, the site is simple to use and searches the top tour operators for good deals.

Thomas Cook
www.thomascook.co.uk
This high-street chain has created a bright, eye-catching web site that's perfect for young and old, new or experienced travellers. Search for package deals or villas, or by age with Club 18-30 and over 50s holidays on offer. Standard brochure stuff, though special requirements vary, with golf, cabaret dancers and bridge for over-50s and nightlife a must for the young ones.

All-in-ones One-stop shops

Club 18-30
www.club18-30.co.uk
A loud fuchsia-and-yellow homepage with a pulsating heartbeat ringing in the background – this could only be the Club 18-30 site. Search through the resort guides to get an idea of where you'll hear the loudest music and book your fun, fun trip. As you generally pay more for specialist holidays, the descriptions and pictures are deliberately made comprehensive and enticing enough to encourage you to buy – as if you really needed any encouragement anyway.

Kuoni
www.kuoni.co.uk
If you're accustomed to passing by the Kuoni brochure at the travel agent's for fear of price overload, you'll be surprised to find cheap deals for such dream destinations as Cuba, Grenada, Egypt and Goa to name but a few. Top offers when we visited included a five-night Egyptian stay in a four-star hotel with a Nile view for £400. Stylewise, the destination guides include history and places of interest. You can search by price, destination or date, and Kuoni uses a step-by-step buying guide to put the less confident at ease.

Last Minute

www.lastminute.com

Forget all the media pot-shots against this company. The bright design of this site eggs you on to buy a holiday through its enthusiasm. The boxed captions include all the key information you need to save you wasting time browsing fruitlessly. You do need to register, but this takes about three seconds and they send you regular updates of the best offers as compensation.

TraveloCity

www.travelocity.co.uk

Huge promises but smaller returns. Supposedly you can book holidays, flights and hire cars from this site, but a recent search failed to come up with any matches for what we wanted. Having been advised to be slightly more flexible on the details of our desired trip, we called customer service to explain that no date, destination or duration preference had been expressed, but they still seemed unable to suggest a holiday, anywhere.

Trrravel

www.trrravel.com

One of the best-designed sites, Trrravel have had the foresight to use scroll-down menus and quick links to avoid over-active homepages which can often put people off. The auction section is a fun way to search. If you're willing to travel the next day, two weeks in Majorca can be picked up for £149. However, the best deals were those in the ski section, with a week's skiing in France in January 2001 for £219. Once again, though, it's a case of making your selection and then waiting for the telephone to ring.

Virgin Holidays

www.virginholidays.co.uk

The suitably sunny homepage clearly maps out all the online offers with late deals, package and flight-only deals to the Mediterranean and Florida, and to more exotic locations. After selecting the part of the world you wish to explore, things get more complicated, with no clear signs pointing to the online booking section. Once resolved, simply fill in the standard requirements. If they can't find exactly what you're looking for, they come up with a list of alternatives, not always suitable. Each resort, hotel and flight is described in detail.

Flights Just get up and go

Buzz

www.buzzaway.com
Buzz is one to note for the future
as the low-cost-flights-to-Europe
company gradually adds more cities
to its destination list. Popular city
breaks include Paris and Milan, along
with such rather more adventurous
destinations as Helsinki and Berlin. On
the downside, Buzz is slow to offer flights
from anywhere in the UK besides London
Stansted. Booking is easy and you receive
an almighty £2 discount for booking online.

Deck Chair

www.deckchair.com
Pick any departure point and destination in the world and
Bob Geldof's Deck Chair (well, not his personal deck chair) will scour the
globe and every flight company for a price to suit. Unfortunately things go a
little pear-shaped from here as the process by which you move from selecting
your flights to actually buying them is a bit too much like hard work.

EasyJet

www.easyjet.com
Hurray! Cheap European flights from UK airports other than London Stansted
and Luton. Those in Liverpool can fly to hot spots Amsterdam, Barcelona and
Nice, to name but a few, for as little as £50 return. Standard booking system
applies and again you receive discounts if you book online.

Go-Fly

www.go-fly.com
British Airways' venture into low-cost flights, Go flies to holiday hot-spots
Tenerife and Alicante. The cheapest flights remain those that are booked last
minute. Easy to navigate with resort guides, insurance, car hire and a hotel
booking service, Go, like most of the cheap-flight specialists, disappoints in
the price stakes. For example, an outward flight to Barcelona may only cost
£15, but the return trip will likely set you back around ten times that amount.

Ryanair

www.ryanair.i.e.
Another low-cost flight site, Ryanair flies to more unusual destinations, such
as Aarhus in Denmark and Perpignan in France, along with the more run-of-

the-mill Genoa and Dublin. Don't get too excited by the £9 return flights blurb on the homepage: this covers a very limited range. Flights are still cheap, but most flights from UK locations outside London Stansted fly via Dublin.

Travel Select
www.travelselect.com
As basic as it can get, this site uses plain pages from which you select your route and see what they can come up with. Not for those looking for the cheapest options – £165 for a ticket to Barcelona is a typical offering – but a useful site for those after a no-nonsense approach.

You can also try:
British Airways
www.british-airways.com
Prices here can often compete with those of the cheap-flight merchants, but the timetables and airport codes can be confusing. Perhaps one for the frequent flyer who knows their Luton from their Ljubljana.

British Midland
www.iflybritishmidland.com
Less publicised therefore more chance of available flights.

By Sea Wave goodbye

Drive Alive
www.drive-alive.com
Despite the name, these motoring holidays to Europe begin with a ferry crossing. Their aim is to take the hassle out of planning your trip by handling all the booking arrangements on your behalf. This may sound like a glorified tour operator but the system is quite unique. Enter your proposed dates, returns and destinations for ferry crossings and then navigate your way around France, selecting from a long list of hotels where you would like to stay. It calculates the price and books for you. All you have to do is the driving.

P & O Ferries
www.poef.com/poef/index.htm
Ferry crossings to Europe remain the cheapest option. From this site you can do everything apart from confirm your booking. Fill in the form (complete with meal preferences and insurance requirements) and a P & O rep will call you back ASAP to finalise your holiday. Special offers begin at £39 per person to Bruges, with alternative destinations including Bilbao and Rotterdam.

Korea move

See the Stalinist Las Vegas!

For the adventurous, independent traveller, there is only one part of the world which now counts as seriously unexplored: North Korea. The People's Democratic Republic (or the weirdest place on Earth as it is often described) may seem like the most closed society on this planet but it has not been slow on the uptake when it comes to the Internet.

In the capital Pyongyang stands a rare realistic statue of North Korea's great late leader Kim Il Sung suffering from backache

If you fancy a different type of package holiday you can browse some of the options on www.stat.ualberta.ca/people/schmu/kitc.html, the official site for the Korea International Travel Company and the brainchild of Kim Il Sung, the late, lamented (in Pyongyang) leader. This site says that 30,000 tourists arrive every year in a republic, which calls itself "the eastern country of courtesy". The packages on offer here all start in the capital Pyongyang, the Stalinist Las Vegas. But you can't order online, only by telex, mail or fax. Conveniently neither the snail mail nor the telex address (or the fax number) are included in this site, although it does have a picture of a statue of Kim 1.

You probably won't be going to North Korea for the climate, but you can check the weather in the capital on http://as.orientation.com/dispatch/home.html. Whenever this visitor checked, the weather ran the whole gamut from "partly cloudy" to "cloudy". If you're still not deterred, you can order package tours of North Korea by email, through Dutch travel agent VNC on www.vnc.nl/korea. A typical tour costs £707. If you want to order from a UK agent, try www.bestravel.co.uk/northkorea.htm where the tours start at £779 with a train journey from Beijing to Pyongyang.

Want to check the news before you go? There's nowhere better than www.kcna.co.jp – the official site for the official Korean news agency – to catch up on which ambassador is presenting his credentials. You've probably heard some of the fuss about North Korea and its nuclear missiles. They do get into trouble for pointing them at the wrong people (i.e. everybody) and for peace of mind you might want to check out the country's nuclear arsenal on www.fas.org/nuke/guide/dprk/nuke/index.html. If that puts you off, don't worry: you can still travel virtually to North Korea by reading David and Bill's travel diary on www.ozemail.com.au/~davidf/homepage/nk_1994.htm.

Rail Old-time romance

Great Western Trains
www.great-western-trains.co.uk
Fancy a trip to Bath Spa, Taunton or even Swindon? Train-operating company
Great Western have embraced technology and allow you to book your tickets
online. The simple system asks the same questions they would if you rang up,
but your boss won't know you're using company time to book some fun.

The Train Line
www.thetrainline.com
Buying with The Train Line turned out to be quite a complicated process. First
you need to register before you can do anything and once in, it's advisable to
know exactly where you want to go. Scroll-down destination menus would be
helpful. (If you really want to confuse the site, try to book a trip by sleeper.)
Search according to the cheapest or fastest journey, whichever you prefer.

Virgin Trains
www.virgintrains.co.uk
Similar system to The Train Line, the only difference being that they don't
rashly claim to cover the whole country, just the Bransonised bits.

Resting places A room with a view

Bed & Breakfast
www.beduk.co.uk
Grim-looking home page hiding a selection of B&Bs
complete with full descriptions, images and room
rates. You can't book online, but send your requests to
the company and they'll make the arrangements.

Book That
www.bookthat.com
A database of villas, country houses and apartments covering the
UK, France, Spain, Portugal and Italy. Prices range from £500 to
£1000 depending on the season.

Easy Stay
www.easystay.co.uk
Easy Stay is easy to search and easy on the eye. Select a region and browse
through lists of B&Bs and swanky hotels. Search Hot Deals for hotels easy on

Decked out in mellow yellow, Easy Stay's online directory covers everything from bed and breakfasts to hotels which are listed in the English dictionary as the definition of "swanky"

your pocket with up to 50 per cent discounts if you mention Easy. You can't book direct online but you can make reservation enquiries.

Hotels Online
www.hol.co.uk
The best advice here is to look at as many hotels in your chosen area as possible, since some provide extensive information and others barely leave their postal details. Simply select a destination, browse and book.

Hoseasons Holidays
www.hoseasons.co.uk
A dull and lifeless site in terms of style, but here you can choose from boating and holiday park holidays in the UK and Europe. Prices vary considerably, but this could be the ideal site for large groups looking for a cheap getaway.

B&B In London
www.londonhometohome.com
Looking for somewhere to stay while you're on that shopping-and-theatre trip to The Smoke? This excellent site is a real find. Home To Home is a west London B&B agency that will find you a classy and comfortable home from home at rates much cheaper than hotels. Booking is by fax or email.

Travel Web
www.travelweb.com
You can book flights as well as hotel rooms from this US site, but they list prices in dollars only which is a hassle. Although the accommodation section again sticks to the native currency of the hotels, they make up for this with a comprehensive directory of worldwide hotels with descriptions and pictures. Make your search as nit-picky as you like, down to whether you want an alarm clock, and you'll be offered a wide choice every time.

Worldwide Apartments
www.nothotels.com
This sophisticated site looks more like an advertisement for interior design than accommodation, but the apartments here aren't your average B&Bs. Select anywhere in the world and the Foxton's database should be able to find something to suit your taste, if not necessarily your bank balance. Prices begin at £60 per person, per night but the last minute deals we found for London were more around the £200 mark. There's no online booking, but you can make online information requests or use their call-back service.

Useful info Weather, bugs, cash points...

Travel Xtras
www.travelxtras.com
It's the week before your holiday and you've forgotten to buy your mosquito repellent. Travel Xtras can sort you out no problem. Try the handy waterproof pouch so you need never hide your valuables in the sand again.

The Foreign Office
www.fco.gov.uk/travel/
Official travel and visa advice and contact details for British embassies.

Oanda.Com
www.oanda.com
A bit like a public information ad, this lists the exchange rates for 164 countries.

VISA
www.visa.com/cgi-bin/vee/main.html
The location of every cash point in the world. Trivia buffs can't keep away.

World Meteorological Association
www.wmo.ch
Weather news and updates whether your destination is Brunei or Bromsgrove.

Caravanserai offers tours to Libya and Iran – destinations which could best be described as "up and coming"

Independents For something completely different

Bales Worldwide

www.balesworldwide.com

You won't find Aiya Napa or the Costa del Sol here, only luxury holidays at luxury prices. Explore Thailand, China, South America or even Iceland. Each itinerary includes details of what you get for your of thousands of pounds, including insurance, meals and guides, along with a brief run-down of the delights ahead. The descriptions are a bit short and could do with more pictures. You can book online if this doesn't bother you, or order the brochure from the site to get a better picture. For the experienced traveller only.

Caravanserai

www.caravanserai-tours.com/

Clearly Caravanserai Tours has no pretensions to being the next Thomas Cook as it specialises in tours to Iran and Libya, two destinations which have yet to have their own Exposed series on Sky One. This is a nice, uncluttered site that never takes its eye off the fact that it's the destinations that you're interested in. You can email them your requirements for tours to either country.

Indian Magic

www.indianmagic.co.uk

This site caters for first-time visitors to India as well as those heading back for more. Chose from the overview trip taking in the sights of Jaipur and Delhi for £1500, or head for Rajastan to visit a camel breeding farm and spend an evening with an astrologer. The site is easy to navigate with simple headings from which you can scroll down the itinerary lists for each trip. Thankfully it hasn't overdone the decoration. No online booking, but fill in the order form with your chosen tour number and dates of travel and they'll get back to you.

Magic of Bolivia
www.bolivia.co.uk
For many, Bolivian magic is defined by Lake Titicaca but Che Guevara's bones were found there recently and a "Che is God" concert is being organised (obviously Eric Clapton won't be playing). It's part of this site's unique charm that it seems as keen to share such snippets as it is to get you to click on a button for a Bolivian holiday. Online ordering was planned when the site was inspected. Meantime, you can download an itinerary. Nice to see an online store which doesn't stress everything with exclamation marks.

Pack Your Bags
www.packyourbags.co.uk
Pack Your Bags is both a useful late-deals site where you can find your bargain break and email your request, and a source for holidays of a more adventurous nature. Be as one with the wolves and bears in Transylvania for a week at £718, or search for the hidden secrets of Zeus on an archaeological dig in Turkey for around £900. Each comes with a full day-by-day itinerary and pictures to whet your appetite.

The Russian Experience
www.trans-siberian.co.uk
Not in fact the full Russian experience: you don't get to be the victim of rampant hyperinflation or wait for months for your wages to turn up. But this company does offer you the chance to stay with a typical Russian family as well as do the more predictable stuff like travel on the Trans-Siberian Express (which is as basic as the Orient Express is luxurious). Order by email from a site which also allows you to download the brochures.

Sherpa Expeditions
www.sherpa-walking-holidays.co.uk
The title of this site is slightly misleading: not every holiday here involves a duel with the world's highest mountain and a close encounter with someone called Tensing. You can go walking or trekking across Corsica or even the Cotswolds. You can book by email and phone over your credit card details.

STA Travel
www.statravel.co.uk
If you're a student or under 26, this offers you cheap flights and insurance to destinations all over the world. Current offers include return flights to Australia with a free stop-off in Los Angeles for £525. If you have problems connecting to STA's server to search its database, you can always ring its service line for bookings. If this is your first foray into serious travelling, the site also contains useful healthcare and resort information.

Wild Dog
www.wild-dog.com
There's a lot of information to plough through, so you'll need to take your time using this online directory, but it'll be worth it in the long run. Aside from the online flight and hotel-booking service which scans more than 100 operators for the best deals, Wild Dog is particularly useful if you're looking for such adventures as gorilla-tracking in Uganda. You can't book online but they do provide descriptions, a brochure request service and contact details.

Wildlife Worldwide
www.wildlife-ww.co.uk
Walruses in the Arctic, jaguars in Ecuador and rhinos in Namibia are just a few of the beasts eager to be observed. If you're not sure what's happening in the wildlife kingdom, you can look at their wildlife calendar and request brochures to cover your next trip. If you're satisfied with the day-by-day itinerary which maps out each trip you can email them details of your chosen holidays and they'll reply. Not for the budget traveller but it could be money well spent.

Car hire — The open road, a set of wheels, no petrol...

Hertz
www.hertz.com
If you're looking for that little bit of adventure, renting a car and exploring the countrysides of Cyprus, Morocco or Costa Rica is an idea. Hertz can help in all these locations. Choose your destination, dates of travel and an Escort, Mondeo or any of the Ford classics. Most prices work out at around £15 a day.

Car Hire 4 Less
www.carhire4less.co.uk
This site specialises in searching reputable vendors (including Budget and Hertz) and coming up with discounted prices. This said, they failed to beat Hertz on matching deals on our most recent visit.

Autocar Rental
www.autocarrental.co.uk
It's a simple system – you tell them how, when and where you want your car and they'll email you in return with a quote.

Easy RentaCar
www.easyrentacar.com
Yet another Easy venture. This one enables you to pick up a Mercedes A class to tour London, Barcelona or Paris. Nice, clean, text-led site, let down by a rather temperamental mechanism for checking prices and availability.

Winter Vacations to chill you out

1 Ski
www.1ski.com

This site takes information to the extreme. Here, you can read up on any ski resort in the world, down to the tiniest detail: difficulty ratings, snow reports, events diary and techniques. If this whets your appetite, you should also be able to find a skiing holiday, although the usual enquiry and call-back service does apply. On the downside, the Top Ten deals section is over-ambitious. The week-long trip to Soldeau, promised for £123, turned out to be closer to the £300 mark. Still worth browsing.

Center Parcs
www.centerparcs.com

A viable alternative if your bank balance won't stretch to a week in the Canaries, the Center Parcs website teems with greenery, much like the forest villages themselves. Here you can read about and view the villas housing two to eight persons, the restaurants, bars, heated outdoor pools and pamper palaces. Center Parcs doesn't accept credit card details online but you can make a reservation (a week in Sherwood Forest works out for only £65 each) and it'll call you back within two days. You can also make specifications for adjoining villas, en-suite facilities and even Turkish baths.

IGLU
www.iglu.com

This site looks fantastic with lots of snow pics and everything you need to know to book a skiing holiday. Resort and hotel guides, snow reports, even webcams and 3D maps are all there to browse. But only once you start to search do you realise – after they come up with no matches from the widest criteria possible for the whole of Canada – that there's something missing beyond the homepage. Everything else is right, with even a demo of how to buy online. But this isn't much good if there are no holidays…

Inghams
www.inghams.co.uk

This would be a comprehensive site to book from if Inghams could just organise the navigation a bit better. You can choose from ski resorts, lakes and mountain villas, and city breaks. For skiing, resorts are rated by piste and the level of expertise needed to avoid broken bones. You can book online but you are warned on the homepage that if you don't enter anything in the first 15 minutes the connection will time out. Not as clear as it could be.

Watersports

Offline surfing is now so mega that someone will soon decide it's the new rock'n'roll. Meantime, feast your browsers on this little lot...

Diving Daisy

www.divingdaisy.freeuk.com

Strictly for the Newquay set. Busy blue and pink interface in the style of Miss Teenage fanzine reveals that it in fact sells only après scuba diving T-shirts. Buy direct by credit card, and if you order over four items you'll get a freebie. Less expensive than most surf shops at £25 and under, including delivery.

Jag Wet Suits

www.jagwetsuits.co.uk

Jag, one of the UK's biggest suppliers of all things neoprene, has outfits and accessories for every occasion. No cavorting babes here – just neat product illustrations with brief descriptions. Jag will ring/email you for free (whether you live in Aruba, Ivory Coast or Zimbabwe) to answer any queries and take orders – or you can just go ahead and use your credit card.

Marine Products

www.marine-products.com

This Salt Lake City-based store ships international orders in 5-10 days. Shipping costs are calculated once you've ordered but nothing is charged to you unless you agree. More unusual items include water trampolines for $700.

Robin Hood Watersports

www.roho.co.uk

Despite the envy-inducing images of expert water babies, Robin Hood starts at the bottom of the ladder with Kayak Starter Packs for £299, and moves on to the radical wave boards with flashy designs and flashy prices, some over £1000. If you're really keen, everything is delivered the next day for £7.50.

Simply Scuba

www.simplyscuba.co.uk

With dive equipment and courses to buy, news and reviews, Simply Scuba is as comprehensive as it gets. If you're new to the sport the review sections will tell you the difference between your Aqua-Lung and your Typhoon dry suit.

Weddings & Bar Mitzvahs

Big day approaching? Why not let the Web ease the strain of planning? There are loads of sites with plenty of cool goods from tiaras to furry handcuffs to make it a truly special event

General | From stag/hen nights to biodegradable confetti

Confetti

www.confetti.co.uk

Alongside the usual guff about etiquette, there's some cracking stuff here to calm a harassed bride. Our favourite is the rotating dresses section where you can see what a selection of gowns looks like from all angles before you try them on. In the shopping section there are excellent gifts (not just for weddings but other occasions too, such as Mother's Day or 21st birthdays), plus items for the modern wedding like biodegradable, heart-shaped confetti and disposable camera multipacks. There's also a selection of pretty and reasonably priced tiaras for those who not fortunate to have a diamond one in the family, and jewellery thank-you gifts for bridesmaids.

Hens and Stags

www.clickandbuild.com/cnb/shop/hensandstags

Online shop for party supplies aimed at hen parties and stag nights. Fake breasts, furry handcuffs, inflatable men and women – you get the drift. Prices are reasonable with some definite savings if you buy a complete party pack. Delivery is £4 but be prepared to wait up to 14 days for your order to arrive.

Martha Stewart

www.marthastewart.com

Martha is the uncrowned US queen of the stylish wedding. Her web site has a whole section devoted to wedding ideas (think discreet luxury rather than raucous knees-up). In the Martha By Mail section, you can buy things like her signature wedding favour boxes, glass cake-stands and general all-round unique loveliness for the upmarket wedding. They ship internationally, but you have to phone the details of your order to the US to find out shipping costs.

Ultimate Wedding
www.ultimatewedding.com
Another online wedding mall from the US, with loads of fun products such as printed matchbooks or personalised champagne bottles filled with jellybeans. Overseas shipping is calculated separately on your order, depending on size.

Web Wedding
www.webwedding.co.uk
The gifts section is handily broken down into categories – mother of the bride, best man (lovely waistcoats) etc – with lots of presents for everyone involved which can be gift-wrapped and delivered anywhere in the country. There are also books on speeches and organisation, and while the wedding dress search engine (based on price, train length and shape) is a little limited, new styles are being added. But carriage charges are only calculated once you've started the ordering process and can be quite hefty (£6.50 on a £40 order).

Wed Guide
www.wedguide.com
Fantastic prices on American wedding accessories such as bubble-blowers or car and cake decorations. There are lots of things here that you won't find in the UK to add an individual touch to your big day, so it's worth the extra effort of calling in your order to check shipping details.

 **"Just one more for the album"**

The Guild of Wedding Photographers
www.gwp-uk.co.uk
Advice on what to look for in a good photographer, plus contact details and links to Guild members.

Studio Images
www.studioimages.co.uk
Representing photographers all over the UK who specialise in modern wedding photography. There are loads of pictures to look through to help you choose, and an online request form for more information or contact details.

PIC Productions
www.pic.clara.net
These wedding videographers provide plenty of stills from actual wedding videos so that you can get a real idea of the coverage and service they offer. You can e-mail them for quotes or further information.

Weddings & Bar Mitzvahs

 **Something different for your invitations**

ABC Publishers
www.shadicards.com
Suppliers of invitations and cards for Indian and Pakistani weddings, including Muslim, Hindu, and Sikh ceremonies, although many designs are suitable for non-Asian weddings too. There are lots of different designs, and insert paper is included in the price for you to print on your own printer (they even offer clip-art to download) or they can print the inserts for you at an extra cost.

ARTeMISS Design
www.artemissdesign.fsnet.co.uk
Easy to use with lots of photos of their designs, this is a great site for brides looking for something a bit different for their invitations. Cards are handmade using high-quality paper and fabrics, and a range of art techniques such as collage or watercolour. The mail order page was down when we tested it, but you can email through the site for further details.

Big Leap Designs
www.bigleapdesigns.com
This is a very impressive, bright and modern wedding invitation and thank-you card site. There are plenty of designs to choose from and they also do orders of service, candles, place cards, evening invitations and reply cards. The order form is comprehensive right down to the wording (don't worry – you will be sent a proof before they print) and the customer service is exemplary.

Wedding locations **and other unusual ideas**

County Marquees
www.countymarquee.co.uk
Home counties marquee hire for celebrations of all sizes. The site can be a bit slow but there are letters from satisfied clients and plenty of pictures on show.

Federation of Professional Toastmasters
www.federationtoastmasters.fsnet.co.uk
If you're planning a big do, consider hiring a toastmaster (generally a man with a moustached, a red jacket and a loud voice) to keep things running smoothly.

For Better For Worse
www.forbetterforworse.co.uk
Directory for a wide variety of sites for UK civil weddings. There are stately homes, country house hotels and unusual venues such as football grounds.

The Occasional Poet
www.theoccasionalpoet.com
Commission a poem which is tailored to you and your intended's lives. Forty lines costs you $100 and will save anyone struggling to write personal vows.

Polhawn Fort
www.polhawn-fort.co.uk
For something extra special, why not hire a real-life fortress on the stunning Cornish coast? Available for weddings and receptions most of the year.

The Printed Candle Company
www.printedcandle.com
Candles of various shapes and sizes which can be printed with your names and wedding images, plus lots of gift ideas for bridesmaids. This US company will ship internationally, but allow at least six weeks for your order to arrive.

Bar & Bat Mitzvahs Make it a kosher event

Five Star Software
www.fivestarsoftware.com/mitzvah/barmitzvah.htm
Download a free trial version of this Bar and Bat Mitzvah planning software, or buy the full program online to help you track every detail of your day.

Jewish.co.uk
www.jewish.co.uk
General site with a useful directory of specialist firms who supply invitations, photographers and kosher catering for a Bar or Bat Mitzvah celebration.

Maria's Celebration Cakes
www.fsmarketplace.co.uk/ubik.dll/store/mariascelebrationcakes
This online cake order service has a selection of Bar Mitzvah keepsake tins filled with fruitcake, complete with coloured decorations and mini Menorah.

Rosenblums World of Judaica
www.alljudaica.com
Original Bar and Bat Mitzvah gifts as well as supplies for the ceremony and books on Judaism can all be found on this US-based site. The site is secure, but for international orders you have to phone your order; delivery is via UPS.

Talit.com
www.jewishheart.com
Online mall of Jewish products directly from Israel. Many items are handmade and holy products such as Talis are certified kosher. Prices are in US $ but they ship anywhere; deliveries to the UK cost $12 and should take eight days.

Weird stuff

Fear not - not every
Internet novelty has
to do with flatulence
or Bill and Monica.
Surf and ye shall
find– from a redneck
doll to a combined
telephone and blender…

A noble title
www.elitetitles.co.uk/

This site should probably be rechristened FantasistsRUs. "C'mon ladies – for 200 smackers you can call yourself a marchioness!" It's the kind of offer even a certain sitcom market-trader might find a bit fishy but as the site says, a proper title would cost you £8,000 so by clicking the order form here, the aspiring noble can save £7,800! Of course, your reign as baron(ess) will not entitle you to the usual privileges: the right to pass this honour on to your offspring, or be thrown out of the House of Lords by New Labour. An off-the-shelf title could be yours in just 14 days, though a title with its own bit of land costs £995 and could take up to eight weeks for all the formal guff to go through. A small price to pay for ersatz nobility.

Cattle mutilation T-shirts
www.ufoshirts.com/

Tasteful t-shirts featuring a drawing of a cow with a bullet hole where part of its midriff should be are just one of the highlights on this site. The designs may be naff but at $15 a throw, these t-shirts are pretty cheap. If you need extra protection from "government truth beams and cosmic rays", the manufacturers advise you to line the shirts with aluminium foil.

Demotivational calendars
www.despair.com/index2.html

For those who, like that supreme loafer Philip Larkin, don't want to let the toad called work squat on their life and are proud of it, this is the ultimate site. The online catalogue contains an amazing array of demotivational posters and calendars, containing such perversely inspiring slogans as "If at first you don't succeed, failure may be your style". Despair.com does ship outside the US for a charge of $20 an order – almost worth it to buy the Pessimists Mug which comes complete with the recommendation "This mug really makes everything taste bitter". Not to be missed.

Diving maps for the Red Sea

www.venus.co.uk/diveplan/intro.htm

Fancy diving in the Red Sea but scared that your lack of local knowledge will let you down? Well, shed those fears and get ready to scuba because for £30 you can buy a dive plan pack which includes a 16-page guide describing each site and incredibly detailed maps packed with such useful information as "much small life".

Email the rest of the universe

www.messagetospace.com/index2.html

Sending a message into space could, the people at the Message to Space company politely suggest, release your inner self and enhance your creativity. Whether it does either, both or none of the above probably depends on the sender, but one thing's for certain: it will cost you $10.95 for a one-page message and $4.95 for each subsequent page.

Flightless fruit flies

http://drosophila.herpetology.com/

Inspecting the shipping and returns policies of a site is usually the dullest part of online shopping but not here. To the FAQ "what is our liability?" the Drosophila Company (snappy motto: "Flightless fruitflies for reptiles and amphibians") replies, "We only guarantee live delivery and you must notify us within 24 hours of any DOA vials." A vial contains 25 to 50 adult fruitflies, so if they are on Dead On Arrival that's probably the fruitfly equivalent of genocide. The company does deliver overseas but only if you order at least 100 cultures. Inviting 5000 genetically impaired (and biologically grounded) fruitflies into your home doesn't sound that drastic. After all, they only live for 25 to 30 days (not good news if they get sent by surface mail by mistake). But they do spend most of their 25-30 days on this Earth breeding. So if you fancy having your pad taken over by thousands of sex-crazed, rotten-fruit gorging fruitflies which can't fly, this is most definitely the site for you.

A GOTTLE OF GEER!

If you harbour a secret desire to be Keith Harris (and your doctor cannot suggest a cure) log on to www.axtell.com/vent. html. All you really need is a Net-friendly computer, a cuddly toy to stick your hand up and a willingness to ignore the baffled looks from your workmates as you mutter "Gottle of geer! Gottle of geer!" incoherently into your screen.

———————————

After ten minutes you should feel qualified to join the International Ventriloquist's Association on www.inquisite.com.

———————————

And remember, to paraphrase an old cliché, on the Internet no one can see your lips move.

Food-blender and telephone

www.cycoactive.com/blender/

It's a telephone and a food-blender all in one! This astonishing device comes complete with a testimonial from Bill Jenkins who brought it for a friend's wedding in Boulder, Colorado, and says: "It was incredible… the groom kept ringing it on his mobile all night… it was the only gift they carried home with them." If you think it's a tasteless wedding present, recall the Blendmaster's wise words: "It's their fault for getting married." This site is so well done that it's only when you email for info that you're convinced it isn't a spoof.

Humorous underwear

www.cautionunderwear.com

Not even Kenny Everett's character Cupid Stunt would describe this site as "in the best possible taste". If men's boxer shorts decorated with a road sign which says "Slippery when wet" tickles your funny bone, this is for you.

Musical Coca-Cola carousel

www.franklinmint.com

"A musical masterpiece of carousel artistry that moves round and round, up and down" is how the Franklin Mint Company describes this musical carousel, decorated with authentic vintage Coca Cola signage, which costs only $245. At least you can't order online from the UK; the time expended in ringing up the London sales office should bring most people to their senses.

Nancy Sinatra fridge magnets

www.fridgedoor.com

Quite frankly your fridge isn't pulling its weight. Why should it be allowed to just sit there, big, white and blank, just keeping things cool when it could be contributing to the ambience of your palatial abode by wearing, for example, a tasteful Nancy Sinatra fridge magnet complete with red boots? These people "gladly accept international orders" which sounds a tad desperate.

Robopup

http://shop.store.yahoo.com/faoschwarz/poochi.html

Dr Who fans still mourning the demise of the allegedly loveable robodog K9 may or may not find solace in this interactive puppy with the less than appealing name of Poo-Chi. This virtual pet thinks you were born to make him happy: the more you play with him the happier he gets. Such is the demand, even at $29.95, that customers can only buy two each and the sellers say smugly "Immediate delivery is not guaranteed." So it's like that is it?

Snowthrowers

www.cleanairgardening.com/

Snow-clearing is not a problem most of us have to grapple with on a regular basis, but if you're a sucker for the kind of American movie where Ma and Pa spend much of the screen time clearing away snow from their extravagantly proportioned house, then the Toro electric power curve 1200 snowthrower is worth $270 (without shipping) and it's a cheaper way of getting in the mood than moving to Nebraska.

Redneck doll

http://www.spumco.com

From those terribly amusing people who brought you Ren and Stimpy comes the subversively named site, Spumco, probably the Web's finest cartoon show. Buy a George Liquor doll for just $34.95 plus $20 shipping and, the blurb

From the creators of Ren & Stimpy comes this online comic book, complete with hidden fun sound effects

promises: "He'll teach you to be a God-fearing American, no matter what foreign country you're from. Girls! Give one of these to your boyfriend. George will make a man out of him for you!" But don't order in July because everyone in the studio store goes on holiday. All month.

Samurai-style helmet

www.majestic-n.com/

The place to go if you're willing to spend $235 on "an authentic style samurai helmet". (Note the careful interjection of the word "style" in that description.) If that doesn't tempt you, why not buy a fairy, gargoyle or a skull-shaped piggy-bank? The generous people from Majestic Novelties have also been known to give away stuff like a miniature barbarian axe, which is promoted with the slogan "Get them while they're hot!". Thankfully you need an ID and password to visit sister site SwordsRUs. No, we're not making this up.

Virtual makeover

www.compucloz.com

Digital makeovers sound deeply superficial but The Digital Looking Glass take this subject very seriously indeed – it's the company's avowed aim to become the "dressing room of the digerati". Ignore all the corporate guff (this site is really aimed at retailers) and get a total head-to-toe makeover online.

Woolly mammoth teeth

www.twoguysfossils.com

Elton John need look no further for his next hair transplant. For $60 he can buy some two-million-year-old hair with one careless owner: a Siberian woolly mammoth. But hurry, Elton – there are only four samples left! Among the other prehistoric artefacts on this site are 1/10 scale models of tyrannosaurus rex, a sabre-toothed tiger's skull and what's left of a 36-million-year-old wolf spider. Two Guys Fossils does deliver overseas, although charges vary from $9-$50.

White goods

Whether your fridge is only managing to keep the milk lukewarm or you just blew up the oven, there are plenty of websites that can rescue you from any domestic crisis. There's even a site that will go comparison shopping for you

General | Because electrical shops are so dreary

Argos

www.argos.co.uk

Microwaves might be the largest household appliances on offer, but Argos' refreshingly vibrant design at least offers relief from the repetitively boring white goods sites which follow. Argos sells vacuum cleaners, microwaves and heaters online, along with smaller electrical accessories. Descriptions and pictures are available for each but discounts are generally just a few pounds.

Benfleet Electronic Services

www.bes-direct.co.uk

Opting for the kitchen-white backdrop, BES sells everything from cookers and microwaves to fridges and freezers. The site is easy to navigate, but it is below par when it comes to providing additional information on each model. For those models with an info stamp beside them, you can read all the specs and view adequate pictures. Otherwise it's a case of trying to deduce what a Cannon Cambridge cooker with double slot oven actually looks like. No discounts are listed for the prices, but the brands range from luxury Neff and Smeg items to high-street regulars Zanussi and Hotpoint.

Best Buy Appliances

www.best-buy-appliances.co.uk

You don't get much better price guarantees than the 110 per cent refund of the difference offered if you find a purchased item cheaper elsewhere within seven days. Putting its emphasis firmly on price, this family-run business sells top brands in kitchen and home appliances, including Bosch, Whirlpool, Zanussi and Hotpoint, and everything is delivered free of charge. The extensive catalogue contains more, if not different, items than you'll generally find on the high street, although it's the American section containing the walk-in fridges, complete with juicer, that everyone wants.

Comet

www.comet.co.uk

Cookers, fridges, washer-dryers – all the usual housewares. Delivery for these is charged at £11.95, and there's a handy Sunday delivery for only £3 more. The best prices are not the best on the Net but Comet is a name that won't disappear overnight and you can complain in person if things go wrong.

Co-op

www.electrical.coop.co.uk

This site has a stylish design with fast connection to the sub-categories and a search facility for cooking, cooling and washing appliances (the cleaning and smaller item sections were under construction when we visited). Here it really is better to buy online, as the e-Coop undercuts the bricks-and-mortar stores by around £50 in most cases. Delivery is set at £11.95.

Direct Sales

www.directsales.org.uk

Direct Sales refers to phone sales rather than online purchases, yet the unique service they offer is worth a look. Linked to top household-appliance names from Whirlpool and Bosch to Neff and AEG, the site lists the items they have on sale at discount prices (£400 for a Neff fridge/freezer, for example). All you have to do is note down the code and make a call. It's sparse in details, so this is really a site for those who already know what they're looking for.

Electrical Direct

www.electricaldirect.co.uk

Hundreds of pounds worth of discounts across the board are on offer here. What's more, if you take a few minutes to join their Privilege Club you can benefit from even cheaper prices with a WAP mobile phone (at the time of our visit) thrown into the bargain. The search categories offer the neat advantage of listing their findings by brand or price, depending on your requirements.

Freenet

www.freenet.ltd.uk

You may well be thinking 'bargain basement' as the shocking-yellow home page hits you in the face, but discounts are few. The organisation is well thought out, however: the sub-categories get as detailed as slimline-dryers and electric slot-in ovens, so you don't need to waste time browsing. But you still have to make your choice based on brief descriptions and small images, so this site is probably best used by those who know exactly what they want.

Helpful
www.helpful.co.uk

Helpful has taken into account what consumers really want by stating what offers are available upfront on the opening page. These include free delivery, free installation on the majority of items, and a three-year guarantee. From here on in, you select a category, browse by brand or price, and make your selection. Helpful has also had the common sense to realise that not everyone feels comfortable buying hundreds of pounds worth of goods with only single-line descriptions to go on. Click on the point descriptions and you'll get the complete explanation.

Home Electrical Direct
www.hed.co.uk

This customer-friendly site offers free delivery and a buy-now, pay-nine-months-later option. Simply laid out, the spec sheets are brief but adequate, including images of each item with its own individual order form. The price listings aren't backed up by high-street comparisons but you'll already know these if you've shopped around.

Intersaver
www.intersaver.co.uk

There isn't much fun to be had shopping for a washing machine but Intersaver has managed to think of almost everything to make your search a little less painful. The prices may not be exactly bargain basement, but reductions of £40, £50 or £60 apply to most items, making it worth a visit. A very handy scroll-down menu on each product description page allows you to see exactly how much high street stores such as Currys or Comet are selling the same model for. As if this wasn't enough, the company will deliver most items between the hours of 4pm and 9pm, it having dawned on the management that they're not the only ones busy at work.

Miller Bros
www.millerbros.co.uk

Nothing special, but it's worth a look for discounts on many top name brands, including Zanussi, Belling, AEG and Ariston. If you have time to spare then browse the catalogue sub-sections; alternatively if you know what you want search by brand or product. There's a flat-rate charge of £10 for delivery, which should take four days.

Powerhouse On-line

www.powerhouse-online.co.uk

The standard deal. Choose from laundry, cooking, refrigeration etc, pick an appliance and either search for a particular model or view the entire stock. The descriptions are minimal, however, and you need to be an expert to work out the difference between A, B and C-class washing machines. On the plus side, the delivery charge on large appliances is only £10.

QED

www.qed-uk.com

A web designer out there is having a laugh. Exactly the same site design as Miller Bros, same products and same layout, but with different prices. QED, however, should be your first port of call as the site offers hundreds of pounds in discounts and free delivery. The price quoted as high street on this site is generally the one that Miller Brothers charges.

Value Direct

www.value-direct.co.uk

The smooth and clear navigation allows you to make your search as simple or as detailed as you like, but it's advisable to use the step-by-step approach as it took this reviewer several attempts at narrowing down the criteria enough to find any results. The price comparison tool is also helpful when checking off what each model can do. Buying is simple and you can spread your payments over two years: simply choose the credit option and wait for your request to be approved.

We Sell It

www.we-sell-it.co.uk

Wordy and jumbled, We Sell It is nevertheless recommended for its range of ever-trendy Smeg appliances. Fridges, freezers and cookers are all available: read the specs (including diagrams of how your built-in appliances will fit, and pictures of the various functions) and place your order. Delivery is free if it's more than £200, and you're not likely to get a Smeg model for much less than that.

These sites are also worth checking out:

Tempo

www.tempo.co.uk

Be Direct

www.bedirect.co.uk

Easy Buy Appliances

www.easybuyappliances.co.uk

Small appliances — Not just any old iron

Americana From The Heart

http://shop.store.yahoo.com/americanafromtheheart

This site deserves an honorary mention even though it sells ironing boards not irons. Americana makes the kind of schmaltzy all-American kind of products which are designed to leave a hole in the wallet and a lump in the throat of any right thinking American. Their ironing board is described as "America with birdhouses" but you have to see it on screen to gauge the full scale of the atrocity. Americana From The Heart does deliver to the UK and there's also a lighthouse themed board. The site says supply is limited. Right. As in "limited to the number we can sell".

KITCHEN SINKS

That ultimate kitchen item, the much-thrown sink, is the house speciality at In-Sinks. Browse through luscious stainless steel, granite and ceramic designs you won't find at MFI. The designer brands, including Kohler, Luisina and Blanco, may not mean anything to those who aren't fanatical about doing the dishes but they are luxury additions to any kitchen. Prices range from £200 to £800 including delivery, which should take three to five days.

In-Sinks
www.kitchen-sinks.co.uk

Global Power

www.globalpower.co.uk

It isn't immediately obvious what Global Power sell. You need to focus on the image bar surrounding the picture of the helpful sales assistant to enter the shop. Once in, you'll find a limited range of white goods and a comprehensive store of smaller appliances including coffee-makers, toasters and kettles. Standard £20 white models are included alongside such luxurious items as a Delonghi espresso and cappuccino-maker for £90 and the ultimate toaster for £165. Buying is simple.

Ifex

www.ifexonline.com

You have to scroll through the list of items at this online department store until you reach Kitchen Appliances. Everything looks the same so far, but Ifex sells some of the more unusual white goods around. Do you have a burning need for a crumb vacuum? There's a Guzzini model for £16.95. Or, you could buy the ultimate American appliance, the waffle iron, selling at a slightly pricier £280, and well-heeled margarita drinkers will be thrilled with a £428 Dualit ice crusher.

Priceright
www.priceright.co.uk

The yellow and mint-green design of this site coordinates well with the appliances sold within. According to the site's sales spiel, their limited catalogue of stock means that selling is based on a first-come, first-served basis, but this seems less than convincing and most shoppers will be able to cope by searching elsewhere. Toasters, kettles etc can work out as much as £20 to £30 cheaper than the high street and, if you become a member, you can benefit from an extra 5% discount off your online purchases.

Vacuum cleaners | Dust bunnies beware

Dyson
www.dyson.co.uk

Dyson is the must-have fashion accessory for every houseproud man or woman. By the time you're through with this stylishly designed site you'll know everything there is to know about vacuum cleaners. There are six models in the range, and you can read all the specifications to learn what the funny nozzles do, and buy, or not. The shopping cart symbol is there but neither this visitor's Explorer or Netscape browser could add a thing to it.

Hoover
www.hoover.co.uk

You can't buy Hoovers from here but the riveting explanation of its Triple Vortex cleaning system with "continuous triple section power 300 G-force" is a must read. You need to have Flash to be treated to the fastest moving animation this side of *The Simpsons* only without the humour or the content. This is the kind of website which wins awards. And loses customers.

Vacuum Cleaners Direct
www.vacuumcleanersdirect.co.uk

Best stick to the scroll-down navigation bar at the top of the page rather than trying to decipher the wordy, confusing home page. Using the product-search wizard you can make your search as simple or as comprehensive as you like, down to your upright or canister preferences, attachments and price limit. This site is good for specialist models, wet-and-dry, three-in-one, four-in-one and so on, with more info than most buyers need.

Vacuum World
www.vacuumworld.co.uk

Find the tools, bags, belts and rollers to fit your own machine from the largest range of vacuum-cleaner accessories online. Just select the brand and scroll through the pix till you come across something which resembles that machine lurking under your stairs. It's that easy. Well, almost.

Wines and Spirits

Fed up with carting all those clinking bottles back from the supermarket? Get someone else to do it for you with these wine and spirits delivery sites that offer everything from an amusing little Pinot Noir to a hardman-humbling tequila. Now we just need someone to take care of all the empties...

Wines | Far too good to drink out of a bag

Allez Vins
www.allezvins.co.uk

Blissfully easy-to-use site from this French regional wine specialist with clear instructions and no having to search around for information on products and services. Allez Vins imports wine directly, mostly from smaller and independent vineyards, so it's a very good place to look for something you may not be able to find at the usual high-street outlet. Since they try to use their own vans, delivery might end up taking four weeks, although urgent orders can be dealt with, and it's free within many postcodes. If you live outside those areas though, it will cost you £6.50.

Berry Bros & Rudd
www.bbr.co.uk

Can you serve red wine with salmon? Well, yes, as long as it's dry and fruity like the selection recommended here in the hugely useful food and wine matching section. This is a top class wine merchant where you can find delicious vintages or simply outstanding everyday wines, as well as learn about your choices and the site's own recommendations before you buy. A great place for people who would like to drink better. Delivery costs £7.50 for orders under £100, free over that, and your wine will be with you in six working days.

Bordeaux Direct

www.bordeauxdirect.com

A misleading name for this site which actually sells wines from all over the world. Savings of over £20 are offered on their mixed cases and there's an intriguing magical mystery section where you can buy random mixed cases for £30 off the original price. If you don't like the wine, for whatever reason, they will replace it or give you a refund.

Buy Wine Online

www.buywineonline.co.uk

Outstanding prices on good wine delivered right to your door. Plenty of choice to make up your own case or you can follow the experts and buy a ready-made selection. The wine advice section is a good overview of the mysteries of wine appreciation and might help you understand which wines you may prefer. There's secure credit card ordering or send a cheque if you can wait the seven days for it to clear. Delivery is within five days and costs £4.95.

Discount Champagne

www.discount-champagne.com

Good champagne, including a number of vintages, sold in cases at knock-down prices. The site is basic, as is the customer service set-up, but all this means is that their overheads are low and the savings are passed on to the customer. Case prices include delivery to the UK mainland.

Drinks Direct

www.drinks-direct.com

More a gift service than a wine merchant, but there are nevertheless some nice treat cases of wine here which you can keep for yourself if you're not feeling that generous. The Around The World case for £44 would keep you quite happy for a few days. Delivery costs £5.99 and will be made within two days unless you specify otherwise.

> **Buy Wine Online has a wine advice section that will help the novice without blowing the budget**

Enjoyment

www.enjoyment.co.uk

Online version of the Thresher, Victoria Wine, Wine Rack and Bottoms Up chain of off-licences. You can search for wine by country, location, price or vintage (or a combination of any criteria). Single bottles are at ten per cent less than they cost on the high street, or you can put together a mixed case or buy one of Enjoyment's own selections at a discount of at least 15 per cent. If you particularly like what you've bought, there's a personal notes section to keep track of your favourites. Delivery costs £4.99 per address for up to five cases, but be careful of ordering individual bottles as they will charge £6.99 per address for these, making it far less cost-effective.

Grainier Direct

www.grainier-direct.com

French champagne house selling their own brand vintage and non-vintage fizz from a quarter bottle to a 20-bottle Nebuchadnezzar. Since you're buying direct the prices are excellent, although you do have to buy at least six bottles to get the best deals. They can also make personalised labels for a special occasion. Delivery charges vary so check before you buy.

Laymont and Shaw Ltd

www.laymont-shaw.co.uk

Hoping to recapture that summer holiday feeling of sipping a glass of local wine while watching the sunset? Well, this site can't do anything about the sunset, but it does sell a good range of quality Spanish, Portuguese and Southern French wines. At first it may seem you have to request a catalogue in order to buy, but if you look carefully on the Welcome page, there's a link to secure ordering which also pops up on some, but not all, of the wine list pages. Prices quoted include delivery and your order should be received within three working days.

Mad About Wine

www.madaboutwine.com

Good selection of worldwide wines with a range of prices from a Cuvée de Vignerons Blanc at £3.69 to a bottle of 1905 Sauternes for £5351.59. Their mixed cases, like Party Solutions, are good value and make life a bit easier for those in a hurry. They also sell a limited range of beers and spirits. There's a useful freight calculator for you to check delivery charges before you put anything in your basket (it's one of the few sites that can send wine overseas) but UK delivery seems to come out at £4.99 no matter what the number of bottles.

Maison De Pierre

www.maisondepierre.co.uk

Despite the name, it's not just French wine that you will find on this simple and effective site, but a good selection of other European and New World bottles as well, all selected from independent growers with a strong emphasis on quality. There are some very good deals in the Special Offers section, particularly the Country Case for only £48.68, and they also stock a range of ports and liqueurs. Delivery is free to much of the South of England, or if you are buying at least five cases.

Now 365
www.now365.com

Priding itself on quality service with fast delivery (although you can't actually get booze delivered 365 days of the year), this is a good site for party supplies with low prices on basic wines and spirits and they even do wine boxes for alcohol emergencies. Delivery costs vary depending on your address (sometimes it's free) and they have a guaranteed next-day service if you're really desperate.

Orchard Hive and Vine
www.winesuppliers.co.uk

Try something a little different with this selection of English and Welsh wines available online. A number of vineyards are represented, all making wine from grapes grown in this country (as opposed to British wine which is made here from imported concentrate). Orders must be for a minimum of 12 bottles and cost £8 for delivery within one week.

And for the morning after "Aaarghhh!"

Ever since man first woke up with a mouth that felt like it had been cleaned with a toilet brush, he's been searching for the ultimate answer to the morning after. Here's what the online gurus recommend:

Beer Geer
www.beergeer.com

Hangover cures listed and rated by a website that should know.

Estronaut
www.estronaut. com/a/hangovers.htm

Alcohol advice for women who can't remember how they got home.

Sob'r-K
www.hangoverstopper.com

Miracle pills said to cure even the hairiest of hangovers. You have to remember to take them while you're still drinking, though...

Wrecked
www.wrecked.co.uk

Prevention being better than cure, one look at this drinking information site will put you off the sauce for life. Go on, have a peek, you owe it to your liver.

Rouge & Blanc

www.rouge-blanc.com

France-based (although they sell wine from all over the world) comprehensive wine site with plenty of advice and special offers for the unsure. The bargains section has some excellent everyday drinking tips on offer, or you could consult their wedding service if you need advice on what to serve on your big day. All orders cost £2.99 for delivery and will be with you in three days.

Stanley Ball Ltd

www.stanley-ball.co.uk

Independent wine merchant selling a range of wines which can be labelled to suit the customer. The site has examples of some bottles and there's an online form for further enquiries.

Wine Today

www.winetoday.com

News, reviews and advice on building a cellar or becoming a wine connoisseur from this comprehensive appreciation site. There's no online shop here, but plenty of links to individual vineyards around the world as well as merchants selling wine and wine accessories online.

Wychwood Wines

www.wychwoodwines.co.uk

A well laid out home page tells you everything you need to know about this importer who concentrates on wines from small vineyards all over the world. Argentina, Chile and South Africa are represented along with the more traditional wine countries, and most bottles are reasonably priced between £4 and £10. They encourage feedback about their service and offer a case of wine every quarter to the most constructive comment received. Weekday deliveries cost £6 but are free on orders over £150.

Black Mountain Liqueur is almost guaranteed to evoke images of the mountains and valleys of Wales

 **Make mine a double**

Black Mountain Liqueur

www.celticspirit.co.uk

And people say there isn't anything to do in Wales. Black Mountain Liqueur is a traditional cordial that is brewed in the Wye valley from local apples and blackcurrants and packs a comforting punch served after meals or over ice. Bottles cost £12 each and delivery is free within the UK.

Drinx

www.drinx.com

If it's got alcohol in it, you'll probably find it here. The wine choice is limited and prices are not much cheaper than those you will find on the high street, but there are some reasonable bargains to be had in the house wines section. The spirits section is more comprehensive, with even a section devoted to fruit schnapps for the very brave. Delivery costs £5.50 for an order of any size and your goods will be with you in two to three days.

Last Orders

www.lastorders.com

There's nothing particularly out of the ordinary on this booze-soaked site, but it does offer all the top brand names you know and love at discounted prices. The wine selection is fairly limited, but you'll find a wide range of spirits and alcopops as well as some cider and beers. Orders placed before 3.30pm will be delivered the next working day for £3.99, so it's good place for last-minute party planning. They're working on a same-day evening and weekend delivery service for really impromptu gatherings.

The Whisky Shop

www.whiskyshop.com/

From familiar blends, to rare single malts (how about a bottle of 40 year old Bowmore for £4000?), this site will keep any whisk(e)y drinker more than happy. It's well-designed with lots of info on the products and how to shop. Delivery is calculated when you order and starts at £6.50.

EVERYONE'S RUIN – ABSINTHE

Absinthe is enjoying a new dose of popularity at the moment and there are websites devoted to the scary green stuff popping up all over the Internet.

You can see what all the fuss about this unbelievably strong wormwood-infused spirit is and even buy yourself the odd bottle at the following sites, although be warned, it has been reputed to induce hallucinations. This may, of course, could be just what you're after... One site even suggests an absinthe and Red Bull cocktail for people who really don't care if they live to see their next birthday.

Eabsinthe.Com
www.eabsinthe.com

La Boheme
www.laboheme.uk.com

Stuff that doesn't fit anywhere
else, like the glossary and index

REFERENCE

What (almost) all the technical words men in real English

GLOSSARY

Access Provider
Company which sells Internet connections, more usually known as an Internet Service Providers (hence the initials ISP)

Acrobat Reader
Stand-alone program or Web browser plug-in from Adobe that lets you view a PDF file in its original format and appearance. The Acrobat Reader is free and some online stores will allow you download their catalogues as PDF files.

Address
The identifier you need to access a Web site: http://www.roughguides.com (see URL).

AltaVista
Search engine at http://www.altavista.com

Applet
Small (Java) program embedded in an HTML page. When you open that Web page, the browser downloads the applet and runs it on your computer. Don't worry – applets cannot read or write data on to your computer. Applets only work if the browser you're using supports Java.

AUP – Acceptable Use Policy
AUP is a policy for the use of the Internet laid own by an organisation. Some companies (including your own) may use a AUP filter to exclude some Internet services for staff. Parents can also set AUP limits by using a filter to make sure their children cannot view pornographic sites.

Attachment
A file included with email. If, for example, you bought travel insurance over the Web you would probably get a file, confirming the policy you'd bought, attached to the return email.

Autoresponder
A software program running on a computer server, linked full-time to the Net.

If someone sends an email to an autoresponder's email address, the autoresponder automatically and immediately emails this person a standard answer (for example: "Thank you for your message. I will reply shortly"), and sends the incoming message to whoever owns the autoresponder.

Banner

An advertisement, in the form of a graphic image on the Web, usually found at the top of a Web page. Most banner ads are animated GIFs.

Bookmark

Netscape browser feature which lets you save a link to a Web page. You can always use this bookmark to return to that page without keying in the address again. In Explorer, the same feature is called a Favourite.

Bot

Virtual robots which behave like search engines, only instead of finding the best Web pages they find products you have told them you want to buy.

Bps – Bits Per Second

Just a measure of how fast data is moved from one place to another, normally in thousands of bits per second (Kbps) or million of bits per second (Mbps). A bit is the basic unit of data. A 56K modem, still the one most commonly used by people surfing the Net for pleasure, can transport 56,600 bits per second.

Broadband

Rapid Internet access.

Browser – Web Browser

The software program which allows you to surf the Web. At this moment in cyberhistory, almost everyone uses Internet Explorer or Netscape Navigator.

Browsing

What you do when you visit the Internet, aka surfing.

Cache

Computer memory or directory on your hard disk where your browser stores the Web pages you have most recently visited.

Client/Server

A client is a computer system that requests a service of another computer system (a server) on a network.

Compression

Technology that reduces the size of a file in order to transfer it rapidly.

Cookie

The small text-file a Web server sends to your computer hard disk via your browser. Cookies contain information such as log-in or registration information, online shopping cart information, user preferences, etc. This information can be retrieved by other pages on the site, so the site can be customised. For example, when you're shopping online, the cookie contains a list of all the items in your shopping cart. When it's time to pay, the server takes the cookie from your browser to see what you have bought and invoices you.

Cyberspace

The term first coined by the science-fiction writer William Gibson to describe the virtual world which exists within the marriage of computers, telecommunication networks and digital media.

Data encryption key

String of characters used to encode a message. This encoded message can only be read by someone with another related key.

DNS – Domain Name Server or Domain Name System

A Domain Name Server maps IP numbers to a more easily remembered name. When you type http://www.roughguides.com into your browser, the DNS (specified when you installed dial-up networking) searches for a matching IP address. If the DNS doesn't find an entry in its database, it will ask other DNSes until the entry is found, and you will see the Rough Guides site. Otherwise, you'll get an error message from your browser.

Domain name

A unique name which identifies an Internet site. A domain name always points to one specific server, while this server may host many domain names. If you look at the URL for this page, you'll see www.roughguides.com at the beginning. The "www" points your computer to the server and "roughguides.com" is our domain name.

Download

What happens when a Web page comes up on your screen. You can use your browser or File Transfer Protocol program to download files to your computer.

E-commerce

Selling goods or services over the Internet. Customers choose what they want to buy (often using a virtual shopping cart) and then type their credit card details into a secure payment form on the site.

Email

Electronic mail which is sent and received via the Internet.

Encryption

Technology which scrambles the contents of a file before sending it over the Internet. The recipient must have software to decrypt this file. If you want to transmit "hot stuff" like credit card information, you have to use some form of encryption. PGP (Pretty Good Privacy) is one such encryption program.

Excite

Search engine at http://www.excite.com

FAQ – Frequently Asked Questions

You will find one of these on most websites you visit. An FAQ is simply a file which is supposed to contain answers to the most common questions asked on a particular subject.

Favourite

The Explorer equivalent to a Netscape Communicator Bookmark.

File

Anything stored on a computer, like an image, text or a program.

Firewall

Internet security which defends a Local Area Network against hackers. Hardware and software combine to act as a firewall to divide the LAN into two parts. Normal data is available outside the firewall, while hot stuff is kept inside the firewall. A firewall can also be designed by a company to make sure that, for example, you cannot buy products over the Net from your computer at work.

Frame

Technology introduced in Netscape 2.0 which allows Web designers to break the browser window into several smaller windows, each of which can load different HTML pages.

GIF – Graphics Interchange Format

A compressed graphic format used widely on the Net. Mostly used to show clip-art images (photographic images are usually in a format called JPEG). The GIF 89a standard permits the use of multiple images in a single file, and many online shops will use a GIF file to show some animation on their website.

Hacker

Someone who breaks through computer security for fun. If someone does it with criminal intent they are called a cracker.

Hit

A single request from a browser to a server. Some servers also count each graphic on that page as a hit. This is why the boast that X site has Y million hits a month is now a devalued way of measuring a website's popularity.

Homepage

The main page of a website. The term is also applied to any website, typically created by a private individual, which only has one page.

Host

The server on which a website is stored. Hosting companies store websites of their customers on powerful Web servers (with fast, permanent connections to the Internet) so, theoretically at least, you should always be able to access the page you want, providing the owner has not taken it down (off the Web) for some reason.

HTML

Hyper Text Mark-Up Language. This is the language used to create Web documents.

Hyperlink

A highlighted word (or graphic) within a Web page (technically, these pages are often described as hypertext documents). When you click a hyperlink, it will take you to another place within the same page, or to another page somewhere else on the Net.

Hypermedia

Pictures, videos, and audio on a Web page that act as hyperlinks.

Hyperspace

Less commonly used variant of cyberspace.

Hypertext

Text that includes links to other Web pages. By clicking on a link, the reader can jump straight from one Web page to another related page.

Internet Explorer

Web browser from Microsoft.

IP – Internet Protocol

The rules that provide basic Internet functions. Without IP, computers would not be able to find each other.

IP address

A unique 32-bit Internet address consisting of four numbers, separated by dots and sometimes called a "dotted quad". Every server – connected to the Internet – has an IP number. The Domain Name Server converts this number into the domain name.

ISP – Internet Service Provider

Most common usage is the same as Access Provider. But it also means any company that provides Internet services such as website development.

Java

A platform-independent programming language invented by Sun Microsystems, which Web developers use to create applets. Java-enabled Web pages can include animations, calculators, scrolling text, sound effects and even games. Although many Web designers like Java, many people using the Web surf with a Java-disabled browser because they don't want to wait until some applet is entirely loaded into their browser. It's not uncommon when accessing a website to get a pop-up box full of numbers and code headlined "Java error messages". Don't worry – this doesn't mean your terminal is crashing. Just click on the box to shut it and keep on browsing.

JPEG – Joint Photographic Experts Group

Image compression standard, optimised for full-colour (millions of colours) digital images. You can choose the amount of compression, but the higher the compression rate, the lower quality the image. Virtually every full-colour photograph you see on the Web is a JPEG file, while GIFs are used to show clip-art images.

Link

Marked text (usually underlined) or picture within a Web page. With one click of your mouse, a link takes you to another Web page (or to another place on the same page). Depending on the type of file, when you click on a link it will be retrieved and displayed, played or downloaded.

Log in

Entering into a computer system. Also the account name (or user ID) you must enter before you can access some computer systems. Many websites ask you to log in before viewing their pages. Before you do, it's worth checking what the site's policy on privacy is. You don't want to give your email address to a company which is going to pass it on to loads of other companies without your knowledge. In commercial cyberspace, email addresses are as prized as cigarettes are in prison.

Mirror or mirror site

More or less an exact copy of another site. Mirror sites are created when too many people want to access the original site. If, for instance, you are trying to buy goods from a global company you may be pointed to the mirror site nearest to you to make it quicker for you to access the pages.

Modem

Abbreviation of MOdulator-DEModulator. A modem allows computers to send information to each other on ordinary telephone lines.

MP3 or MPEG 3

A compressed musical format (see www.mp3.com) which enables you to download music to your computer from the Internet.

Navigator

Netscape's Web browser.

Page

One single document on the Internet.

Patch
A temporary or interim add-on which fixes or upgrades software. Often available from the companies for free (for example, iMac users can download a free patch onto their computer, designed to manage modem communications somewhat better.)

PDF – Portable Document Format
A file format created by Adobe (see Acrobat Reader) designed to make sure the file can be read on different computer platforms. Created for offline reading of brochures, reports and documents with complex graphic design. When you download a pdf file, you get the whole document in a single file.

PGP – Pretty Good Privacy
Program, developed by Phil Zimmerman, which protects files from being read by others. You can also use PGP to attach a digital signature to a file to prove you are the sender.

Plug-in
Small piece of software, usually from a third party developer, which adds new features to another (larger) software application. When visiting sites, you may often be asked to plug in programs like Flash or RealAudioPlayer. Downloading these software packages can be very time-consuming so you have to decide whether it's worth it. There is also a risk that a plug-in may carry a virus.

Portal
A website which attracts visitors by offering free information, or free services. When you are on a portal site, you can use this site as a base from which to explore the Web. The most famous portals are the major search engines.

Protocol
A set of rules and conventions that describes the behaviour which computers must follow in order to understand each other.

Search engine
Website which allows you to search for keywords on Web pages rather than having to know the specific Web address. Every search engine has its own strategy for collecting data, which is why one particular search produces different results on different search engines.

Server
A (powerful) computer that has a permanent connection to the Internet. Websites are stored on a Web server.

Site
A place on the Web. Refers to a home page or to a collection of Web pages.

Snail mail

Mail delivered to your door by the postie instead of being delivered to your computer by a network.

Spam

Junk email, considered a serious breach of netiquette.

SSL – Secure Sockets Layer

Protocol that allows encrypted messages to pass across the Internet. SSL uses public key encryption to pass data between your browser and a given server (for example, to submit credit card information). A URL that begins with "https" indicates that an SSL connection will be used. In Netscape, you can also check if a site you are using is secure, and you should see a gold padlock at the bottom of your window if the site to which you are sending your credit card details is protected.

Surfer

Slightly passé version of browser.

Time out

When you request a Web page and the server that hosts the Web page doesn't respond within a certain amount of time, you may get the message "connection timed out". Try again immediately if it's urgent, if not, leave it five minutes. If it persists, the site may be down temporarily or permanently.

URL – Uniform Resource Locator

Web address. Our home page's URL is: http://www.roughguides.com

User ID

Unique identifier that you must enter every time you want to access a particular service on the Internet. The user ID is always accompanied by a password.

Webmaster

The person responsible for the Web server (usually the system administrator).

World Wide Web

Hence the WWW. Graphic and and text documents published on the Internet inter-connected through clickable "hypertext" links.

XML

eXtensible Mark-up Language, to give it its full name, is a new language for writing Web pages and it's set to replace HTML (Hypertext Mark-up Language), some think by early 2001.

Yahoo!

Search engine at http://www.yahoo.com

The Rough Guide to Internet Shopping Offline Browser

INDEX

Index

From boxing nuns to emu oil and a tour of Old Plovdiv

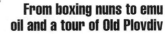

57 THINGS TO BUY ONLINE

Okay, you want to buy something. And by 'something' we don't mean anything as dull as groceries. Here are 57 varieties of stuff you can buy at the click of your mouse. The goods listed on auction may have been sold but if you follow the web address you should find other equally ludicrous bargains

1 A copy of John Lennon's birth certificate, £2.99
www.goldenlegends.co.uk

2 Clear glass telephone pole insulator, $5
http://auctions.yahoo.com

3 A complete medical history of potential sperm donors, $15
www.thespermbankofca.org

4 A six-yard flag of the Armenian Republic, £120
http://www.flagmakers.com/cgi/shoplink.pl?page=contents.html

5 Guinea-pig-shaped clear glass oil lamp, £9.99
www.winking-cavy.co.uk/glass.htm

6 A bar of Bug Off! shampoo soap to get rid of head lice, £3.50
http://www.strange.co.uk/soap/prods.htm

7 Dancing Elvis telephone (his hips swivel when the phone rings), $84.95
www.elvis-presley.com

8 Whirlpool table: a circular pool table with only three pockets , £2150
www.drinkstuff.com/pubgames.htm

9 A CD of marches and songs of the French Foreign Legion, £22
www.frenchforeignlegion.org/merch

10 A snowdome of the Great Wall of China, $16
www.snowdomes.com/gscatalog.html

11 The first ever issue of Eagle comic, £4
www.comicshack.uk.com/ie.htm

12 A Celly Massage cellulite-remover, £39.99
www.premierdirect.co.uk/start.htm

13 An ostrich clock decorated with paper toile yellow roses and violets
http://freespace.virgin.net/eggsclusive.design

14 A standard-sized US-style mailbox, £37.99
www.mmbef.clara.net/usmailboxes

15 Maria, the fighting nun, quality punching hand puppet, £8.99
www.sillyjokes.co.uk/wacky-products/fighting-nun.html

16 A hand-held lightning detector, $195
www.scientificsales.com/conligh.htm

17 An Edvard Munch coffee mug showing his painting The Scream, £5.95
www.classicouk.com/finartmug.htm

18 A four-person liferaft for use in commercial aviation, £821.33
http://www.avnet.co.uk/gtaviatn/betashop/files/shopguide.htm

19 More than 3000 acres of tropical rainforest in Brazil, $500,000
http://page.auctions.yahoo.com/uk/auction/30603360

20 One programme for the Toto reunion concert in 1999, £5.99
www.pushposters.co.uk

21 Starfish-decorated toilet seat and lid, £85 (plus £40 for matching mirror)
www.cooloo.com/pages/starfish.htm

22 A rare 1738 map of the world showing California as an island, £350
www.antique-atlas.co.uk/world.html

23 Deluxe beginners' kit for beekeepers (already assembled), £285.11
www.thorne.co.uk/thorne7.htm

24 Clinton Senate Hearings admission ticket, £35
www.politicos.co.uk/bookstore

25 Three six-month-old, four-horned chameleons, £120
www.thereptilehouse.co.uk

26 Wild Maine blueberry pie filling sample, free!
www.fruitfillings.com/samples.html

27 An hour's one-to-one tuition in driving a lorry, £25
http://autopass.co.uk:80

28 One pack of 12 five-star HB pencils, 48p (exc VAT)
http://www.office-supplies-on-line.ltd.uk

29 Full-size replica of Doctor Who's Tardis, £1895
www.thisplanetearth.co.uk/page2.html

30 Cornish Cormorant 12ft dinghy, £7721
www.allthingscornish.com

31 Sherlock Holmes chess set, £208.51
www.poshgifts.com

32 Extra-large Mexico red legs tarantula T-shirt, £14
www.seriousbite.com/welcome.htm

33 Valentine One high performance radar detector, £545
www.snooper.co.uk

34 One bottle of golden emu oil for muscle rubs, £9.95
www.pion-tc.co.uk

35 Crossword Compiler 5 Windows software, £28
www.netword.demon.co.uk

36 'Lifesize' statue of Lara Croft, £910
http://auction.yahoo.co.uk

37 William Wallace reproduction claymore sword, £439
www.macallen.force9.co.uk/index.html

38 Left-handed computer keyboard, £91
https://shop.anythingleft-handed.co.uk/shop.html

39 Charles Rennie Mackintosh geometric cufflinks, £16.75 (exc VAT)
http://www.scottish-jewellery.co.uk

40 First edition of *Some account of the Roman Catacombs especially the cemetery of San Callisto compiled from the works of . . . Rossi with the consent of the author* by Rev. Spenser and Rev. Brownlow, £100
http://dogbert.abebooks.com/abe/IList

41 16,000 items of lingerie seized in police raid, £10,000 (retail value £600,000)
www.bluecycle.com

42 A set of Vampire LeStat custom-fit fangs, £140
www.dentaldistortions.com

43 145g of caviar house goose foie gras, £30
https://secure2.cnm-uk.net/jayfruit/caviar/welcome.html

44 Sign from Wembley listing which items cannot be taken into stadium, £43
www.qxl.com

FOR UNDER A TENNER...

You can buy a Barbie inflatable table for just $9.95 from Bluefly.com. But there is a catch: it'll cost you $42 to get it shipped to the UK.

No such snags with Isabel Allende's thinking person's cook book, Aphrodite, yours for £4.99 on http://s1.waterstones.co.uk

If Allende's book disturbs your sleep, take some Potters Nod Off – a snip at £4.75 from www.nutravida.co.uk/index.jsp

One final bargain: a pair of red knee socks from www.organicsdirect.com – yours for just £6.60!

The acceptable face of lavatorial humour: Cooloo's toilet seat designs are not for the squeamish or, at £85, for the parsimonious

45 A day-long tour of Old Plovdiv for one, $30 + $15 for restaurant lunch
www.digitaltravel.com

46 One copy of Sniffin' Glue punk fanzine, issue 4 featuring the Clash, £15
www.soundstravel.demon.co.uk

47 A certificate to show you have leased one acre of the moon, $5
www.geocities.com/Area51/Dreamworld/1510

48 Jay-Be Tiffany's contemporary chaise longue, £655
http://store1.europe.yahoo.com/fol2

49 Twelve bottles of Bateman's Yella Belly organic ale, £18.99
www.lastorders.com/html/home.asp

50 Five kilos of roasted Australian Skybury Estate coffee, £49
www.realcoffee.co.uk/index.html

51 Cezanne's *Tree Trunk With Flowers*, pencil & water colour, undisclosed
www.EuropeanPaintings.com/french

52 Liebherr LTM 1050 all-terrain crane, £160,000
www.ainscough.co.uk

53 Booking Gary Kasparov to give a speech, £27,000 plus expenses
www.speakers.co.uk

54 Haji Japanese wind-up astronaut robot, $295
www.spacetoys.com

55 Download the Blues Brothers theme, free
www.s.nw.edu/~tommym/blues/index.html#using

56 Samba Junior Mulltigoal five-a-side goalposts and net, £104.99
www.go4soccer.com/goalposts.htm

57 Edible birdseed church, with plywood frame, $65
www.catalogcity.com

AVAILABLE NOW – THE LATEST EDITION OF THE
WORLD'S BESTSELLING POCKET NET GUIDE

THE ROUGH GUIDE TO

The
Internet

Angus J. Kennedy

2001 EDITION • FOR PCs AND MACS